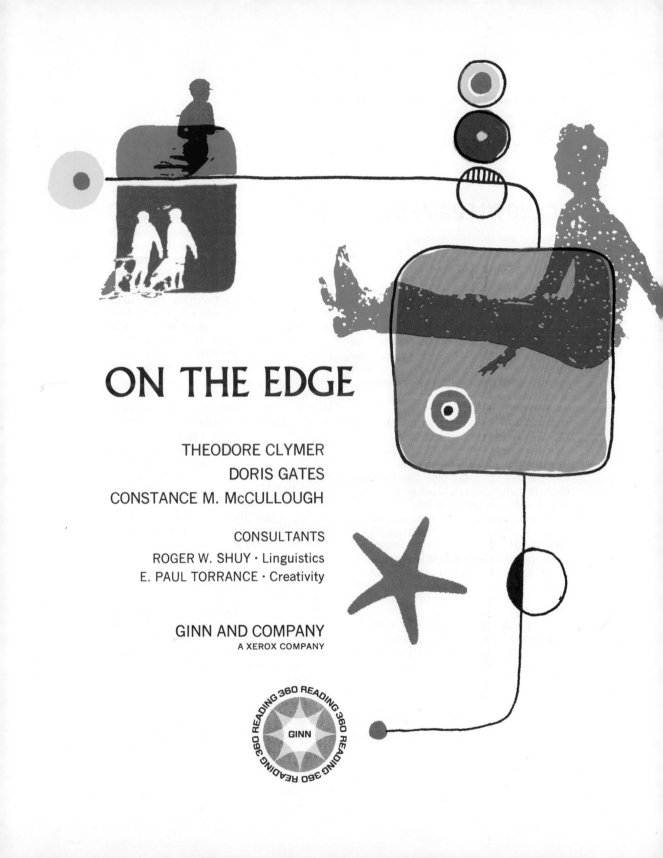

ON THE EDGE

THEODORE CLYMER
DORIS GATES
CONSTANCE M. McCULLOUGH

CONSULTANTS
ROGER W. SHUY · Linguistics
E. PAUL TORRANCE · Creativity

GINN AND COMPANY
A XEROX COMPANY

READING 360 READING 360 READING 360 READING 360 READING 360
GINN

0-663-25209-1

ACKNOWLEDGMENTS

Grateful acknowledgment is made to the following authors and publishers for permission to use copyrighted materials:

Atheneum Publishers, Inc., for "Wild Bird" by Florence Parry Heide. Copyright © 1971 by Florence Parry Heide. From *The Key*. Used by permission of Atheneum Publishers.

Doubleday & Company, Inc., for *The Secret Journey of the Silver Reindeer* by Lee Kingman. Copyright © 1968 by Doubleday & Company, Inc. All Rights Reserved. Used by permission of the Publisher.

E. P. Dutton & Co., for "The Golden Eagle," slightly adapted and abridged from the book *The Golden Eagle* by Robert Murphy. Copyright, ©, 1965 by Robert Murphy. Reprinted by permission of E. P. Dutton & Co., Inc. Also for "The Sea" from the book *The Wandering Moon* by James Reeves. Used by permission of E. P. Dutton & Company, Inc.

Harcourt Brace Jovanovich, Inc., for "To Look at Any Thing" by John Moffitt. © 1961 by John Moffitt. Reprinted from his volume, *The Living Seed,* by permission of Harcourt, Brace & World, Inc. Also for "Fueled" by Marcie Hans. From *Serve Me a Slice of Moon,* © 1965 by Marcie Hans. Reprinted by permission of Harcourt, Brace & World, Inc.

Harper & Row, Publishers, for "A Fair Breeze" and "The Sailboat Race" from *Stuart Little* by E. B. White. Copyright 1945 by E. B. White. Reprinted with permission of Harper & Row, Publishers. Also for "Adventure on the Last Frontier," abridgment and adaptation of pp. 106–127 *Lady with a Spear* by Eugenie Clark. Copyright 1951, 1952, 1953 by Eugenie Clark Konstantinu. By permission of Harper & Row, Publishers.

Holt, Rinehart and Winston, Inc., for "Anansi's Fishing Expedition" from *The Cow-Tail Switch and Other West African Stories* by Harold Courlander and George Herzog. Copyright 1947 by Holt, Rinehart and Winston, Inc. Reprinted by permission of Holt, Rinehart and Winston, Inc.

Houghton Mifflin Company for "Stormalong" from *Yankee Doodle's Cousins* by Anne Malcolmson. Copyright, 1941, by Anne Burnett Malcolmson. Reprinted by permission of the publisher, Houghton Mifflin Company.

Little, Brown and Company for "Sail Calypso," Copyright . . . © 1968 by Adrienne Jones, from *Sail Calypso* by Adrienne Jones, by permission of Little, Brown and Company; for "Ptarmigan," Copyright © 1965, 1966 by David McCord, from *All Day Long* by David McCord, by permission of Little, Brown and Company; for "Seal," copyright © 1956, 1957 by William Jay Smith, from *Boy Blue's Book of Beasts* by William Jay Smith, by permission of Atlantic-Little, Brown and Company; and for "A Bird Came Down the Walk" from *The Poems of Emily Dickinson,* by permission of Little, Brown and Company.

The Macmillan Company for "Curtains for Joey," adapted with permission of The Macmillan Company from *Me 'N' Steve* by Roy O. Brotherton. Copyright © by Roy O. Brotherton 1965. Also for "Call It Courage," reprinted with permission of The Macmillan Company from *Call it Courage* by Armstrong Sperry. Copyright 1940 by The Macmillan Company, renewed 1968 by Armstrong Sperry.

McGraw-Hill Book Company for "Fish Story" from *Light Armour* by Richard Armour. Copyright 1954 by Richard Armour. Used with permission of McGraw-Hill Book Company.

New Directions Publishing Corp. for "The Term" by William Carlos Williams, *Collected*

2

3

The New American Library and Christ's College, Cambridge, England, for "The Story of Perseus" from *Gods, Heroes and Men of Ancient Greece* by W. H. D. Rouse. This extract is printed with the permission of The New American Library and The Master, Fellows and Scholars of Christ's College, Cambridge, England, the owners of the copyright.

Candida Palmer for her story "The 'Empty' Wasn't Empty."

Penguin Books Ltd, London, for "Dew on a Spider Web" by Michael Stone from *Miracles* edited by Richard Lewis. Used by permission of Penguin Books Ltd., British publishers.

Rand McNally & Company for "Forten Sails with Danger," adapted from *Forten the Sailmaker* by Esther M. Douty. Copyright 1968 by Rand McNally & Company.

Marie Rodell, literary agent, for "Adventure on the Last Frontier" from *Lady with a Spear* by Eugenie Clark.

Yale University Press for "Days" from *Blue Smoke* by Karle Wilson Baker. Copyright © 1919 by Yale University Press.

Every effort has been made to trace the ownership of all copyrighted material in this book and to obtain permission for its use.

The illustrations were prepared by the following artists: Donn Albright, Ramon Ameijide, Ben Black, Mike Cassaro, Diane and Leo Dillon, Judy and Todd McKie, David McPhail, Jane Oka, Joan Paley, Don Pulver, William Papas, George Salonovich, Lynn Sweat, and Garth Williams.

The illustrations by Garth Williams for "A Fair Breeze" and "The Sailboat Race" are from the book *Stuart Little* by E. B. White, and used by permission of Harper & Row, Publishers.

The photographs were obtained through the following sources: Fratelli Alinari, 208, 223, 225, 238; Berlin Art Museum, 235; Leonard Rue Enterprises, 256 (top); Douglas Faulkner, 265, 266, 267, 268, 271, 275, 279; Owen Franken, 96; Robert Houston, 33, 88, 90, 91, 92, 94 (top left), 95 (top right), 97, 98, 99, 100, 101 (top left), 103, 107; The Louvre, 228; The Metropolitan Museum of Art, 200 (Gift of John Taylor Johnston, 1881), 244 (Gift of J. Pierpont Morgan, 1917); Anna Kaufman Moon, 101; Paul Nesbit from National Audubon Society, 293; Allen Roberts, 250, 251, 253 (right), 256 (bottom), 262; William M. Stephens, 276; Robert Strindberg, 252, 253 (left); U.S. News and World Report, 93.

4

CONTENTS

6

ON THE EDGE

10

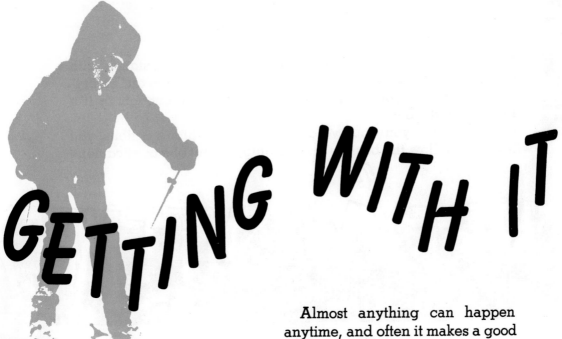

GETTING WITH IT

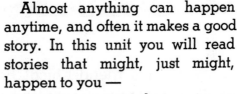

Almost anything can happen anytime, and often it makes a good story. In this unit you will read stories that might, just might, happen to you —

if you went exploring in an empty old house.

if you were part of a neighborhood baby-sitting service.

if you searched for a monster in a lake.

if you were an Indian boy walking in the city with your grandfather

if you went sailing on the ocean.

So, if you think "Nothing exciting will ever happen to me," don't be too sure. Get with it and read on!

There's something spooky about an empty house. It stands with hollow eyes and stares you down. But if you must go into an "empty" for a good reason, you do. That is, if you are brave enough, or if a pal will go with you.

Whether or not you approve of Benny's and Chico's actions, you will want to follow the boys as they get into and out of a predicament.

"EMPTY" WASN'T EMPTY

Benny and his friend Chico had been guessing about the snow all the way home from school, along Washington Boulevard and West Park, and now down Thirty-third Street.

"Up there it looks ready to let loose," Chico observed hopefully, his face lifted to the heavy gray sky bulging low over the tall city buildings.

"Yeah—but there's gotta be seven inches for no school," Benny reminded him, kicking his shoe against a piece of hard ice left from last week's snow. A new sugar sprinkling flecked the red brick sidewalk.

They reached their block, Sycamore Avenue at Thirty-third, and stopped in front of Altmann's Delicatessen at the corner, wedged hard between the narrow-angled streets. Old Mrs. Altmann, spying them from the window, tapped her bony finger against the glass, beckoning urgently.

12

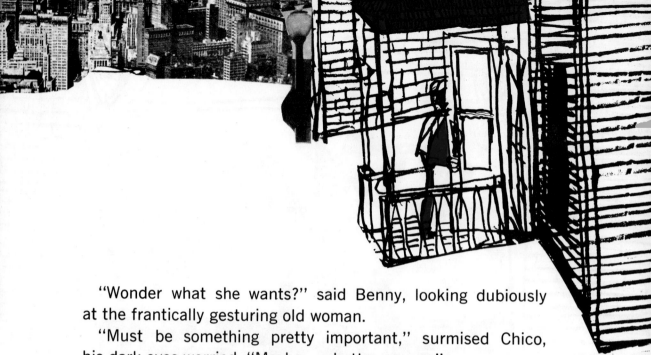

"Wonder what she wants?" said Benny, looking dubiously at the frantically gesturing old woman.

"Must be something pretty important," surmised Chico, his dark eyes worried. "Maybe we better go see."

"Yeah," agreed Benny, "come on."

Inside the warm little store, smelling pleasantly of cheese and pickles, the boys rested their school books on the counter as they listened to Mrs. Altmann's hasty explanation.

"Go quick, boys," she was saying, holding out a ring of keys toward Benny who was the taller of the two. "I need some things from the 'empty' and my Otto is down with the flu. A bad storm is coming and I am short these things." She handed Benny a penciled list along with the keys. "Do you think you can find them in the 'empty'?"

"Sure we can," Benny assured her. "We've helped Mr. Altmann lots of times."

"It's easier now," Mrs. Altmann said. "Since the cold weather, we don't keep many groceries in the 'empty.' Just stuff that won't freeze. And take this carton back." She pointed to a carton full of empty bottles over near the door. "You do this for me and I give you each a quarter."

14

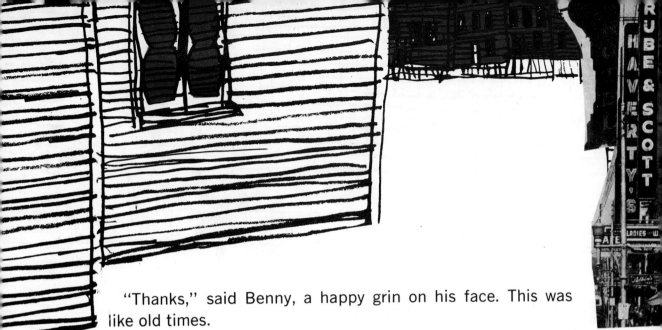

"Thanks," said Benny, a happy grin on his face. This was like old times.

Chico's dark eyes were dancing. "We'll be real careful and we won't forget a thing."

"Just be careful you don't let nothing drop. I want no busted packages," warned Mrs. Altmann.

Benny picked up the carton of empty bottles and with Chico behind him started for the "empty." The old house had been so smoke-damaged by fire which burned down the one adjoining it that it had to be abandoned. The rubble from the burned house had been trucked away, so now there was a vacant lot along side the "empty."

When the boys reached the stone steps, Benny set the carton down and ran up with the keys to unlock the door. The lock was stubborn at first, but at last he swung the door open on creaking hinges to reveal a narrow, gloomy hallway with a battered stairway going up one side. The front windows were kept shuttered so only a dim light seeped along the hall from the back of the house, past the stairs, meeting at last the square patch of daylight by the open door. Benny pushed the door wide, then ran back for the carton. He carried it into

the house and to the large front room off the hall. There he
set it down with a clatter of banging bottles and reached
high to turn on the single light bulb hanging from a discolored
cord in the very middle of the ceiling. There were several
half-filled cartons scattered about the room and as Benny
read from the list, Chico scampered about like an enthusiastic
retriever gathering what was needed. At last all the items
were assembled in a neat pile near the door.

"Guess that's it," said Benny, slipping the list into a pocket
of his jeans.

Chico sat back on his heels and sent a glance around the
scarred old room.

"Sometimes I wish Tyrone was back living here again. We had
a lot of fun in this room."

"You can have Tyrone," said Benny. "I don't want any part
of him. Not since he told on us."

"Funny how he did that." Chico's face wore a puzzled frown.
"He was always such a good guy."

"Might be the new neighborhood he moved to. Maybe we
aren't good enough for Tyrone any more. In my book, a squealer
just ain't good enough for me."

16

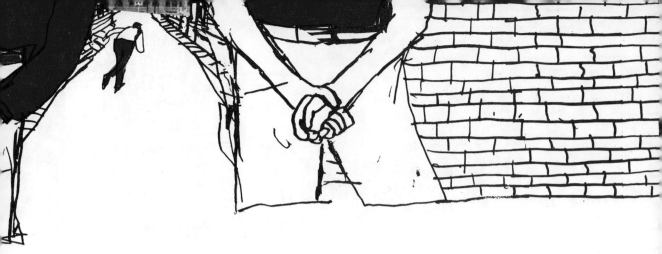

Until the fire, Tyrone had been a good friend of Benny and Chico. But when the landlord decided that the old house wasn't worth the repairs it would need to make it habitable after the fire in the one adjoining it, Tyrone's family had had to move away. The three boys continued going to the same school, but everything else was different. Most important, Tyrone was different. Benny and Chico had run into him several times in the neighborhood of the "empty." But each time when they had tried to be as friendly as ever, Tyrone had not responded to their friendliness. Once he turned and ran when he saw them coming.

"He looked like he was cryin'," Chico had then said, his voice full of concern. "What's he got to cry about?"

"Don't know," Benny had replied. "Maybe he's homesick."

They had more or less accepted his strange behavior, hopeful that in time Tyrone would be his old friendly self again.

Then something had happened which even Benny and Chico could not forgive. Tyrone had betrayed them. He had gone to Mr. Altmann and told on them. Anyway, that's what he had said he was going to do and the boys believed he had.

It was last time they had gone on an errand to the "empty."

They had gathered up all the things that Mr. Altmann had wanted, and were ready to leave when Chico suggested that they have a look around.

They had explored as far as the deserted kitchen, when an angry voice behind them had demanded, "What do you think you're doin'?"

Chico and Benny had whirled around to see Tyrone standing in the door to the kitchen, staring at them.

"Mr. Altmann sent us here to get some stuff for him," Benny explained. "Not that it's any of your business."

"We'll see about that," Tyrone answered. "Mr. Altmann sure don't want you foolin' around back here with the front door wide open for anybody to walk in and help himself."

Whether Tyrone had really told or Mr. Altmann just wanted to save quarters, that was the last time he ever asked them to run an errand. They badly missed the quarters and they never forgave Tyrone.

Now, today, they began gathering into their arms the items from Mrs. Altmann's list.

"Wonder what ever happened to that old cat he was so nuts about," Chico said.

18

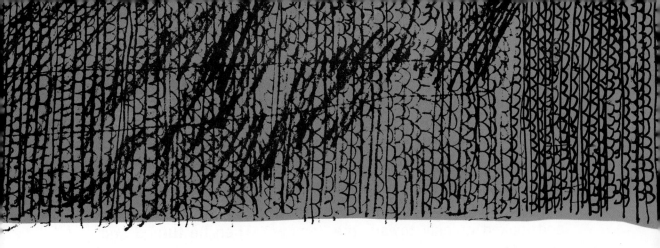

"The Altmanns had it for a while," Benny reminded him.

"Not after it got into the herring," Chico said.

Benny grinned, suddenly recalling the afternoon that Mrs. Altmann had pursued the cat for half a block waving a broom and screeching, the cat running for dear life with a fish hanging out of its mouth.

Their arms full, they started out of the "empty." Benny slammed the door shut on its automatic lock. Had he happened to glance inside he might have seen a face appear over the bannisters of the stairway an instant before the door closed.

Next morning the bustling, noisy city lay crippled under a deep white cover. The snowplows screeched and labored up Sycamore. It was noon before Benny, with Chico's help, had the sidewalk clear outside his father's barber shop. Here were the seven inches they had hoped for and the schools were closed. And here was the white, freshly fallen snow to play in. Stacking their snow shovels, they made for the vacant lot beside the "empty."

"Let's play forts," said Benny. "The first guy to knock out the other's fort will be the winner. You make yours here by the street and I'll make mine up by the 'empty.'"

Accepting this arrangement, Chico squatted down in the snow and began scooping and piling it into a high wall facing the "empty" toward which Benny was trudging.

"Whoever gets his fort finished first can start firing," Chico called, working frantically.

Benny didn't reply, but his steps quickened and the snow spurted away from his hurrying feet. Suddenly he stopped and looked quickly toward the "empty." Then he turned and called to Chico.

"Hey, Chico, hold it. Look what I found."

Chico rose slowly, his face dubious. Was this a trick to slow him down? Already a good high heap of snow stood between him and his future target. But it wasn't like Benny to play a trick.

Benny made an impatient gesture toward his friend. "Come on, what are you waitin' for?"

Chico hastened over to where Benny stood and his gaze followed Benny's pointing arm. "Look there at that upstairs window."

The window was grimy and there was darkness behind it, but even so, Chico could see at once the face of a cat close against the glass. He could even see the pink of the cat's mouth and knew that it was crying.

"What does that look like to you?" demanded Benny.

"It's Tyrone's cat," said Chico almost in a whisper.

"Yeah," said Benny, "and it's shut in there and starving. Might of slipped in yesterday when we went to get the stuff for Mrs. Altmann."

"We can't let it starve," said Chico.

"Come on," said Benny. "We'll go get the keys from Mrs. Altmann and let the poor thing out."

20

"Wonder where it's been living," said Chico, and they trotted through the snow, the building of forts forgotten.

"Search me," Benny replied. "I haven't seen it since the day she chased it with the broom."

They reached the store all out of breath only to find it locked.

"Old man Altmann must be worse," said Benny. "Guess Mrs. Altmann couldn't mind the store and him too."

"Whadda we do now?" demanded Chico.

"We bang," Benny told him, fitting action to the words.

But though he banged on the door and rattled its lock, no Mrs. Altmann came to let them in.

"Now what?" asked Chico.

"We gotta get into the 'empty,' that's what," said Benny.

"You mean break in?" Chico sounded scared.

"It ain't the same as if the Altmanns hadn't let us in before," Benny reasoned. "They know us and we'll tell 'em about it later. Besides, ain't nothin' in there much but some empty bottles. Not like before the cold came."

This seemed to satisfy Chico and together they ran toward the "empty."

First they tested all the downstairs windows, but all of them

22

were firmly closed and locked. Benny went around back and studied the short flight of steps and the door at the top of them. Above the door was a transom.

"You know, Chico," he said at last. "I think if you stood on my shoulders, you could reach up to that transom and if it isn't locked, you could push it open and crawl in."

"I ain't gonna bust nothin'," said Chico, looking worried.

"Who asked you to? We ain't gonna bust nothin'. Come on."

It wasn't much of a feat to climb up onto Benny's shoulders, though he complained once when Chico's foot hit his ear.

"Take it easy," Benny cautioned.

Gingerly, bracing one hand against the door, Chico reached up to give the transom a cautious shove. His hand brushed the sill and a handful of snow dropped onto his face. The transom swung in.

"Good," cried Benny, indifferent to Chico's plight. "Now get hold of the edge and I'll help boost you in."

Somehow, with a good deal of scrambling, they managed it and Benny heard the thump which signaled Chico's landing on the floor of the hallway inside. Seconds later, he had opened the door and Benny slid in.

EEEOOOWW EEOOWW

A gray, winter light came bleakly in from the dirty window over the kitchen sink. The window in the door had been boarded over. Across the room, the door to the cellar was ajar.

Chico went on ahead toward the front hall and the stairway, calling, "Kitty, kitty." But no cat appeared.

"It's upstairs," said Benny. "Come on," and he started up.

Halfway to the top, he was flung back against the wall as a flying object descended past him.

"Open the back door, Chico. Maybe it'll run out," he cried.

Chico headed back toward the kitchen, and Benny continued up the stairs. Reaching the top, he paused for a look around. Three doors opened onto the landing, shedding their light onto it. Suddenly Benny tensed. He had heard something! The room to the left. A funny sound, almost human, yet slightly different. There it was again, almost like a cat's cry. But the cat was gone!

Slowly, Benny started into the room. Just inside the door he paused. The room was a proper mess. An old mattress was up-ended against one wall, newspapers were scattered about, and over near the mattress was a shiny pie plate, such as a bakery pie comes in. An old sofa with a broken leg leaned

in one corner. On it was a carton. As Benny started toward
it, he caught that sound again. This time there could be no
doubt, and a smile came to Benny's lips.

Kittens! There, curled tightly on an old gray sweater on the
bottom of the carton, were three tiny kittens. Two were black
and one had gray stripes. The gray one had lifted his head to
cry piteously, but his eyes were shut, as were the eyes of the
other two. They couldn't be more than a few days old.

"Hey, Chico," Benny called. "Come see what I found."

Chico came banging up the stairs and into the room. He
approached the old sofa slowly at a signal from Benny.

"Golly," he breathed, reaching in to put a gentle hand on
the crying one. Suddenly he straightened. "The mother cat
ran out. Now how will she get back to 'em?"

"She can't," said Benny. "We'll have to take the kittens
to my house."

"Will the mother cat find them there?"

"Probably not," admitted Benny. "But they'll die of starvation if we leave 'em here."

"They'll die anyway," said Chico, "because they're too little
to lap milk. They gotta have their mother."

For a moment the boys were silent as they considered their problem. It was unthinkable that they should leave the "empty" open for the mother cat's return. It was useless to consider catching her, for she had become as wild as a bobcat.

Suddenly in the very depths of the old house, they heard a noise. It sounded as if someone had bumped into something. *Who could be in the "empty"?* The boys looked at each other quickly, their faces frightened.

"Let's get out of here," said Benny, whirling toward the door.

"But the kittens," protested Chico, his face crinkling with concern. "They'll *die*."

"Not so loud," cautioned Benny in a whisper. "You coming, or am I going to leave you here to face whoever is down there?"

Chico gave a last despairing look at the kittens. "I'm coming," he said.

Moving as quietly as possible, they descended the stairs and headed toward the kitchen and the back exit. So far they had seen no one and had heard nothing. Now they were at the kitchen door, Chico so close at Benny's heels that when the former stopped, the smaller boy ran smack into him.

"What. . .?" began Chico in an irritated whisper, and then he looked over Benny's shoulder.

There in the center of the kitchen, tense and staring. was Tyrone. His head was bare, his hood hanging down his back from the collar of his heavy jacket. In his mittened hands was a paper bag. His face was white and his chest heaving. Behind him the cellar door was opened wide.

"What're you two doin' here?" he said at last. "You got no business here."

Benny recovered from his surprise to say, "We got as much as you have."

"I came to feed my cat," said Tyrone. "Why did you come?"

"Same reason, sort of," said Benny. "We came to let her out. She was cryin' at the upstairs window. We let her out before we knew about the kittens."

"How'd you get in?" said Tyrone. "The store ain't open."

"We found that out," said Benny. He and Chico were now standing in the kitchen and the atmosphere was getting more relaxed. "We figured somebody had to do something about the cat, so we tried that transom," nodding toward the back door, "and it wasn't locked. Chico made it in."

27

Tyrone looked from one to the other. "Didn't know you cared about cats," he said.

"Figured the cat was hungry, that's all," said Benny.

Tyrone nodded. "She was hungry all right. I'm late and she couldn't get out on account of the snow."

"You been comin' here right along?" asked Benny.

Tyrone nodded again, his face troubled. "There's a busted window in one of the cellar wells and I know how to work the bars loose and unlock it. I learned about it when I lived here. The cat kept comin' back here all the time; wouldn't stay in the new place. She got in through the busted window, only today the well was full of snow and I had to clear it out. I had to sneak food in here because I didn't want old lady Altmann to know about the cat. She wouldn't have let it stay."

"That's why you acted so mean the day you found me and Chico back here in the kitchen," said Benny. "You didn't want us to find out about the cat."

"But you had no business squealing on us," said Chico.

"I never did," said Tyrone. "I only said that to keep you out of here. I never told nobody."

Benny and Chico exchanged glances and something like a smile passed between them.

"We ain't gonna tell on you, neither," said Benny.

"That's right," said Chico. Then he added, "What're you goin' to do with the kittens?"

"I been thinkin' about that while we've been talkin'," Tyrone answered him. "I been thinkin' that if I was to get the kittens home, the cat would stay home to take care of 'em. Only my mother wouldn't let me keep three kittens. I know she wouldn't."

There was a moment's silence, then Chico spoke. "How would it be if you kept the three till they were big enough

to lap and then gave one to me and one to Benny? My mother would let me have one. How about you, Benny?"

Benny's face registered sudden interest. "I could ask her. I got a feeling she'll let me. A cat's a good thing around a shop too."

"You can have the two black ones," said Tyrone. "Now let's go upstairs and wait till the cat comes back. She can get in now I've cleaned the snow away from the window."

Together, the three trooped back upstairs. The kittens had stopped crying and were curled against each other, sound asleep. Crouching around the carton, the boys talked in whispers. It was almost like old times again in the old house, Tyrone's old house.

All at once the kittens began to stir.

"Hey, you guys," whispered Tyrone. "I think she's comin' back. I got to catch her and get her home. So you two have to get out of sight, 'cause she's scary. When I get hold of her, I'll wrap her up good in the sweater, then you can take the kittens and we'll beat it for my house."

And that's just the way it worked out. The mother cat wailed in Tyrone's arms and looked anxiously at the other two boys

30

who had her kittens cuddled close inside their jackets. But with the sweater wrapped firmly around her, she was helpless to escape.

They descended the stairs to the front hall.

"How're we goin' to get out of here?" asked Benny.

"I know," said Chico, promptly. "We're goin' right out that front door and slam it shut behind us, and then we're goin' straight to the Altmann's store and make her let us in. And we're goin' to tell her all about everything and how the 'empty' wasn't empty. She'll understand, all right. See if she doesn't."

And Mrs. Altmann did. She even went so far as to ask for the gray kitten.

"I always sorta liked kittens," she explained.

— *Candida Palmer*

THINKING IT OVER

1. A good title excites interest and gives clues to what the story is about. Do you think "The 'Empty' Wasn't Empty" is a good title? Why or why not?

2. All three of the boys entered the "empty" without permission. Do you think Tyrone was right or wrong in doing this? What about Benny and Chico? Explain your answers.

3. Of the two boys, Benny and Chico, which one was the leader? Be ready to support your answer with evidence from the story.

THOUGHTS AT WORK

1. In several places the author used little "tricks" to keep the reader guessing. For instance, "Not since he told on us" makes you want to read on. Find other examples like this.

2. Sometimes a misunderstanding can cause a friendship to end. How was that true in this story? Tell about a time when you and a friend had a misunderstanding.

3. Why do you think Tyrone didn't want Benny and Chico to know that he was keeping a cat in the "empty"?

4. An author sometimes interrupts a story and explains events that happened before the story took place. This technique is called a flashback. List the pages where a flashback is used and be ready to explain how you know it is a flashback.

5. Why do you think Tyrone's cat wouldn't stay in the new place? Why wouldn't his mother allow him to keep three kittens?

6. Suppose Benny and Chico had left with the kittens before Tyrone returned with the food. What do you think might have happened?

THE TERM

A rumpled sheet
of brown paper
about the length

and apparent bulk
of a man was
rolling with the

wind slowly over
and over in
the street as

a car drove down
upon it and
crushed it to

the ground. Unlike
a man it rose
again rolling

with the wind over
and over to be as
it was before.

—William Carlos Williams

Summer is a good time to earn pocket money. There may be a lawn to mow, some errands to run, or cars to wash. But baby-sitting may prove to be the most interesting of all. It's the job when you must match wits with the unexpected, as Henry Reed soon discovered.

The story you are about to read took place on a fine summer day. You may hope that you never experience such a day, but for Henry it was a good start on his new summertime service.

THE BARBECUE FOR THE BOSS

This story is an adventure in the life of Henry Reed, who has come to spend the summer with his aunt and uncle in a little community in New Jersey. Henry has just formed a business which he calls HENRY REED'S BABY-SITTING SERVICE. As the story opens, he has just successfully finished his first job and is hopeful that Midge, a girl who lives nearby and whom Henry has known since the previous summer, will join his service. Henry tells the story in his own words.

I'm fairly certain now that Midge is going to join the firm. She was a big help today; I earned two dollars and fifty cents in the morning and four dollars in the afternoon. Midge earned two dollars, and Mrs. Wittenberg[1] gave both Midge and me a dollar tip.

I arrived at the Wittenberg's this morning at ten-fifteen; I'd never met any of the family before. Mrs. Wittenberg is a tall, pleasant, dark-haired woman about thirty. She said she had asked about me and had had very good reports.

"This is Danny," she said, introducing her four-year-old son. Mrs. Wittenberg wasn't looking at him at the moment, so Danny stuck out his tongue at me. It didn't seem to be a good beginning.

"I'm chairman of the hospital fund drive and we have a meeting at ten-thirty. I should be back by twelve-fifteen or twelve-thirty," she explained as we walked toward the car. "So there's really nothing to do. I'll get lunch for Danny when I get back. I know you two will get along splendidly."

[1] Wittenberg (wit'ən bérg)

35

A big black poodle came bouncing up and sat down beside me. He wagged his entire hind end, he was so friendly. I like poodles. They're almost as nice as beagles. I'd thought of bringing Agony, but decided against it. It was just as well, since the poodle might not have been so friendly toward another dog.

"This is Consommé[1]," Mrs. Wittenberg said. "He's well behaved and knows enough to stay off the road."

She didn't say anything about Danny's being well behaved and I soon figured out that she had a good reason not to. The minute her car was out of sight, Danny grabbed a little wagon that was sitting by the garage, jumped in it, and went rolling down the macadam drive toward the road. The drive has quite a slope, and the way he was gathering speed, I figured he would roll right out to the middle of the street. While the road through Grover's Corner isn't any turn-pike, quite a few cars use it. I could see my baby-sitting career coming to a fast end if anything happened to Danny. I ran like mad and managed to catch him before he got to the road.

"You don't want to go out in the road, Danny," I told him.

"Yes, I do," he answered.

"The cars will run over you," I warned.

"I'll run over them," he said. "I'll knock them right in the ditch."

Danny sure had self-confidence. I wasn't so confident, though, so I pulled him back up the sloping driveway to the garage.

[1] Consommé (kon′ sə mā′)

"Why do you call your dog Consommé?" I asked, to change the subject.

"Cause he shakes like jellied consommé when he wags his tail," Danny said. "He's afraid to go out into the road, the scairdy-cat!"

"Let's go inside," I suggested, and started walking up the drive toward the side door of the house. I figured it would be safer inside until I got used to him.

He didn't say anything, and a second later I heard the wagon behind me. I turned around and he steered straight for me. He skinned both my shins, but I kept my temper.

"That's the end of that," I said, when I could walk again. "You can't use the wagon if you're going to go out into the road."

I took the wagon inside the garage and found a nail on the wall. I lifted the wagon up and hung it beyond Danny's reach. Then I took him by the hand and we went inside.

"I don't like you," he said, glaring at me.

I could have told him my opinion of him, but managed not to. Aunt Mabel warned me that the main thing I would need to be a good baby-sitter was the patience of a saint, but I hadn't figured on needing it so soon.

We had no more trouble the rest of the morning and were having a good time when Mrs. Wittenberg got home about twenty minutes after twelve. She paid me two dollars and a half.

About four-thirty the telephone rang. It was Mrs. Wittenberg. "Henry, could you come over and baby-sit for about an hour? An emergency has come up."

"Sure," I said. "I'll be there in ten minutes."

Danny met me at the kitchen door. Mrs. Wittenberg came hurrying down from upstairs a minute later.

"It was awfully nice of you to come on such short notice," she said. "I'm in sort of a jam. John's boss and his wife have been in Boston visiting their daughter and are on their way back to Cleveland. They just called from New York. There wasn't much else I could do but invite them for dinner and overnight."

She got out her mirror and put on some lipstick. "It isn't like it sounds. They're both very nice, and I'm delighted to have them. It's just that this is un-expected and I'm not prepared for guests for dinner. Naturally I'd like to make a good impression. It's hopeless for me to try to give them directions to here from the turnpike, and even if I could it was Mrs. Bartlett calling and she wouldn't get them straight. So I said I would meet them at the Hightstown exit."

"Can I go along?" Danny asked.

"I think you'd better stay here and help Henry. What I need most, Henry, is to get things organized. I've been trying for ten minutes to get my husband, but the telephone is busy. And I have to go because if they make good time, we'll both get to Hightstown at about the same time." She handed me a slip of paper. "Here's Mr. Wittenberg's number. He's usually there until about five-thirty. Keep calling until you get him. Tell him the Bartletts are coming for dinner and the night, and he's to pick up a nice big steak and we'll cook it on the grill. Also some tomatoes for the salad. Luckily I baked an apple pie this afternoon."

38

I took the piece of paper and wrote down *Bartlett, Steak,* and *Tomatoes.* Mrs. Wittenberg was all flustered about her husband's boss coming to visit, but I was calm and efficient just like my advertisement said.

"John mowed all the lawn except that part to the right of the path there in the back yard," she said, pointing out the kitchen window. "Of course that's just the part that needs mowing if we're going to eat outside. Danny will show you where the mower is. Would you mow that and see that everything around the grill is neat? Then, if you have time, would you lay a charcoal fire? By that time John ought to be home."

"I'm to have the fire ready for lighting, but not to light it?" I asked.

"That's right. I'll leave everything in your hands. I know I can depend on you, Henry."

As soon as she drove off I went inside and tried to call her husband's office. It was busy the first two times I called, but finally a woman answered the telephone.

"Mr. Wittenberg is not in," she said. "He had to go out on an important call and he won't be back this afternoon."

"This is Henry Reed of Henry Reed's Baby-Sitting Service," I told her. "I'm calling for Mrs. Wittenberg and it's very important that I get in touch with him. Is there some place I can call him?"

"I'm afraid there isn't. He asked me to call Mrs. Wittenberg and say that he wouldn't be home until six-thirty or a quarter to seven."

I went outside and mowed the little patch of lawn

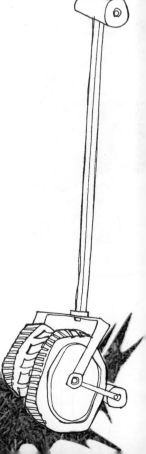

while I thought about this. Mrs. Wittenberg was going to get home before he did, and when she found nothing had been done and there was nothing to cook, she'd be really upset. She was nervous about the whole visit anyhow. I laid the charcoal fire and tidied up around the grill, and then I went inside and called Midge.

"I ought to do something because all the stores will be closed before she gets home," I said after I had explained the situation.

"We've got a couple of packages of potato puffs in the freezer," Midge said. "We could lend her those. Also I'm sure we have tomatoes. But we don't have any steaks. The only thing we've got is a beautiful roast of beef and I'd be shot if I took that."

"Could you bring the potatoes and tomatoes over?" I asked. "I'll see if I can find anything here."

I looked through the refrigerator. There was half a loin of pork, the remains of a piece of corned beef, and some luncheon meat. There was lots of cheese, some dishes with some odds and ends of vegetables, and three bottles of milk. Finally, on the bottom shelf, I found a plastic bag with some uncooked chopped meat. The freezer compartment had an assortment of vegetables and a half gallon of ice cream.

Midge arrived on her bicycle a minute later. "Midge Glass's Emergency Food Service coming to the rescue of the natives!" she called from the driveway.

After I had introduced her to Danny, I told her about the food situation.

"Well, the guests eat hamburgers, I guess," Midge

40

said. "Potato puffs, salad, hamburgers, another vege-
table, and apple pie with ice cream. Not bad at all."

"I like hamburgers," Danny said. "I want two."

"We haven't any rolls," Midge said. "And I know we
haven't any at home."

Aunt Mabel usually keeps several packages in the
freezer, so I called her. We were in luck. Midge stayed
with Danny while I rode home for the rolls. By the
time I got back it was a quarter to six. Mrs. Wittenberg
should have been back from Hightstown, but there was
no sign of her.

"She could have missed them or they might have
been held up by traffic," I said.

"Well, let's get everything ready," Midge said. "We
can make the salad and put it in the icebox, and get
the hamburgers ready. I know how to make a wonderful barbecue sauce if she has catsup, soy sauce, and
mustard."

Cooking isn't too difficult. The three of us had fun.
It got to be six-thirty and still there was no sign of
either of the Wittenbergs. By this time the salad was
made, the potatoes were in the pan in the oven, ready
to be turned on, the rolls were ready to be heated,
and we had a pot with a little bit of water all ready for
the string beans. The hamburgers were made and on a
tray covered with waxed paper, and Midge's special
barbecue sauce was mixed and waiting in a dish. I
went out and lighted the fire.

Mrs. Wittenberg arrived at ten minutes to seven.
The Bartletts had got off the turnpike one exit too
soon and had waited for her for fifteen minutes before

they learned their mistake. I was standing by the barbecue when the two cars came in the driveway. Mrs. Wittenberg looked at the lawn I'd mowed and the outdoor table which was all set, and smiled happily.

"Everything looks lovely, Henry. Is Mr. Wittenberg inside?"

"He's not home yet," I said. "He left word that he'd be home about a quarter to seven."

Mrs. Wittenberg looked rather sick. "Then he didn't get my message?"

"No, he had left the office before you left here. Midge Glass is in the kitchen though. She's my partner. We borrowed a few items from her house and we have things about ready. You'll have to eat hamburgers, though, instead of steak."

"I love hamburgers," Mr. Bartlett said, coming over to look at the fire. "Fire looks about right."

Midge brought out the platter of hamburgers and Mr. Bartlett helped me cook them. In fact he did most of the cooking. Midge had made an extra big pot of her barbecue sauce, and each time Mr. Bartlett turned the hamburgers, he put on more sauce. They were beginning to smell good when Mr. Wittenberg drove in. He barely had time to wash his hands before everything was ready to serve. Midge brought out the potatoes and beans and rolls from the kitchen, and Danny carried the big bowl of salad. It was a well-organized operation and a delicious-looking dinner.

Mrs. Wittenberg asked us to stay, which we had expected. By this time it was a little late for us to get anything at home. We had plenty of everything,

42

so we set up the table for Midge, Danny, and me. Consommé, the poodle, went back and forth between tables and got tidbits from everyone.

Everyone seemed to enjoy the food, especially Mr. Bartlett. He came back twice for hamburgers. "I'll have to get your recipe for that barbecue sauce, young lady," he said to Midge. "Best hamburgers I ever ate."

There wasn't much cleaning up to do except to throw the paper plates and trash in the incinerator. Midge and I cleaned up our table and were ready to go while all the adults at the other table were still eating their pie and drinking their coffee. Mrs. Wittenberg walked down the drive with us.

"I can't tell you how much I appreciate your pitching in like this. Instead of being in an embarrassing situation, I think we've made a very good impression on John's boss."

She paid us and said, "I also owe you some food. I'd better write it down so I'll remember."

"Two packages of potato puffs. four tomatoes, and two packages of hamburger rolls," Midge said.

"What about the hamburger?"

"That was yours," I told her. "I found it in your refrigerator."

Mrs. Wittenberg looked very peculiar. "In a plastic bag?" she asked.

"That's right. On the bottom shelf."

"That was Consommé's ground horse meat," she said, swallowing twice.

Midge began to giggle. "Mr. Bartlett wanted my recipe. Wait till he hears it!"

Mrs. Wittenberg managed to smile. She reached in her purse and handed us both a dollar. "I'm not trying to bribe you, but I'd appreciate it if you'd not say a thing about this to anyone—and especially not until the Bartletts have gone."

Mrs. Wittenberg gave a feeble smile and hurried back to her guests. Midge and I rode off on our bikes. I got to thinking about those horseburgers and wondering what the horse had looked like. My stomach began to churn a little.

"Do you feel a little queasy?" I asked Midge.

"Never felt better," Midge said. "I'm a real chef. Anyone who can take old horse meat and make it into delicious hamburgers, so that the guest of honor comes back for seconds and thirds, is a culinary genius."

I'd had seconds, which didn't make me feel any better. "Don't you feel peculiar, eating horse meat?" I asked.

"Yes, it makes me want to kick up my heels, except I can't because I'm riding a bicycle."

Midge is a good friend and you can depend on her in an emergency, but she can be childish at times. That horse meat didn't bother her a bit. Women are supposed to be more sensitive than men, but I doubt it.

—Keith Robertson

THINKING IT OVER

1. The story was told from Henry's point of view. How do you think Mrs. Wittenberg might have told about the Bartlett's visit and the preparations for it?

2. What words would you use to describe Henry? Midge? Danny? Be ready to give reasons for your choices.

3. At what points in the story did you feel *worried*? When were you *angry*? What parts *amused* you?

THOUGHTS AT WORK

1. If you had to take care of Danny for an afternoon, how might you have kept him out of mischief?

2. On page 44 Henry said that "Mrs. Wittenberg gave a feeble smile." How would you have acted if you had been in the same situation?

3. Mr. Wittenberg was mentioned very little in the story, but he played an important part in the events of the day. Explain why.

4. How do you think the Bartletts would have reacted if they had learned about the horse-meat burgers?

5. List in order all of the jobs Henry and Midge did for the Wittenbergs. Do you believe that they earned their pay? Why or why not?

If you lived near a lake and were bored with a summer of swimming and boating and fishing, you just might liven things up with a strange sea monster. But how would you go about it? As you read this story, you may get some ideas.

The Strange Sea Monster of Strawberry Lake

Dinky Poore didn't really mean to start the story about the huge sea monster in Strawberry Lake. He was only telling a fib because he had to have an excuse for getting home late for supper. So he told his folks he'd been running around the lake trying to get a close look at a huge, snakelike thing he'd seen in the water, and the first thing he knew he was too far from home to get back in time.

His mother and father greeted this tale with some skepticism. But Dinky's two sisters were more impressionable, and that's how the story really got out. They kept pestering him for so many details about the monster that he had to invent a fantastic tale to satisfy them. That's one of the troubles with a lie. You've got to keep adding to it to make it believable to people.

It didn't take long for the story to get around town, and pretty soon Dinky Poore was a celebrity in Mammoth Falls. He even had his picture in the paper, together with an "artist's conception" of the thing he had seen. It was gruesome-looking—something like a dinosaur, but with a scaly, saw-toothed back like a dragon. Dinky was never short on imagination, and he was able to give the artist plenty of details.

It was the artist's sketch in the newspaper that got Henry Mulligan all excited. Henry is first vice-president and also chief of research for the Mad Scientists' Club and is noted for his brainstorms. No one in the club actually believed Dinky had seen a real monster, but we were all willing to play along with a gag—especially when Henry suggested that we could build a monster just like the one shown in the newspaper.

"Build a monster?" Freddy Muldoon's round face was all goggle-eyed. He liked the idea, but he just didn't know how Henry proposed going about it. He rubbed his button nose, which was always itching, and asked, "You mean a real monster that can swim?"

"Don't be a dope," said Dinky.

"I'm not a dope. But who ever heard of a monster that can't swim?"

"The one we build will float," said Henry, rubbing his chin and looking up at the rafters of the club laboratory the way he always did when he was speculating on a new project. "All we need is some canvas and chicken wire, and Jeff Crocker's canoe."

Jeff Crocker is president of our club—mainly because his father owns the barn that we have our lab in, but also because he's just as smart as Henry and maybe a little more scientific. Henry dreams up most of the schemes that we get messed up in; but it is usually Jeff who figures out how to do everything, or how to get us out of what we got into.

Since Henry's plan to build a lake monster seemed like a good one, we held a formal meeting of the club that night to take a vote on it. Naturally, we all voted in favor of it, and three days later we had most of it finished. We built it on a small piece of dry land hidden 'way back in the swampy end of the lake. Henry and Jeff had designed a frame of light lumber and laths that had the shape of a big land lizard, and we suspended this across the gunwales of the canoe. Then we hung chicken wire on the frame and stretched canvas over it. With a little paint and a few shiny tin can lids spotted here and there, we soon had a loathsome-looking creature guaranteed to scare the life out of anyone a hundred yards away from it.

Jeff had to keep putting the brakes on Henry's fancy ideas, but he did let him outfit the head with a pair of red eyes—which were just flashlights with red lenses stuck out through the canvas. Henry installed a switch and circuit breaker in the canoe, so that the "eyes" could be made to blink. After two days of practice back in the swamps we figured we could handle the beast well enough to make a test run out on the lake. The monster's profile stuck up about four feet out of the water, and it was a cinch for four of us to sit upright in the canoe to do the paddling and steering.

Meanwhile, the town was still all excited about the possibility that there was a real, live sea monster in Strawberry Lake. A reporter from one of the big city papers had been in town to interview Dinky Poore, and when folks heard this, a lot of them began to recall seeing strange things on the water. Everybody wanted to get into the act, and pretty soon all sorts of people were volunteering information. Daphne Muldoon got her picture on the front page, not because she had seen the monster, but because she lived in Mammoth Falls and had a good-looking face and pretty legs. Daphne is one of Freddy Muldoon's cousins. Her younger brother, Harmon, used to be a member of our club. But he got kicked out for conduct unbecoming a scientist and for giving away secret information.

The first night we took the beast out was a Saturday, when the lake cabins and beachfront were crowded with weekend visitors. We figured it was best to wait until just before dark, then people couldn't see too well and there were fewer boats on the lake. There are plenty of small islands near the swampy end of Strawberry Lake, and this gave us a good chance to get the monster out into open water for a short run and then scoot it back into the cover of the swamp before anyone could discover where it had gone.

Homer Snodgrass, who is one of the brighter members of our club, had agreed to sit on the front porch of his folks' cabin so that we could get a first-hand report on what the monster looked like from the shore. Jeff and I were sitting in the middle of the canoe and doing the paddling. Mortimer Dalrymple,[1] our electronics wizard, was steering; and Henry sat up

[1] Mortimer Dalrymple (môr′tə mèr) (dal′rim pəl)

50

in the prow, where he could look out through two peepholes.

"Are there many people on the beach?" Jeff asked.

"Scads of them," said Henry. "It's still light enough to see pretty well, but nobody has sighted us yet."

It was dark as black velvet inside the monster, though, and there was a damp, musty odor of canvas and paint. It was a little like being in the Tunnel of Love at an amusement park. I started to giggle, and Jeff told me to shut up or I might spoil everything. But I think he wanted to giggle too, and was afraid I might start him off.

"Don't get all shook up," came Mortimer's quiet voice from somewhere in the darkness back toward the monster's tail. Mortimer is always quiet like that. He never gets excited about anything. "It's half a mile over to the beach. They can't hear us unless we make a real big noise," he pointed out.

51

Suddenly Henry jumped violently, bumping his head on the framework of the beast's spine and rocking the canoe. "They've seen us," he cried.

"What? How do you know?" asked Jeff in a whisper.

"There's a whole bunch of them running out to the end of the boat dock. They're jumping up and down and pointing out here and waving and screaming."

Henry was right. We could hear some shouting now, and a few shrill screams of women.

"Let's rock the boat some!" Mortimer shouted from the back. "Give 'em a good show!" He was excited too, for once.

"I can't see anything now," Henry cried. "My glasses are all wet."

We could hear Henry moving around up front, as Mortimer started rocking the canoe from the rear and swishing the beast's huge tail back and forth through the water. Suddenly there was a splash and a gurgle, and my paddle hit something heavy and soft. Then there was a glurping noise, and something grabbed my paddle and tried to pull it out of my hands. There was a lot of thrashing going on, and I got scared and started hollering at Jeff to help me. The canoe and the whole framework of the monster were rocking violently.

"Maybe we've run into a real monster!" Mortimer snickered.

"Shut up and stop rocking," Jeff shouted. "Where's Henry?"

Just then Henry's head appeared right beside me, and one of his hands grasped the gunwale of the canoe.

52

"Glurp," he said, "my glasses, I—lost 'em."

By this time Mortimer had stopped rocking and we managed to pull Henry back into the canoe.

"Get up front and see where we are," Jeff commanded, shoving me by the shoulder. "We've got to get this monster out of here before somebody starts chasing us in a motorboat. Henry, what were you doing in the water, anyway?"

Henry was choking on lake water, and didn't bother to answer.

When we got back into town that night, we stopped in for a Coke and ice cream at Martin's Ice Cream Parlor, where Homer had agreed to meet us. The whole town was buzzing. Everybody in Martin's was talking about the sea monster, and about how Dinky Poore had been right, after all. We took a booth in a corner, where nobody could overhear us, and listened to Homer's report. There was no doubt the beast had been a sensational success. Homer said it had almost rolled over once and all the women on the beach had screamed. When Homer left the beach, state police cars had arrived and were sweeping the lake with their spotlights. But they didn't see anything, of course.

We took the monster out a couple more times that week, and got to be pretty expert at handling her. The town just about went wild. The newspaper offered a hundred dollars as a prize to anyone who could get a picture of the beast, and people started flocking into Mammoth Falls from all over the state, hoping to get a look at it. Lake cabins were renting for as

54

high as two hundred dollars apiece, when they used to bring fifty a week; and a lot of local families just moved back into town and rented their cabins out to sightseers. All the concessions at the beach were doing a booming business, and the restaurants and the one hotel in town couldn't handle the crowds. Homer's father, who runs a hardware store, said he'd never seen such business.

Pretty soon we realized we had a tiger by the tail. Business was so good, and people in town were so happy, that we didn't dare stop taking the monster out, even though it was wearing us down.

We soon had something worse to worry about, however. Homer Snodgrass came running over to my house right after lunch one day, all breathless.

"Guess what?" said Homer.

"Guess what?" I asked.

"Give the club code word!" he said.

"Skinamaroo!" I said.

"The information you are about to receive is classified *confidential*," Homer panted. "You swear not to tell it to anyone not a member of the Mad Scientists' Club?"

"I swear!"

Then Homer told me that Harmon Muldoon had been in his father's store with two men. They wanted ammunition for an elephant gun. Mr. Snodgrass doesn't carry that kind of ammunition, of course, but he did tell them where they could order it in the city. The two men were from out of town, and they said Harmon had promised to show them an island in the lake where they could set up a campsite and try to get a good shot at the monster when it came out in the evening. They decided to drive to the city to pick up the ammunition.

This news called for an emergency meeting of the club in executive session, and we held it that night in Jeff's barn. Everyone agreed that we couldn't take the beast out again and risk being shot through the head with an elephant gun. But Homer argued that we couldn't disappoint all the merchants and other people in town who were making money on the tourists. Dinky Poore, as usual, was in favor of writing a letter to the President and asking for his help.

While we were arguing, Henry Mulligan suddenly turned his eyes up toward the rafters and started stroking his chin. Whenever this happens, everybody stops talking and waits for Henry to speak. After a decent interval of respectful silence, Henry brought his eyes down and fixed them on Jeff.

"Your father has a small outboard motor that can be mounted on the canoe, hasn't he?"

"Sure," said Jeff. "We use it for fishing at the shallow end of the lake."

"And it's a pretty quiet one, as I remember?"

"It doesn't even scare the fish."

"O.K.," said Henry. "Now, if Homer can bamboozle his father out of a few essential pieces of hardware, I think we have enough equipment here in the lab to rig that motor up so that it can be controlled by radio. Then all we have to do is pick a good spot on the shore for our transmitters—on one of those steep hills on the north side—and we can make the beast do anything we want it to."

"And those hunters can shoot at it all they want, and they won't do anything more than put a few holes in the canvas," observed Mortimer.

"Jeepers," said Dinky. "I bet that'll make Harmon mad!"

In about a week we had most of the club's radio gear rigged up in the canoe so that we could make Jeff's outboard motor speed up, slow down, idle, turn right or left, and reverse itself. We made a few short test runs with it 'way back in the swamp end of the lake, and everything worked fine. This time Jeff agreed to letting Henry add a pump that would squirt water out of the beast's nostrils. And he even gave in to another of Henry's brainstorms. Freddy could make a bellow that sounded like a bull moose on a rampage—because his voice was beginning to change. So Henry figured it would be a good idea to install a loudspeaker in the belly of the monster and let Freddy bellow into a microphone once in a while from the place where we hid the transmitting equipment.

The first trip of the motorized monster was a sensation. Homer and Dinky and I couldn't see much of it–because it was our job to go back in the swamp, get the beast from its hiding place, and start the motor. Then we called Jeff on our walkie-talkie and he directed the operation from the wooded hill where we had our transmitting apparatus. Henry and Mortimer operated the radio controls to steer the beast and make the eyes blink and the nostrils spout water.

Freddy stood by to bellow whenever Jeff tapped him on the shoulder. Jeff watched the monster all the time through binoculars.

She moved through the water much faster now, and every time Freddy let out with the bull-moose call it echoed back and forth among the hills and caused a regular panic on the beach. We got her back into the protection of the swamp just before dark, all right; but we had some anxious moments when she passed the last island out in open water. Four or five shots were fired at her, and Jeff said he could see the bullets splashing in the water. But the beast kept on going as though nothing had happened, and this must have caused Harmon's hunter friends some consternation.

The next day every newspaper in the country must have carried the story. They quoted eyewitnesses who swore that the monster was mad about something, because it was swimming a lot faster and making a frightening noise. A scientist in New York speculated that it might be the mating season for the beast, and suggested the possibility that there might actually be two of them. Within three days there must have been a hundred and fifty reporters in Mammoth Falls from newspapers, magazines, and radio and television stations. Newsreel camera crews were lined up along the beach, and several of them had large searchlights ready to sweep across the surface of the lake at dusk, when the monster usually appeared.

We kept the beast under wraps for a few days, and spent the time visiting with the camera crews and reporters. Most of them were camped on the beach, sleeping in cars and station wagons, because there weren't any rooms available in town. Besides getting a good line on what the reporters were planning to do, we were able to make a little money for the club treasury by running errands for them and operating a lemonade stand. Hot dogs were selling for thirty cents apiece at the beach, and for fifteen cents in town. We did a pretty good business buying them at Martin's Ice Cream Parlor and running them out to the beach in thermos jugs on our bicycles. Freddy Muldoon was able to get five dollars for an old telescope, and Henry traded some of his father's shaving cream for flash bulbs and camera film. We kept Dinky Poore's mother pretty busy making cakes and pies; but we didn't make much money on this venture, because Dinky and Freddy would eat up most of the profit. They also drank too much lemonade, and after the first day Jeff wouldn't let them run the stand any more.

By this time several of the reporters had made camp on the same island the hunters had been on, and rented some high-powered motorboats. They were determined to get close enough to the monster to get some good pictures. There were also a lot of people tramping around the shore every day, trying to get back into the swampy end of the lake. So we decided to move the beast to a new hiding place.

We picked out a deep cove studded with rocks and small islands, about two miles east of the swamp. Late at night, long after the searchlights had been turned off and people had gone to sleep, we towed the monster over there with a rowboat. Early the next morning, before the sun had come up, we took her out for a brief appearance on the lake and caught everybody by surprise. Some early-morning watchers on the beach started shouting, and this woke up a few of the reporters on the island. But the monster was not where they expected her to be, and by the time some of them had scrambled into their boats we had her back into the cove and covered up among a jumble of rocks.

This created quite a lot of confusion, and people began to believe the professor who had claimed there might be two monsters. But we could see that the string was running out for us. There were so many people exploring the lake now and so many "scientific expeditions" on their way to investigate the "phenomenon," as they called it, that we were pretty sure somebody would discover our hiding place sooner or later. Even though most people were too scared to take boats out any more, there were several boats making regular patrols of the lake, and every once in a while a helicopter would fly over it.

We held a meeting to discuss the situation. Dinky Poore argued that Abraham Lincoln said you couldn't fool all of the people all of the time, and we might as well quit while we were ahead and claim the hundred-dollar reward the newspaper was offering. But Henry claimed that P. T. Barnum had proved Lincoln was wrong, and so had a lot of politicians. Homer Snodgrass was in favor of continuing as long as we could, because all the extra tourist business was good for the town, and Mammoth Falls had always been a pretty poor place. But Mortimer and Jeff and I were beginning to feel that we should confess the whole business to Mayor Scragg, because he was getting worried about the monster making the lake unsafe for boating and swimming. We also felt that Harmon Muldoon would get wise to us pretty soon and spill the beans. We had seen him sneaking around the lab a lot lately, and trying to follow us sometimes. We knew Harmon was a pretty bright boy. He had been our radio expert when he was in the club, and he had enough brains to figure out the whole deal eventually.

Freddy wasn't around when the meeting started, but he came busting in now, all out of breath after running all the way from his house. "The jig is up, fellas," he announced. "I think Harmon has snitched on us!"

We all started questioning Freddy at once, of course, and Jeff had to rap for order so that we could get the story straight. It seems that Harmon had been up early in the morning, fiddling with his ham radio outfit, and had picked up Freddy's bellow coming over the air. He recognized it as the sound the monster made, and he knew that it couldn't get on the air unless the monster was sitting next to a microphone.

"Holy smoke!" said Mortimer, slapping himself on the forehead. "We should have had brains enough to change all our frequencies after Harmon left the club. He knows which ones we use."

Freddy explained that Harmon had then gone to the local newspaper and told a reporter what he suspected, in the hopes of claiming the reward. The editors didn't intend to print his story until they had more proof, but they were certainly going to investigate his theory. Freddy got all this information from his father, who works in the composing room.

It didn't take us long to make a decision after getting this news. Mortimer had made good friends with one of the out-of-town reporters on the beach. His name was Bud Stewart and he wrote for the *Cleveland Plain Dealer*, which we knew was a big newspaper. So Jeff and Mortimer went to see him, and told him the story after he had agreed to a proposition. He got his home office to agree to buy the club an oscilloscope and a ten-channel transmitter for our lab, in return for exclusive pictures of the monster. Then we all sat down with Mr. Stewart and mapped out a plan of action.

Early the next morning we took him to our hiding place and uncovered the monster for him so he could take pictures of it. He also wanted to get some pictures of the beast in action, of course, so we planned to take it out for an excursion that very night. We figured that if we waited any longer Harmon Muldoon would have time to show the local newspaper people how to get a fix on the location of our transmitter by tuning in our frequency from two or three different places. Mr. Stewart went out to the airport to hire a helicopter. He planned to fly over the lake just before dusk, and when we saw him we were to unleash the monster.

That night we were all in our positions early, just in case Mr. Stewart misjudged the time. It seemed like a long wait, but he finally appeared and waved to us from the helicopter. We had the beast all ready and started her out to the open water. Those of us who had to stay back in the cove couldn't see what happened next, but we could tell from all the shouts and the way the helicopter was flying that this was the monster's most triumphant appearance. We got all the details later, including a look at Mr. Stewart's pictures.

63

The reporters who were camped on the island were ready for us this time, and three boatloads of them appeared as soon as the monster got out there. They had newsreel cameras mounted in the boats, and they were only about half a mile from the beast when Jeff gave the order to head her back to the cove. But Henry couldn't make her do a tight enough turn, and she started back on the far side of a large island that lay across the mouth of the cove. This island is a huge granite mountaintop that rises up out of the water as high as a hundred feet in some places. Once the beast got behind this mass, Henry lost contact with her, and for a few moments she was running free. For some reason the monster doubled back on its tracks, and to everyone's amazement shot out from behind the island again, heading straight for the boats of the pursuing cameramen. Incredibly, the beast suddenly gained speed and went roaring full throttle at the tiny boats—now less than a quarter of a mile away.

The newspaper men in the boats had been busy signaling their crewmen on the shore to turn on the big searchlights, and they didn't notice that the monster had reversed its course until it had closed almost half the gap between them. When they did turn to see it bearing down on them, with nostrils spouting spray and the red eyes blinking, panic broke loose among them. All three boats suddenly turned to head back for the safety of the beach. One of them nearly collided with another and had to turn so sharply that it capsized, spilling its occupants and its gear into the lake. There

had been five men in the boat, and when they rose to the surface they swam frantically for the nearest island.

Henry and Mortimer, meanwhile, were pushing buttons and flipping switches so fast that the two of them looked like a centipede with a case of poison ivy. But no matter what they did they couldn't regain control of the beast. Suddenly Mortimer shouted, "Harmon Muldoon must be transmitting on our frequency, and he's got a stronger signal than we have! He's got the thing jammed at full throttle. Cut the receiver, Henry!"

Henry threw the emergency switch that cut off the power supply to the main receiver inside the beast. She slowed down so suddenly that the head almost went under water. Freddy was so excited that he gave out with a big "Hooray!" that sounded like the battle cry of a raging bull elephant. You could hear the screams of the people on the beach, as they heard it come out of the loudspeaker.

"Switch to the alternate receiver now!" cried Mortimer, and Henry did so. This one operated on a different frequency, and Mortimer had insisted on installing it in case something went wrong with the main one. Since Harmon couldn't know we were changing frequencies, it was not likely he could jam this one too.

The beast started back toward the cove like a docile cow coming home for supper, and the searchlights on the beach came on, finally. But all that the watchers on the shore could see was the tail of the beast disappearing in the darkness.

66

It was about two hours later that we met Mr. Stewart at Martin's Ice Cream Parlor to discuss what we should do next. The local radio station had just announced that Mayor Scragg had asked the Governor to get the Navy to fire depth charges in the lake in the hope of killing the monster. The reporters and cameramen stranded on the little island had been rescued by a police launch, but they were mad as wet hens and had apparently convinced the Mayor that the beast was a menace to the public health and safety.

We went back out to the lake that night and stripped all our equipment out of the beast, including Jeff Crocker's canoe. We mounted her frame on an old raft that someone had abandoned on the shore. Then we towed her far enough out in the lake so that she would be visible from the shore in the morning, and anchored her there. We hung a wreath of pine cones

on her neck, and Henry and Mortimer rigged up some kind of a diabolical device inside her.

As soon as it was light in the morning we all climbed up to the place on the hillside where our transmitters were located. We could see a few people on the beach looking at the beast through binoculars, but nobody was taking any boats out. When the sun started to peep over the ridge at the east end of the lake, Henry pushed a button and a lot of smoke came billowing out of the monster. All of a sudden she burst into flames that climbed about thirty feet high, and a big column of black smoke went up into the sky. When the smoke had cleared away there was nothing left on the lake but a dirty smear of oil and a few pieces of black debris—and that was the last that anyone ever saw of the strange sea monster of Strawberry Lake.

We packed up our gear and started for home; and Dinky Poore, who is the youngest member of the Mad Scientists' Club, started to cry a little bit as we were trudging through the woods. Since the monster had really been his idea in the beginning, I guess he felt as though he had lost a close relative. But Jeff told him he could have two votes the next time the club had a meeting, and he had stopped blubbering by the time we got home.

—*Bertrand Brinley*

THINKING IT OVER

1. Give as many reasons as you can to explain why the boys built the sea monster.

2. Explain why you believe that this story could or could not have happened.

3. Describe the part of the story which you thought was the most amusing.

THOUGHTS AT WORK

1. Do you think Dinky Poore's fib was important to the story? Explain your answer.

2. The person who told this story was one of the members of the Mad Scientists' Club. Did he consider Henry or Jeff the better scientist? Why do you think so?

3. Below are the names of the members of the Mad Scientists' Club. List three or four words to describe each one and be ready to explain your choices.

   Dinky Poore   Freddy Muldoon   Homer Snodgrass
   Mortimer Dalrymple   Jeff Crocker   Henry Mulligan

4. How did the publicity about the sea monster affect Mammoth Falls? Explain why you think the publicity was good or bad for the town.

5. What do you think would have happened if the boys had not destroyed the monster at the end of the story?

6. What did the narrator mean when he said on page 55, "Pretty soon we realized we had a tiger by the tail"?

7. Pretend you are one of the newspaper reporters assigned to Mammoth Falls. Describe in your own words the day the monster blew up.

This is realistic fiction about two boys who go sailing on the ocean one windy day when there is a hint of storm clouds on the horizon. The sea is not a playground. It can be savage. It can kill. It can demand all the strength and courage a person has.

The two boys change in this story, just as the sea changes before a storm. Watch them carefully as you read about their adventure, and notice how they change.

70

SAIL CALYPSO!

It was Clay who first found the old hulk half buried in the sands. It was he who dug it out and read the name in faded letters across her stern, *Calypso*. Every day of this summer he hastened to the beach right after breakfast to work on the old wreck, to clean the sand from her sides, and to dream of making her sea-worthy again.

Then one morning on arriving at the beach, he saw a boy's head looking up at him from inside the *Calypso*. A stranger in his boat! Clay ran forward furiously to challenge the newcomer. But Paul claimed the boat as his. "I found her too," he said. Clay insisted that he had already begun work on her and hence had a better claim than the younger boy.

For a while they hated each other as each one tried to improve the condition of "his" *Calypso*. But gradually hatred gave way to a grudging tolerance as they saw that each of them had something to contribute and together they could achieve what separately would be impossible for them. Tolerance turned to friendship as the summer sped by. When the time came to practice sailing the *Calypso* in a nearby pond, each boy would have found it hard to imagine sailing her alone.

After that practice sail they were ready for the open sea. Their objective was an island opposite their shore. It had been beckoning them for weeks. So on this particular morning they set forth, reaching the island without mishap. But before they had had time to explore it thoroughly, they noticed that the sky had become overcast and a wind was rising.

"I smell rain," Clay said. The wind blew gusty and damp, cold against his body. He shivered. "C'mon!"

Together he and Paul ran to where the *Calypso* awaited them on the sand.

They launched the boat and worked it through the shallows, Clay at the tiller and Paul at the bow on the lookout for rocks. Free of them at last, Clay brought her about and now they were running before the wind, headed for the mainland.

72

Paul turned an anxious face to Clay who grinned and shouted over the wind, "She'll take us back safe, Paul! Don't you worry."

"She'd better!" Paul, catching some of Clay's spirit, laughed and the shakiness of the sound was covered by the wind. "I don't swim very well. That's an awfully long way to land!"

Then Clay remembered the orange life jackets he had found so long ago, remembered he had thrust them back into the locker and forgotten them. Until now.

"Hey!" he called. "Get those orange things out of the locker. Now's when we need 'em. Just in case . . ."

So Paul found the jackets and hauled them out. He slipped into one, awkward for a moment with the two ties that cinched in front.

"You'd float 'most forever in that!" Clay assured him. "Take the tiller now, and I'll get into the other one."

So finally they were both secure in the jackets and the bright color was somehow reassuring and cheerful in the dark vastness of sea and clouds.

They could still see the mainland far ahead as the swells swept under and past them, hurrying to that low shore, alternately raising them to the dizzy crests, then plunging them with stomach-clutching suddenness into the troughs.

The rain had begun to fall. At first there were only wind-driven spits of stinging drops. Then it came more steadily. Lightning slashed across the black sky. Thunder crashed above them. And the rain increased.

Clay struggled with tiller and sheet. Paul bailed furiously. The water from the downpour mingled with the seawater that the *Calypso* had already shipped. Slowly it rose until it was up as high as the boys' ankles, a small sea of itself, dashing and sloshing about as the boat pitched and yawed in the running swells.

"I can't see land any more!" Paul yelled.

"Me neither!" And for only a second Clay took his eyes from the sail, the mast, and the danger of the swinging boom. "I'm trying to keep the wind behind us! And the swells are running toward the beach! Maybe we ought to try to take the sail in. The water's bound to push us into shore!"

He didn't like to think of the size of the breakers that would be pounding the beach. How would they ever get the *Calypso* in with the waves breaking over her stern! But there was no time to worry about that.

"Shall I lower the sail?" Paul called.

"Yeah. Be careful! Don't go overboard! You'd never get back in! Not the way the *Calypso's* rolling!"

Paul stowed the bailing can. He moved cautiously forward, gripping the rail. When he was opposite the mast, he reached for it, stretching to keep the safety of the rail until he had grasped the spar with one hand. Then wary of the boom, he pulled himself over, squatted there with a tight hold on the mast, and began to work with the halyard. It was wet and his fingers were icy. With the wind behind them the sail jerked and bucked and pulled so tight that he could not manage the soaked line.

Clay close-hauled the sheet, as much as his strength would allow. He managed to pull the boom in almost parallel to the *Calypso's* length. Thus the wind, driving over the stern, had less surface to batter. He knew now they should have lowered the sail long ago. Anxiously he glanced at Paul who still clung to the mast trying to loosen the jammed halyard. Once the other turned and Clay could see him shake his head, but then Paul once more bent doggedly to the task.

"Man, if those clouds would only rise up a little," he muttered to himself, to the *Calypso*. "If I was just sure we're sailing for the beach instead of China . . ."

Then presently, as though the clouds had plucked his wish from the swirling air, they lifted a little above the water's surface and thinned a bit.

Clay was sorry he had uttered the words!

For before the clouds closed in once more, the *Calypso* had topped a white-ridged swell and Clay had his view of the mainland. It was nearer, much nearer, than he had thought it would be! Even from this seaward side he could see the breakers pounding the beach, making a foaming terror of the surf. In that brief view before the clouds closed in once more, the boiling stretch of sea looked like certain death for the *Calypso*.

"Paul!" Clay shouted. "Paul . . ."

The other did not hear him, but seemed welded to the mast as though intending to work through eternity at the task of the jammed line.

Desperate, Clay screamed, "Paul! Paul! We gotta turn her! Watch the boom! We gotta turn! Paul! Watch out. . . ."

Though the wind seemed to smother his cry before it had left his lips, it could not mask another sound — the wild clash of surf along the shore; the thundering, pounding force that would break the *Calypso* into a thousand pieces, that would grind Paul and himself into the sand along the ocean floor.

Once more he screamed, "Paul!"

And as though the desperation reached the other when the sound could not, Paul raised his head and looked back at Clay.

"I'm gonna come around!" Clay shouted. "Keep your head down! Hold on!"

Now Paul shrank against the mast, holding tightly, watching Clay struggle with the yanking sheet. His blue eyes were wide but he seemed calm enough and even managed an encouraging nod, though by now he could hear the roar of the surf and understood their danger. Their eyes held for an instant, then Clay was putting the tiller over just as the *Calypso* started her slide down the steep backslope into a trough.

The valiant little craft managed half the turn before she hit the bottom of the slant. The dark water seemed to pile above her on all sides. Clay forced the tiller as far as it would go. Just as the bow began to finish the arc of its turn, the rising slope of the next wave began to lift her. All might have gone well, but a malignant lash of wind caught the sail from a new angle, yanked it against the *Calypso's* natural roll. She plunged to one side. Her starboard rail raked beneath the water. Clay was thrown violently to the bottom of the boat. In that instant he lost his hold on the tiller, and the sheet whipped free, lashing this way and that.

He wallowed, helpless, in the sloshing water that the *Calypso* had shipped. He clung to one bench, pulled

77

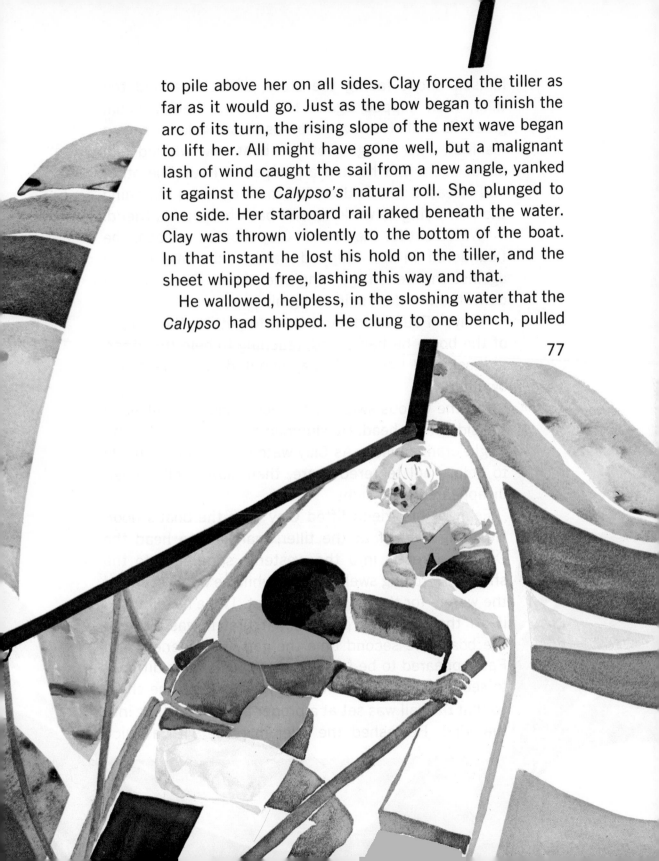

himself about facing the stern, almost reached the tiller, then slipped again. He felt the flailing boom graze his skull. He ducked low as he struggled to regain his feet. The plunging of the boat now whirled him about again and he had a glimpse of Paul. The other had released his hold on the mast and was clutching the rail, trying to work himself back to help his friend.

"Watch out for the boom!" Clay shouted but again he floundered in the shipped water. This time he fell against the bench, gashing one cheek. Blood spread down the wet dark skin along his jaw.

"Clay!" Paul cried. And then forgetting the danger of the boom he half stood, reaching to help the other.

"Look out! Paul . . ." Clay shouted, unaware of his own hurt.

But the vicious swipe of the boom caught Paul along the side of his head. He slumped across the rail, a limp bright orange pillow. As Clay watched in horror, unable to help, Paul teetered there, then slowly rolled over, disappeared from sight.

Fear for his friend lifted Clay from the boat's floor. He flung himself at the tiller, managed to head the *Calypso* directly into the westerly, squarely into the shoreward-rolling swells. All the while he wildly scanned the waters for the bright life jacket. Twice he glimpsed it off the *Calypso's* port rail. At first it was close to the boat. The second time the gap had widened. And Paul appeared to be face down, though it was difficult to see in the gloom. Frantically Clay secured the sheet so that the sail was set at a proper angle for sailing into the wind. He lashed the tiller in place with a quick turn of line to try and keep the *Calypso* heading straight seaward. Maybe he'd have a chance of bringing Paul back to the boat. Maybe—if the surge of the sea offset the *Calypso's* effort to make way—she might stay almost in the same place. Maybe—

Awkward in the bulky jacket, he worked his way along the rail. He kept looking for Paul in the roll of black water. The orange splotch had disappeared. Careful of the boom, he reached the mast. Clinging to the spar he stepped on the bench. Balanced there. Searching. Searching.

And strangely he remembered how Paul had looked that first day. He remembered Paul peering over the rail of the little derelict boat. An owl. A pale owl. He had hated the Owl for taking his new love. For taking the *Calypso*. When had the friendship truly begun? He couldn't remember! Now it was not the *Calypso's* fate that caused the sick panic in his middle.

Paul!

The *Calypso* climbed up the next long slope. As she rose the view broadened.

"Paul!" Clay cried aloud.

There! There, a splash of orange! Closer than Clay could possibly have hoped!

And Paul was not face down. Instead he floundered dizzily. He seemed unable to keep his head clear of the water for more than a few seconds at a time. He'd never make it to shore!

"Paul! Hold on . . ." Clay screamed.

With all of his strength he thrust himself away from the mast, kicked with all of the power of his sinewy

79

legs away from the rail. He arched through the air. Then he was in the water, striking out for the spot he had fixed upon.

His life jacket made swimming difficult, but each time one of the white-topped swells thrust him under, the buoyant jacket popped him back to the surface again.

If he couldn't find Paul soon, it would be too late! Then just as he was sure that the search had failed, he saw a flash of orange. The bright color had shown just at the crest of the swell ahead. He himself floundered in the trough. Now he strained to keep his head clear of the water. Up he rose on the rush of the next wave.

There it was again — the orange jacket! Catching the forward thrust of the swell just below its crest, Clay swam with all of his strength. The orange jacket had settled in the trough and now it began to rise. Furiously Clay pumped with arms, legs, managing to ride just in front of the white crest. He could see Paul's face now, the gaping mouth struggling for breath, the eyes nearly closed against the stinging spray.

Once more Clay thrust forward, snatched at the orange blob. Had it! Shifted his grasp! Now his grip was firm! He slipped one hand under Paul's chin, cupping his fingers over the open mouth, shielding it partly from the dashing brine.

"You're all right!" Clay managed to say close to his friend's ear. "Take it easy, you old Paul."

He was gasping himself from the effort of the swim. For the first time he was grateful for the awkward life jacket. Now it buoyed him and he saved his strength by resting in the harness with his mouth scarcely above the water.

"Go ahead—Breathe—I got you—That's it—See, we're okay—Breathe again—The jackets make us safe —safe as a bathtub—Breathe—That's it—"

Apparently it had been the blow from the boom that had made Paul so helpless, for now, slowly, he began to revive a little. Finally he was able to breathe when he should, hold his breath when the water swept over them. But Clay kept his grip on the other's jacket. Now he remembered the *Calypso*. Their little *Calypso*! Where was she? Was there any hope they could reach her?

Just as he was thinking that she must already have gone down, or maybe was dashing to splinters on the beach, he saw her.

"Hey . . ." he cried despite the wind and the roll of the sea—"there, she's sailing. . . ."

Weakly, Paul twisted his head, but when the wind-driven water slashed into his face, he turned away.

"She's sailing straight out to sea. . . ." Clay gasped, straining to see, blinking the stinging spray from his eyes. "She's leaving us!"

When Clay glanced again at the *Calypso*, he saw that the distance between them had widened. He had secured the sheet and lashed the tiller, and the little boat had picked up the westerly. It was as though her own spirit had taken command. With the weight of the boys gone, the shipped water only acted as ballast and she rode well across the running swells. Now she had managed to free herself of the shoreward-sweeping currents. She was heeling over to leeward, racing gaily across her sea, heading straight away from the land that had too long held her captive. She would not die upon the shore!

"The surf . . ." Clay heard Paul's voice.

He wrenched his gaze from the flying *Calypso*. At this moment they rode high on the crest of a mountain of dark water. The sea had swept them closer to shore. There was the beach, no more than two hundred yards away. But the surf! They had one terrible view of it before they dropped down the back of the swell.

"Next swell's gonna put us in it!" cried Clay.

Now from the trough the water rushed them upward again. It seemed as though this time they shot straight to the sky. They both gasped. For only an instant they looked down on all that surrounded them. The roar and thunder of tons of water crashed on the flat shore. Clay saw that the crest they rode was passing beneath them. He knew it would drop them for the next huge comber to bury. He glanced back. The sea was gathering itself, rising behind them.

But beyond the piling water he caught his last glimpse of the *Calypso*. She was growing small with the distance. She still flew straight away to sea. Her sail stretched jaunty and tight in the gale. Her blue hull gleamed clean and bold.

"Hey, sail, you *Calypso*. . . ." he shouted, but his voice was lost.

The swell dropped them in the trough. The comber behind piled higher. Rising. Rising. Up. Up. Now the

crest seemed to climb upon itself, thin at the top until a pale green light filtered through its arch. It curved over above them. Suddenly they felt themselves sucked upward. For an instant as they swept up the smooth reaching wall of water, they saw they were inside a curving liquid tunnel.

Together they yelled! Then they were whirled up and over into the foaming top. From this height it crashed them down with its own tons of brine. Down, down. Tumbling. Whirling. Then they were scoured for an eternity along the sand of the bottom. At last they shot to the surface. But they had become separated.

Clay gagged, with the salt water strangling him. Then he managed a gasp of air. There was a churning foam all around and before he could truly catch his breath, he was snatched up into another giant, curving wave. Hurled to the bottom. Up to the top again. Gasping, choking. A little air for the lungs. Then up and over and down again. And again. And again, until he was sure each next one would truly finish him. The nightmare of the whirling sea was endless.

One particular thrust of water, more vicious than the rest, crashed him against the sand with such force he blacked out for a moment and then was conscious only enough to be aware that he lay on his back looking up from the pale depths as the water sheeted away, slipping back to the sea. Thus miraculously he found he could breathe air instead of gulping salt water. With gigantic effort he turned over, found himself on his hands and knees in the thin surf of the shore. Before he could struggle to his feet another wave rushed upon him. But it was gone in a moment and Clay found himself standing, staggering, slipping, falling, standing again, moving up the flat of the beach. There he collapsed.

He thought of Paul, but he could not move. He felt himself gag, and salt water poured from his mouth and his nose. He began to shiver, but he still could not force himself to rise.

"Are you all right, Clay?"

The voice was close to him and he felt a hand on his shoulder. He nodded weakly and sat up. There was Paul squatting beside him, his round eyes full of concern.

"You'll feel better in a while, Clay. I guess you just about swallowed the whole ocean." Then after a bit, "You're shaking all over."

After a bit Clay stopped his shivering. He raised his head and looked around. It wasn't raining and he saw that the clouds to the west were beginning to thin. To the south there were a few streaks of pale blue showing. The ocean remained cold and gray and the waves still pounded the shore. But the island was free of the overcast. There it stood, out toward the horizon, and it seemed impossible that they had sailed there and landed on that far, strange shore.

There was not a sign of the *Calypso*. She was gone. Back to her beloved sea.

—*Adrienne Jones*

85

THINKING IT OVER

1. The relationship between Clay and Paul changed. How did they feel toward each other in the beginning? How did they feel at the end? What do you think caused these changes?

2. What, to you, was the most thrilling moment of the story? Why?

3. Certain events cause the reader to fear for the safety of the boys. Beneath the headings below write each event and tell if it was seen, heard, or felt.

Event	Seen	Heard	Felt

THOUGHTS AT WORK

1. Both Paul and Clay showed that they had courage, a quick wit, and endurance. Find examples to prove this statement.

2. Where do you think the story reached a peak or climax? Was there more than one climax? If so, where did each occur?

3. Which of the following words best describe the movement of the story?

    dramatic   fantastic   rapid
    steady   deliberate   exciting

    What are some other words which describe the action of the story?

4. We are not told where the story took place. Find clues which tell you if the story took place on the East or the West Coast.

5. The author used verbs very effectively. For instance, "Paul *shrank* against the mast." Look on pages 74–77 to find at least five more good examples.

6. Personification is a device used to make an object seem human. How did the author make the *Calypso* seem human—like a person? What kind of personality did it have?

7. How did the boys seem to feel as they watched their *Calypso* "racing gaily across her sea"? How would you have felt?

THE SEA

The sea is a hungry dog,
Giant and gray.
He rolls on the beach all day.
With his clashing teeth and shaggy jaws

Hour upon hour he gnaws
The rumbling, tumbling stones,
And "Bones, bones, bones, bones!"
The giant sea-dog moans,
Licking his greasy paws.

And when the night wind roars
And the moon rocks in the stormy cloud,
He bounds to his feet and snuffs and sniffs,
Shaking his wet sides over the cliffs,
And howls and hollos long and loud.

But on quiet days in May or June,
When even the grasses on the dune
Play no more their reedy tune,
With his head between his paws
He lies on the sandy shores,
So quiet, so quiet, he scarcely snores.

—James Reeves

Wild Bird

In the stories you have read so far in this unit, you have seen how "getting with it" means different things to different people. As you read this story you will see that the boy and his grandfather have different values and different points of view which they try to communicate to each other. What do you think that grandfather is trying to tell the boy?

I live in a room in the city with my grandfather. I have lived there as long as I can remember. It is not a pretty room, but it has a sink, and my grandfather says that is lucky. And on the wall is a picture of a hill with trees, and the sky in the picture is gold and red. My grandfather found the picture in a magazine. He tells me that is what a sunset looks like.

First thing in the morning my grandfather is awake. He walks over to the window to see if it is a day for walking. He does not like to stay in our room, and there is nowhere else to be. And so we walk.

But before we leave, we have something to eat, my grandfather and I.

First on our little burner, my grandfather makes coffee, and then while we are drinking our coffee my grandfather makes oatmeal. My grandfather says I must have oatmeal each day. He says that is the way my mother would have wanted me to eat.

"Tell me about my mother," I say.

My grandfather has told me many times of my mother, but today I want him to tell me again.

"Beautiful, and brown as the bark of a tree," says my grandfather, "with a smile to shame the sun. And fast as the brook she ran, and her laughter set the birds to singing."

"Why did she die?" I ask.

"No one dies if they are remembered," says my grandfather. "And we remember her, you and I."

The oatmeal is ready and today my grandfather opens a can of milk and pours some on my oatmeal, and I drink the rest of the milk from the can. Otherwise it will turn sour before we are back in the room again.

We finish our oatmeal. We make our beds and wash our mugs and our oatmeal bowls in the sink. My grandfather likes to have everything clean and neat. Sometimes, says my grandfather, strangers come to make sure he is taking care of me, and if the room is not clean then they will not let him keep me. So we spend much time sweeping the floor, and washing it, and wiping the window. The soot keeps coming in.

And we always open our cans carefully, and when they are empty we wash them out and put them back on the shelf. That way it looks as if we have many things to eat, if the strangers come to see if my grandfather is taking care of me. And we use the clean cans to drink out of, too. We do not have many dishes.

Before we leave, my grandfather makes sure there are two cans of soup for tonight, two cans that have not been opened yet.

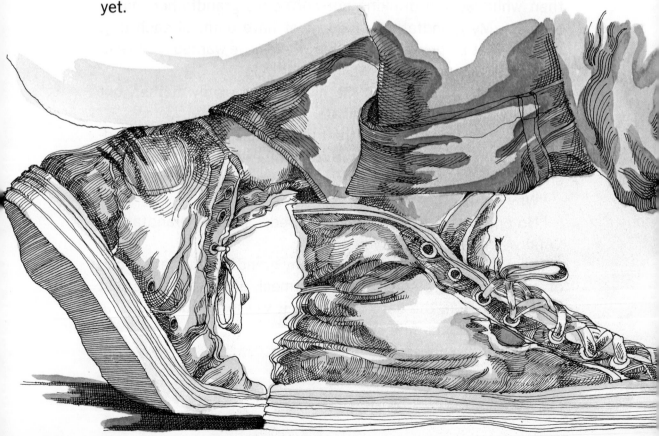

"Two, because tonight we will be hungry from our walk," says my grandfather. "Today we will walk all day."

While my grandfather goes down the hall to the bathroom, I pull the box where I have my bird out from under the bureau and put seeds in. My grandfather does not know about my bird. When he comes back, my grandfather closes the window and locks it, and locks our door as we leave. He carries our bag of garbage.

"Rest well, room," says my grandfather, laying his hand on the door. "Rest well, and try to grow a little while we are away."

Our room is on the third floor. We walk down the narrow stairs and outside. My grandfather puts our bag of garbage in one of the big cans that are lined against the building. They are already filled to overflowing, but he pushes the lid down and makes our bag fit in.

Now we walk in the city, my grandfather and I.

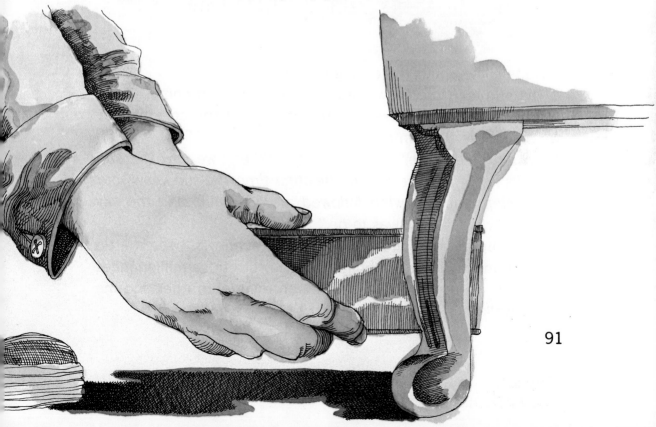

He tells me about the days gone by.

The sun is in the air we breathe, hot and hard coming from the bricks and the glass and the stone and the cement, but we do not see the sun at all.

"In the other time," says my grandfather, *"we saw the sun from its rising to its setting. In the other time, the sun knew your every step, and the wind followed at your back, and the sky told you what the day was to be."*

I look up at the buildings and at the shadows. I see a little sky, but mostly I see the buildings. They stretch a million miles high. I wonder if they will ever fall on my grandfather and me as we walk.

92

I bump into people because I do not look where I am going, and they are angry with me, so now I try to watch. People are often angry with me, although they have never seen me before.

"Now men try to shut out the Great Spirit above with their buildings, but He still watches," says my grandfather. "And they try to shut out the Dark One below with their cement, but He still waits."

My feet in my tennis shoes are hot and sore on the hot sidewalk.

"In the other time," says my grandfather, "the earth was sweet and cool under your feet."

"I don't remember," I say.

"Sometimes a man has to make believe," says my grandfather. "Sometimes a man has to pretend."

"Your summer moccasins were soft and made with love," says my grandfather. "A man could tell by the designs on your moccasins the things you would want a man to know about your life. A man could tell by the print of them in the earth that you were of our tribe. And now you leave no mark upon the land. No trace of you on the white man's sidewalk."

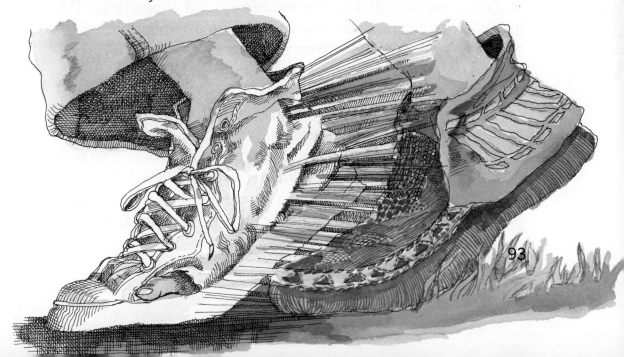

93

I look down at my tennis shoes. My toes are showing through the holes.

"Your summer moccasins were bright and beautiful so the Mother Earth with her flowers would not mind your passing over her," says my grandfather.

"Can Mother Earth see my shoes through the sidewalks now?" I ask. But my grandfather does not hear me. We pass many buildings. There are many people; there is much noise. Now we pass a place with loud music that blares in our ears.

"In the days gone by," says my grandfather, *"you held music in your hand."*

"The beaks of twenty birds were in your tortoise shell and you could shake a thousand thousand songs."

"How old was I then?" I ask.

"A hundred years from being born," says my grandfather.

"I don't understand," I say.

"You need not understand," says my grandfather. *"For now it is enough to listen. Listen and remember. Remember, and tell your sons and your grandsons."*

We walk the hot city streets. I stay close to my grandfather so I can hear him, and so the crowds will not separate us. If I lose him now I cannot find my way back to our room.

"When you were born," says my grandfather, *"they rode through the camp, they beat the drum to say a new manchild had come."*

"You said I was born in the city, and the doctor couldn't come in time, and my mother died," I say.

"When one of you was born," says my grandfather. *"The one before you, or the one before him, or the one before . . ."*

My grandfather and I stand at a corner and wait for the lights to change and the cars to stop so we may cross the street.

"When you were born, you were wrapped in the softest skins of rabbit and deer. You were put on a cradle board, and rocked to sleep by the hand of the wind. And forever after that the wind was your friend."

"What was my name?" I ask, although my grandfather has told me many times before.

"Your name was Golden Eagle," says my grandfather.

I walk close beside him. "Did I have wings?" I ask, but my grandfather does not hear me.

We cross the street.

"Remember," says my grandfather, "something of you lived before you lived. Those who went before you left something of themselves inside you. If you try, you can remember what it was, but you have to try. And your grandsons will carry something of you. And they will have to try to remember what part of you they carry . . ."

There are many people on the sidewalks, sometimes I have to walk behind my grandfather, there is no room to walk beside him. But he keeps talking.

"When you were born," my grandfather says, "the other you, one of the ones who came before you, tiny moccasins were put on your feet. Your grandmother had made them, and sewed on them designs made with porcupine quills. She dyed the quills. I remember the colors," says my grandfather. "The red came from buffalo berries, and the yellow from wild sunflowers, and the black from wild grapes. I remember," says my grandfather. "I remember the colors."

"I think I remember, too," I lie, but my grandfather does not hear me.

"She put holes in the soles of your baby moccasins," he says. *"Then if Death would come your way, He would think the moccasins already worn out, and not fit for the long journey."*

"Can you fool Death, Grandfather?" I ask.

"You can try," says my grandfather, *"you can try."*

My grandfather and I are hungry, and we stop to eat. We sit on little stools at a dirty counter and have hot dogs and pop.

"You grew straight and tall," says my grandfather, *"taller and straighter and stronger than you could ever grow in the city. Close to the earth as the grass you were, and wherever you went the earth was waiting to feed you. Wild currants and blackberries and wild strawberries and the eggs of wild birds."*

"I have a wild bird," I say. "I caught it and put it in a box and it tried to get out and it flapped its wings," I say, but my grandfather does not hear me.

97

"And animals," he says, as we walk along in the close heat. "You were quick and straight with the bow and arrow. You would bring back rabbits and weasels . . . remember the day of the fox? You were proud and we sang around the fire. Fire to cook by and fire to dance by . . . we were always close to fire. Our fire was the child of the sun," says my grandfather.

The day grows hotter. We walk in a crowded street.

"Fleet as the wind on your horse you would ride, swift as an arrow," says my grandfather.

"I've never seen a horse," I say.

My grandfather and I walk along and he is quiet.

I think my grandfather has not heard me. "I've never seen a horse," I say again. "Today let us go where I could see one."

"Your horse was brown and red like an autumn leaf," says my grandfather. "And you and the horse and the wind were one."

The teacher at the school told us when she was a little girl, horses pulled milk in wagons. She used to go out and give the horse a lump of sugar. It was long ago, she said.

We are shoved and pushed in the moving crowd.

We stop to watch a building being built. We watch a building being torn down. The sounds hurt my ears.

My grandfather shakes his head. "In the city," says my grandfather, "men build and tear down, build and tear down, because there is nothing else for them to do with their hands."

Now we must go somewhere to rest. My grandfather is tired. He knows good resting places where we can sit down and where we are away from the noise and the crowds and the cars. He shows me how I can tell a resting place from any other building. Sometimes there is a cross on the top: He shows me.

Inside the resting place there are long benches. We sit.

"In the other time," says my grandfather, "you could always be alone and quiet. You could let new thoughts come your way. Now the new thoughts try to come, but they are driven away by the noise and the crowds. They cannot find their way through the city to come to you."

We sit together for a time and we are quiet, and we wait for the new thoughts to find us.

I think again of the teacher at school. She has very pale skin and pale hair, and pale blue eyes that never see me.

"The early settlers of our country were very brave," she said. "They were not afraid of the Indians, even though the Indians would attack them and kill even the women and the children. We are very proud of our brave forefathers, facing work and hardship and danger and death because they loved their land."

After a while we walk again. We walk along the city streets, and every door we pass is closed. Some of the doors and windows have gates across them.

"In the other time, every family had an owner stick," says my grandfather. *"You could put it near the things you owned and everyone knew what belonged to you, and they would take nothing. Our owner stick had the head of an eagle carved on the top, and the sign of the sun. Our family could leave all we owned on the plain while we were waiting for the buffalo to run. Our owner stick was there, and that was enough. Now men have doors and locks and gates."*

"Where is our owner stick now?" I ask, but he does not hear me.

We walk and walk. My grandfather says nothing.

Some of the bigger boys at school sing songs at me. They do not like me.

See the heap big Indian go
with his arrow and his bow
by the shores of Gitchee Galpo
heap big Indian get a scalpo
Indian get-um scalps a-plenty
five scalps, ten scalps, fifteen, twenty.

"Tell me about the buffalos," I say to my grandfather. I like for him to talk.

"There were many, many. As far as you could see, when they were running," says my grandfather. "And then one day the earth swallowed them up and the buffalo ran no more."

"Where did they go?" I ask.

"One day, one day the earth will open and they will come again," says my grandfather.

"How do you know?" I ask.

"My grandfather told me," says my grandfather.

"Is that how you remember?" I ask. "Because your grand-father remembered, and told you?"

My grandfather does not hear me.

We walk in the city, my grandfather and I.

Every time we walk we go a different direction, every time we take different turnings. We walk a long way. It is very crowded. I am very hot, I am very tired. There are so many people. I wonder if they are walking, like my grandfather and me, be-cause they do not want to stay in their rooms.

"You must be strong," says my grandfather, "so you can walk farther and farther. Some day, if we go far enough, if we make the right turns, we will find our way out of this place of many buildings. Some day we will take the right path, and there will be much grass and much sky, and there will be trees and birds and berries, and I will teach you the ways of the antelope and the deer and the elk and the buffalo."

"I thought the buffaloes were swallowed up by the earth," I say, but my grandfather does not hear me.

"And I will teach you the ways of the fox and the coyote and the rattlesnake," says my grandfather. "And the windsong will be in your ears and the earthsong under your feet."

"Will my horse be there?" I ask, but my grandfather does not hear me.

It is growing dark when we come back. The garbage cans still sit on the sidewalk unemptied.

The lights are blinking on and off.

"You cannot see the night sun here," says my grandfather, "but you used to sleep under it at night and watch it passing by. And the stars were close enough to touch if you tried. You never tried because you thought they might be hot, but you could have touched them if you'd wanted."

102

We walk up the stairs. They are very dirty. Someone has written new words on the walls. My grandfather takes out his key and opens the door of our room. He opens the window. He lifts the two cans of soup down from our shelf.

"Do you want to see my wild bird?" I ask my grandfather.

He does not hear me. He sits on the bed.

I pull the box from under the bureau. I do not hear the bird flapping its wings. I open the box and my wild bird is in a corner. He is quiet and still, but he is alive.

"Look," I say, and show my grandfather. "This is my wild bird."

My grandfather looks in the box. He picks up the bird in his hands and walks over to the window.

"Fly, wild bird," says my grandfather. "Fly away, wild bird."

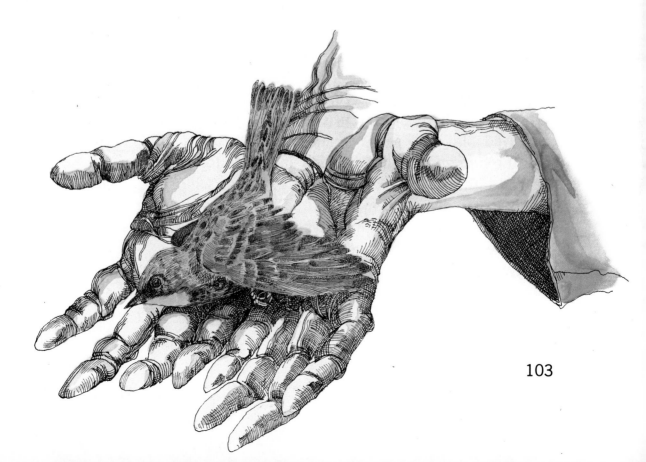

But the bird does not fly. It sits in my grandfather's hands with its eyes half shut. It leans into my grandfather's hands and trembles.

"Fly, wild bird," says my grandfather.

My grandfather looks out of the window to the next building. "Fly, wild bird," he says, holding the bird to the window. He puts the bird on the window ledge and turns to me.

"Wild birds die in boxes or cages or rooms," he says. "They forget how to fly, and they are afraid to try, and they die."

For the first time in all my days my grandfather touches me. He shakes me by the shoulders.

"Fly, wild bird, fly!" says my grandfather to me.

And for the first time in all my days I am ashamed of my grandfather. He has told me no man in our tribe has ever cried. And now he cries.

104

—*Florence Parry Heide*

THINKING IT OVER

1. Why does Grandfather recall the past? What effect does this have upon the boy?

2. What reasons can you suggest for the grandfather not answering many of the boy's questions?

3. Why does the grandfather set the bird free? What do you think Grandfather is trying to tell his grandson?

THOUGHTS AT WORK

1. In the story, the grandfather is afraid of strangers who check the condition of their room. Who are these "strangers" and why is he afraid of them?

2. What do you think the grandfather means when he says "No one dies if they are remembered?"

3. Why does the grandfather say to the boy, "You need not understand. For now it is enough to listen"?

4. Why do the boy's classmates tease him. What does their song tell you about their views of the American Indian? Why do some people hold such views?

5. In the story the boy asks, "Is that how you remember? . . . Because your grandfather remembered and told you?" Do you think that all of the grandfather's memories are personal ones or are they based on stories which he may have heard from others? Explain your answer.

6. What significance is there to the grandfather's grabbing the boy by the shoulders and shaking him? What does this gesture tell you about grandfather's feelings?

7. What are some of the customs and legends of grandfather's tribe which you learned about as a result of reading this story? How do they help you understand and value Indian culture?

STARS

O, sweep of stars over Harlem Streets,
O, little breath of oblivion that is night.
   A city building
   To a mother's song.
   A city dreaming
   To a lullaby.
Reach up your hand, dark boy, and take a star.
Out of the little breath of oblivion
   That is night
   Take just
   One star.

— *Langston Hughes*

BIBLIOGRAPHY

Two on an Island, by Bianca Bradbury.
> Being marooned on a small uninhabited island can be a terrifying experience, especially when no one knows you are there.

D. J.'s Worst Enemy, by Robert Burch.
> Having a worst enemy is bad enough but imagine adding to that a tagging-along small brother with the ability to imitate any kind of sound.

Lady Ellen Grae, by Vera and Bill Cleaver.
> This eleven-year-old tomboy, who enjoys telling "whoppers," is back in her second book, this time learning to be a lady.

The Alley, by Eleanor Estes.
> The alley in Brooklyn is a quiet place until there is a robbery and Billy Maloon begins to "case" the neighborhood.

Dan and the Miranda, by Wilson Gage and Glen Rounds.
> In this amusing story Dan becomes more and more enchanted with spiders in a most unscientific manner.

From the Mixed-up Files of Mrs. Basil E. Frankweiler, by E. L. Konigsburg.
> When Claudia and Jamie run away—to live in the big city museum—they meet some unexpected problems and discover a mystery.

Adam Bookout, by Louisa R. Shotwell.
> Tired of living with his two aunts, Adam boards a bus for New York. But life with other relatives only brings fresh problems and trouble.

The Egypt Game, by Zilpha Keatley Snyder.
> The six, who create their own game in the old storage shed, do not know it will turn into a neighborhood mystery.

A Wonderful, Terrible Time, by Mary Stoltz.
> The unexpected happens when Sue and Mady go to camp, one enjoying the experience, the other stubbornly rejecting it.

THE MANY

FACES OF HUMOR

What's so funny? You may keep a stony silence as someone else laughs aloud. Or you may smile broadly and chuckle over something that is not funny to another person. Not everyone thinks the same things are funny. Humor has many faces—that is, we laugh for different reasons.

109

Many Americans have chuckled over a tale of exaggeration. Wherever work was hard and life lonely, these tales of the super-man—Paul Bunyan, Pecos Bill, or John Henry—doing difficult, dangerous tasks with the greatest of ease gave men something to laugh about.

Stormalong was a sea-going, tall-tale hero. What parts of his story do you think the sailors of yesterday might have enjoyed most of all?

STORMALONG

Stormy's gone, that good old man,
To my way, hay, storm along, John!
Stormy's gone, that good old man,
To my aye, aye, aye, Mister Stormalong.

Stormy's gone, of course. He died before the last Yankee clipper furled her silver sails. But stories about "that good old man" are told still wherever old sailors gather. Just where Old Stormalong was born isn't important. He first appeared on a wharf in Boston Harbor. The captain of the *Lady of the Sea*, the largest clipper ship in the China trade, was signing on men. Stormy gave his full name, Alfred Bullrod Stormalong. Without looking up from his ledger, the captain wrote down the initials, "A.B."

A. B. Stormalong stood five fathoms tall, which is the same as thirty feet. The captain glanced up at his new man. He whistled with surprise. "Phew!" he said. "There's an able-bodied seaman for you, boys."

Someone noticed that the giant's initials stood for just that. From that day to this sailors have tacked A. B. after their names. This shows that

they are able-bodied seamen like Stormy.

Old Stormalong's size and strength helped him a lot on the sea. He didn't have to climb the rigging to furl the topsails. He just reached up from the deck and did it. He could hold the pilot's wheel with his little finger even in the worst weather. In less than a week he'd been promoted from common sailor to bos'n.

The cook didn't care much for his company, however. He made too much work in the galley. He had a weakness for food. He knew a good deal about cooking and wanted everything prepared just so. Besides, he wanted lots of it.

He liked a couple of ostrich eggs fried sunny-side-up for breakfast. For lunch he expected a dory full of soup. After his meals he used to lie out on deck in the sun and pick his teeth with an oar.

But Old Stormy was too valuable a man to dismiss

because of the cook's grumbling. There were many occasions on which the *Lady of the Sea* would have become the *Lady on the Bottom of the Sea*, had it not been for her bos'n.

Once, for instance, in the warm waters of the tropical Atlantic, the captain gave orders to hoist sail and weigh anchor after a morning of deep-sea fishing. The crew heaved and strained at the capstan bars. The anchor refused to budge. Something was holding it fast to the bottom. Not even when Stormalong heaved along with the crew would the heavy iron stir.

So Old Stormy stuck a knife into his belt and dove overboard to have a 'look-see.' Hand over hand he climbed down the anchor chain. Suddenly great waves arose. A commotion began on the ocean floor. The surface frothed and churned. From below came sounds of battle. The crew could see dimly two

113

dark forms struggling in the water's depths. Then the long, black, slimy arm of a giant octopus slapped into the air.

At the sight of it the crew gave up their bos'n for lost. No human being could possibly fight single-handed one of those great devils of the sea and come out alive. But before they had a chance to arrange a funeral service for him, Old Stormalong climbed slowly up the chain and pulled himself on deck.

"Phew!" he sighed. "That old octopus was a tough one. Had hold of the anchor with fifty arms and grabbed the bottom with the other fifty. He won't trouble us now, though. Tied him tighter than a schoolboy's shoe-lace. Tied every one of his arms in a double knot."

A year or so after this adventure Old Stormy lost his taste for the sailor's life. He said it was the food. He was tired of hardtack and dried

114

fish. He had a hankering for some tender, fresh green vegetables.

His shipmates, however, guessed that the real trouble was lack of space. The *Lady of the Sea* was the biggest clipper afloat, but even so she cramped her bos'n. He couldn't sleep stretched out anywhere on board.

After a last voyage around Cape Horn, Stormalong left the wharf at Boston with his pay in his pocket and an eighteen-foot oar over his shoulder. He bade his friends good-by. He said he was going to walk west, due west. He would stop and settle down as soon as someone asked what the long pole might be. He figured that any county whose inhabitants didn't recognize an oar was far enough from the coast for him.

The *Lady's* crew heard nothing from their shipmate for several years. Then in the San Francisco gold rush the mate had news. Stormy had bought a township and was one of the best farmers in the whole U.S.A. Stormy a farmer? The mate couldn't believe his ears. But when he was told of Farmer Stormalong's miracles, he knew it was his man, without a doubt.

Stormalong specialized in potatoes. During his first growing season the whole countryside dried up. It didn't rain for six weeks. The little spring that fed the horse trough gave only enough water for the stock. There was not an extra drop with which to irrigate the crops.

Then Old Stormalong went to work. He labored over those drooping, dying plants until the perspiration ran from him in rivers. He sprinkled those potatoes with the sweat of his brow. At the end of the season, when other farmers were moaning over their burnt acres, he drove to market with a bumper crop of the largest, tastiest spuds ever mashed with cream and butter.

In spite of this success, Stormy wearied of farm life. He was a restless fellow. Often at night when he had milked the cows and locked the hen roost, he sat in front of his stove and dreamed about the old days on the ocean. At last he couldn't deny to himself that the sea was calling him back.

Word spread through the countryside about a new ship, the *Courser*. It was so huge that it couldn't enter Boston Harbor. The inlanders thought it was just another Yankee yarn. They laughed about it as they sat on the front porch of the country store. But to Stormalong the *Courser* was more than a fable. It was a dream come true.

He sold his farm and returned to the East. For several days he hung around the waterfront, looking like the ghost of his former self. His ruddy salt-sea color was gone, his eyes had lost their shine, and all the "shellbacks," or

sailors, who had known him in the old days realized that he was a sick man, yearning for the feel of the spray.

They couldn't tell him much about the whereabouts of the big ship he was seeking. It was a real boat, all right. It had anchored outside of Cape Cod some time before with a cargo of elephants for Mr. Barnum's circus. The *Lady of the Sea* had been pressed into service as a tender to bring the freight to shore.

The more the old bos'n heard about the *Courser* the more his mouth watered to see her and join her crew. At last, when a whaler brought word that she was cruising along the Grand Banks off Nova Scotia,[1] Stormy couldn't stand it any longer. He dove off T Wharf and swam out to sea.

The next time his old friends saw him, he was the captain of the big vessel. The old fire was back in his eyes, his

[1] Nova Scotia (nō′və skō′shə)

116

cheeks were brown as mahogany, and his spirit was dancing. For the *Courser* was the only ship in all the world which suited him. He was the only skipper in all the world to do her justice.

She was so long from stem to stern that it took a man on horseback a good twenty-four hours to make the trip. A string of Arab ponies were stabled in front of the forebitts for the use of the officers on duty. The masts were hinged to let the sun and moon go by. The mainsail had been cut and hemmed in the Sahara[1] Desert, the only expanse of land large enough for the operation. When a storm blew up from the horizon, the skipper had to give the order to man the topsails a good week in advance. It took the men that long to climb the rigging.

This last fact had its disadvantages, of course. Until the United States Weather

[1] Sahara (sə hãr′ə)

Bureau caught on to the trick of sending out weather reports in advance, the *Courser* was often caught in a hurricane without notice enough to furl in her cloth. She was large enough to ride out any storm, even in full sail, without much damage. But there was no way of telling how far off her course she'd be blown in the process.

One time, for instance, during a North Atlantic winter gale, the *Courser* was pushed this way and that until she ended up in the North Sea. As you know, the North Sea is just a little sea, and not in the same class with an honest-to-goodness ocean. In fact, it was so small and crowded with islands that the *Courser* couldn't turn around.

There to port lay Norway and Denmark. Straight ahead lay the continent of Europe, and to starboard the British Isles. Stormy roared with anguish. He feared lest his clipper, his lovely queen of

117

the five oceans, would have to join the lowly North Sea fishing fleet for the rest of time.

There was a way out, however. When Stormalong and the mate measured the English Channel, they found that at high tide it was an inch or two wider than the *Courser*. With luck they might squeeze through it and out into the Atlantic again.

So the skipper sent the officers to Holland to buy up all the soap in sight. Then he put his crew to work, soaping the sides of the big boat. They slapped the greasy stuff on thick until the *Courser* was as slippery as an eel.

Captain A. B. Stormalong himself took the pilot's wheel and steered. Just at the turn of tide, with her full sails set, the *Courser* glided through into the broad Atlantic Ocean. But she had a close call. The headlands on the English coast scraped most of the soap off the starboard side of the vessel. To this day

the cliffs at Dover have been white.

After this adventure Old Stormy was talked about in every port in the world. No sailor could deny that his highest ambition was to ship on the *Courser* under "that good old man."

Great was the mourning from Portsmouth[1] to Hong Kong when news of Stormalong's death finally came. Several reports of it were spread around. One version had it that he was drowned in a storm off Cape Hope. But most of the tales agreed that he died of indigestion. His magnificent appetite had finished him.

His old shipmates gathered for the funeral. They made him a shroud of the finest China silk. They dug his grave with a silver spade. They lowered his coffin into the ground with a silver chain, the color of his sails. And the tears that fell from the eyes of those hard old salts drenched the earth like the rain of a nor'easter.

[1] Portsmouth (pôrts'məth)

Old Stormy has heard an angel call,
To my way, hay, storm along, John.
So sing his dirge now, one and all,
To my aye, aye, aye, Mister Stormalong.

—*Anne Malcolmson*

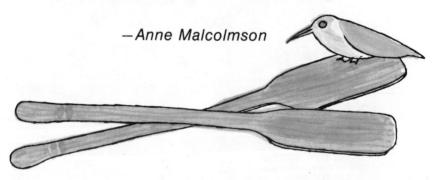

THINKING IT OVER

1. In your opinion, which of Stormalong's adventures was the most humorous? Why?

2. This tall tale includes many exaggerations about Stormalong. Name at least ten.

3. Tell what each of the following "sea-going" terms means.

bos'n	hardtack	stern
galley	clipper ship	port
dory	tender	starboard
capstan	stem	fathom

THOUGHTS AT WORK

1. Judging from this story, what things do you think sailors might wish for? Name as many as you can.

2. Write a description of the *Courser* and then draw a picture showing how you think it looked.

3. What is meant by "He died before the last Yankee clipper furled her silver sails"?

4. Now that you know what Stormalong could do, write a new adventure for him.

5. If Stormalong were to visit America today, which modern inventions do you think would impress him the most?

6. Why do you think that Stormalong was not satisfied with farm life? Would you rather be a farmer or a sailor? Why?

7. Think of a story you have read or heard which is funny because of exaggerations. Be ready to tell the story.

In "Stormalong" everything was exaggerated as though you were looking through a telescope. Do you know what happens when you view things through the *other* end of the telescope? Exaggeration in reverse! Look for examples of this exaggeration in, "A Fair Breeze" and "The Sailboat Race," which are two chapters from E. B. White's book, *Stuart Little*.

122

A FAIR BREEZE

One morning when the wind was from the west, Stuart put on his sailor suit and his sailor hat, took his spyglass down from the shelf, and set out for a walk, full of the joy of life and the fear of dogs. With a rolling gait he sauntered along toward Fifth Avenue, keeping a sharp lookout.

Whenever he spied a dog through his glass, Stuart would hurry to the nearest doorman, climb his trouser-leg, and hide in the tails of his uniform. And once, when no doorman was handy, he had to crawl into a yesterday's paper and roll himself up in the second section till danger was past.

At the corner of Fifth Avenue there were several people waiting for the uptown bus, and Stuart joined them. Nobody noticed him, because he wasn't tall enough to be noticed.

"I'm not tall enough to be noticed," thought Stuart, "yet I'm tall enough to want to go to Seventy-second Street."

When the bus came into view, all the men waved their canes and brief cases at the driver, and Stuart waved his spyglass. Then, knowing that the step of the bus would be too high for him, Stuart seized hold of the cuff of a gentleman's pants and was swung aboard without any trouble or inconvenience whatever.

Stuart never paid any fare on buses, because he wasn't big enough to carry an ordinary dime. The only time he had ever attempted to carry a dime, he had rolled the coin along like a hoop while he raced along beside it; but it had got away from him on a hill and had been snatched up by an old woman with no teeth. After that experience Stuart contented himself with the tiny coins which his father made for him out of tin foil. They were handsome little things, although rather hard to see without putting on your spectacles.

When the conductor came around to collect the fares, Stuart fished in his purse and pulled out a coin no bigger than the eye of a grasshopper.

"What's that you're offering me?" asked the conductor.

"It's one of my dimes," said Stuart.

"Is it, now?" said the conductor. "Well, I'd have a fine time explaining that to the bus company. Why, you're no bigger than a dime yourself."

"Yes I am," replied Stuart angrily. "I'm more than twice as big as a dime. A dime only comes up to here on me." And Stuart pointed to his hip. "Furthermore," he added, "I didn't come on this bus to be insulted."

"I beg pardon," said the conductor. "You'll have to forgive me, for I had no idea that in all the world there was such a small sailor."

"Live and learn," muttered Stuart, tartly, putting his change purse back in his pocket.

When the bus stopped at Seventy-second Street, Stuart jumped out and hurried across to the sailboat pond in Central Park. Over the pond the west wind blew, and into the teeth of the west wind sailed the sloops and schooners, their rails well down, their wet

124

decks gleaming. The owners, boys and grown men, raced around the cement shores hoping to arrive at the other side in time to keep the boats from bumping. Some of the toy boats were not as small as you might think, for when you got close to them you found that their mainmast was taller than a man's head, and they were beautifully made, with everything shipshape and ready for sea. To Stuart they seemed enormous,

and he hoped he would be able to get aboard one of them and sail away to the far corners of the pond. (He was an adventurous little fellow and loved the feel of the breeze in his face and the cry of the gulls overhead and the heave of the great swell under him.)

As he sat cross-legged on the wall that surrounds the pond, gazing out at the ships through his spyglass, Stuart noticed one boat that seemed to him finer and prouder than any other. Her name was *Wasp*. She was

125

a big, black schooner flying the American flag. She had a clipper bow, and on her foredeck was mounted a three-inch cannon. She's the ship for me, thought Stuart. And the next time she sailed in, he ran over to where she was being turned around.

"Excuse me, sir," said Stuart to the man who was turning her, "but are you the owner of the schooner *Wasp*?"

"I am," replied the man, surprised to be addressed by a mouse in a sailor suit.

"I'm looking for a berth in a good ship," continued Stuart, "and I thought perhaps you might sign me on. I'm strong and I'm quick."

"Are you sober?" asked the owner of the *Wasp*.

"I do my work," said Stuart, crisply.

The man looked sharply at him. He couldn't help admiring the trim appearance and bold manner of this diminutive seafaring character.

"Well," he said at length, pointing the prow of the *Wasp* out toward the center of the pond, "I'll tell you what I'll do with you. You see that big racing sloop out there?"

"I do," said Stuart.

"That's the *Lillian B. Womrath*," said the man, "and I hate her with all my heart."

"Then so do I," cried Stuart, loyally.

"I hate her because she is always bumping into my boat," continued the man, "and because her owner is a lazy boy who doesn't understand sailing and who hardly knows a squall from a squid."

"Or a jib from a jibe," cried Stuart.

126

"Or a luff from a leech," bellowed the man.

"Or a deck from a dock," screamed Stuart.

"Or a mast from a mist," yelled the man. "But hold on, now, no more of this! I'll tell you what we'll do. The *Lillian B. Womrath* has always been able to beat the *Wasp* sailing, but I believe that if my schooner were properly handled it would be a different story. Nobody knows how I suffer, standing here on shore, helpless, watching the *Wasp* blunder along, when all she needs is a steady hand on her helm. So, my young friend, I'll let you sail the *Wasp* across the pond and back, and if you can beat that detestable sloop I'll give you a regular job."

"Aye, aye, sir!" said Stuart, swinging himself aboard the schooner and taking his place at the wheel. "Ready about!"

"One moment," said the man. "Do you mind telling me *how* you propose to beat the other boat?"

"I intend to crack on more sail," said Stuart.

"Not in *my* boat, thank you," replied the man quickly. "I don't want you capsizing in a squall."

"Well, then," said Stuart, "I'll catch the sloop broad on, and rake her with fire from my forward gun."

"Foul means!" said the man. "I want this to be a boat race, not a naval engagement."

"Well, then," said Stuart cheerfully, "I'll sail the *Wasp* straight and true, and let the *Lillian B. Womrath* go yawing all over the pond."

"Bravo!" cried the man, "and good luck go with you!" And so saying, he let go of the *Wasp's* prow. A puff of air bellied out the schooner's headsails and she paid off and filled away on the port tack, heeling gracefully over to the breeze while Stuart twirled her wheel and braced himself against a deck cleat.

"By the by," yelled the man, "you haven't told me your name."

"Name is Stuart Little," called Stuart at the top of his lungs. "I'm the second son of Frederick C. Little, of this city."

"*Bon voyage*, Stuart," hollered his friend, "take care of yourself and bring the *Wasp* home safe."

"That I will," shouted Stuart. And he was so proud and happy, he let go of the wheel for a second and did a little dance on the sloping deck, never noticing how narrowly he escaped hitting a tramp steamer that was drifting in his path, with her engines disabled and her decks awash.

THE SAILBOAT RACE

When the people in Central Park learned that one of the toy sailboats was being steered by a mouse in a sailor suit, they all came running. Soon the shores of the pond were so crowded that a policeman was sent from headquarters to announce that everybody would have to stop pushing, but nobody did. People in New York like to push each other. The most excited person of all was the boy who owned the *Lillian B. Womrath*. He was a fat, sulky boy of twelve, named LeRoy. He wore a blue serge suit and a white necktie stained with orange juice.

"Come back here!" he called to Stuart. "Come back here and get on *my* boat. I want you to steer *my* boat. I will pay you five dollars a week and you can have every Thursday afternoon off and a radio in your room."

"I thank you for your kind offer," replied Stuart, "but I am happy aboard the *Wasp* — happier than I have ever been before in all my life." And with that he spun the wheel over smartly and headed his schooner down toward the starting line, where LeRoy was turning his boat around by poking it with a long stick, ready for the start of the race.

"I'll be the referee," said a man in a bright green suit. "Is the *Wasp* ready?"

"Ready, sir!" shouted Stuart, touching his hat.

"Is the *Lillian B. Womrath* ready?" asked the referee.

129

"Sure, I'm ready," said LeRoy.

"To the north end of the pond and back again!" shouted the referee. "On your mark, get set, GO!"

"Go!" cried the people along the shore.

"Go!" cried the owner of the *Wasp*.

"Go!" yelled the policeman.

And away went the two boats for the north end of the pond, while the seagulls wheeled and cried overhead and the taxicabs tooted and honked from Seventy-second Street and the west wind (which had come halfway across America to get to Central Park) sang and whistled in the rigging and blew spray across the decks, stinging Stuart's cheeks with tiny fragments of flying peanut shell tossed up from the foamy deep. "This is the life for me!" Stuart murmured to himself. "What a ship! What a day! What a race!"

Before the two boats had gone many feet, however, an accident happened on shore. The people were pushing each other harder and harder in their eagerness to see the sport, and although they really didn't mean to, they pushed the policeman so hard they pushed him right off the concrete wall and into the pond. He hit the water in a sitting position, and got wet clear up to the third button of his jacket. He was soaked.

This particular policeman was not only a big, heavy man, but he had just eaten a big, heavy meal, and the wave he made went curling outward, cresting and billowing, upsetting all manner of small craft and causing every owner of a boat on the pond to scream with delight and consternation.

When Stuart saw the great wave approaching he jumped for the rigging, but he was too late. Towering above the *Wasp* like a mountain, the wave came crashing and piling along the deck, caught Stuart up and swept him over the side and into the water, where everybody supposed he would drown. Stuart had no intention of drowning. He kicked hard with his feet,

and thrashed hard with his tail, and in a minute or two he climbed back aboard the schooner, cold and wet but quite unharmed. As he took his place at the helm, he could hear people cheering for him and calling, "Atta mouse, Stuart! Atta mouse!" He looked over and saw that the wave had capsized the *Lillian B. Womrath* but that she had righted herself and was sailing on her course, close by. And she stayed close alongside till both boats reached the north end of the pond. Here Stuart put the *Wasp* about and LeRoy turned the *Lillian* around with his stick, and away the two boats went for the finish line.

"This race isn't over yet," thought Stuart.

The first warning he had that there was trouble ahead came when he glanced into the *Wasp's* cabin and observed that the barometer had fallen sharply. That can mean only one thing at sea—dirty weather. Suddenly a dark cloud swept across the sun, blotting it out and leaving the earth in shadow. Stuart shivered in his wet clothes. He turned up his sailor blouse closer around his neck, and when he spied the *Wasp's* owner among the crowd on shore he waved his hat and called out:

"Dirty weather ahead, sir! Wind backing into the south-west, seas confused, glass falling."

"Never mind the weather!" cried the owner. "Watch out for flotsam dead ahead!"

Stuart peered ahead into the gathering storm, but saw nothing except gray waves with white crests. The world seemed cold and ominous. Stuart glanced behind him. There came the sloop, boiling along fast, rolling up a bow wave and gaining steadily.

"Look out, Stuart! Look out where you're going!"

Stuart strained his eyes, and suddenly, dead ahead, right in the path of the *Wasp*, he saw an enormous paper bag looming up on the surface of the pond. The bag was empty and riding high, its open end gaping wide like the mouth of a cave. Stuart spun the wheel over but it was too late: the *Wasp* drove her bowsprit straight into the bag and with a fearful *whooosh* the schooner slowed down and came up into the wind with all sails flapping. Just at this moment Stuart heard a splintering crash, saw the bow of the *Lillian* plow through his rigging, and felt the whole ship tremble from stem to stern with the force of the collision.

"A collision!" shouted the crowd on shore.

In a jiffy the two boats were in a terrible tangle. Little boys on shore screamed and danced up and down. Meanwhile the paper bag sprang a leak and began to fill.

The *Wasp* couldn't move because of the bag. The *Lillian B. Womrath* couldn't move because her nose was stuck in the *Wasp's* rigging.

Waving his arms, Stuart ran forward and fired off his gun. Then he heard, above the other voices on shore, the voice of the owner of the *Wasp* yelling directions and telling him what to do.

"Stuart! Stuart! Down jib! Down staysail!"

Stuart jumped for the halyards, and the jib and the forestaysail came rippling down.

"Cut away all paper bags!" roared the owner.

Stuart whipped out his pocketknife and slashed away bravely at the soggy bag until he had the deck cleared.

"Now back your foresail and give her a full!" screamed the owner of the *Wasp*.

Stuart grabbed the foresail boom and pulled with all his might. Slowly the schooner paid off and began to gather headway. And as she heeled over to the breeze she rolled her rail out from under the *Lillian's*

nose, shook herself free, and stood away to the southard. A loud cheer went up from the bank. Stuart sprang to the wheel and answered it. Then he looked back, and to his great joy he perceived that the *Lillian* had gone off in a wild direction and was yawing all over the pond.

Straight and true sailed the *Wasp*, with Stuart at the helm. After she had crossed the finish line, Stuart brought her alongside the wall, and was taken ashore and highly praised for his fine seamanship and daring. The owner was delighted and said it was the happiest day of his life. He introduced himself to Stuart, said that in private life he was Dr. Paul Carey, a surgeon-dentist. He said model boats were his hobby and that he would be delighted to have Stuart take command of his vessel at any time. Everybody shook hands with Stuart—everybody, that is, except the policeman, who was too wet and mad to shake hands with a mouse.

When Stuart got home that night, his brother George asked him where he had been all day.

"Oh, knocking around town," replied Stuart.

—E. B. White

THINKING IT OVER

1. Stuart was a mouse, but he often behaved like a "typical American boy." When did he act like a boy? When did he act like a mouse?

2. Stuart seemed to know a good bit about sailors and sailing. Find evidence in the story to prove this.

3. Why do you think Stuart Little didn't tell his brother about his adventures?

THOUGHTS AT WORK

1. Tell how Stuart "the mouse" and Stormalong "the giant" were alike. How were they different?

2. Do you believe that Stuart was sensitive about his size? Explain your answer.

3. The "storm" had all the fierce danger of a great ocean gale, yet the author never let you forget that you were in Central Park, New York City. What details described what seemed to be a real storm at sea? What details reminded you that you were in the heart of the city?

4. What three methods did Stuart suggest for winning the race? What was the owner's reason for not approving the first two?

5. Do you think the author liked or disliked LeRoy? Do you like him? Give reasons for your answers.

6. Read the first sentence below, then complete the others.
   a. The tin-foil coin was to Stuart as <u>a dime</u> is to you.
   b. A paper bag was to the *Wasp* as _____ is to an ocean liner.
   c. A pond was to Stuart as _____ is to you.
   d. A breeze was to Stuart's boat as _____ is to a large ship.
   e. A model boat was to Stuart as _____ would be to you.
   f. A dog was to Stuart as _____ might be to you.

7. The *Wasp's* owner and Stuart played with words on pages 126 and 127. Try to create other pairs of sea terms like these.

See how he dives
  From the rocks with a zoom!
  See how he darts
  Through his watery room
Past crabs and eels
And green seaweed,
Past fluffs of sandy
Minnow feed!
See how he swims
With a swerve and a twist,
A flip of the flipper,
A flick of the wrist!
Quicksilver-quick,
Softer than spray,
Down he plunges
And sweeps away;
Before you can think,
Before you can utter
Words like "Dill pickle"
Or "Apple butter,"
Back up he swims
  Past sting-ray and shark,
  Out with a zoom,
  A whoop, a bark;
  Before you can say
  Whatever you wish,
  He plops at your side
  With a mouthful of fish!

—William Jay Smith

138

THE RELUCTANT DRAGON

Dragons are mythical creatures, existing only in the imagination. But people throughout the ancient world believed in them as symbols of both good and evil. In one old English legend St. George slew a dragon. It is this St. George who appears in the play *The Reluctant Dragon*, based on the story by Kenneth Grahame found in his book *Dream Days*.

Characters

BOY

HIS MOTHER

HIS FATHER

THE HEAD OF THE RELUCTANT DRAGON

HIS LEFT PAW

HIS RIGHT PAW

HIS TAIL

EIGHT VILLAGERS

ST. GEORGE

The play takes place Long Ago in the shepherd country of England. At the back right corner of the stage is the cottage where the BOY lives. Later in the play, it is the Village Inn. The rest of the stage is open countryside with a few bushes and rocks, a wind-blown tree. At stage left is the rocky entrance to an enormous cave. In the cottage BOY sits on a little stool reading a big book and his MOTHER sits on a little stool sewing. After a bit of homey quiet, the FATHER rushes onto the stage from off right.

FATHER *(Shaking with fear)*. It's all up with me, Maria! Never no more can I go up on them there Downs!

MOTHER *(Calmly)*. Now don't you take on like that, but tell us all about it first, whatever it is as has given you this shake-up, and then me and you and the Son here, between us, we ought to be able to get to the bottom of it!

FATHER. It began some nights ago. You know that cave up there—I never liked it somehow, and the sheep never liked it neither, and when sheep don't like a thing there is generally some reason for it. Well, for some time past there's been faint noises coming from that cave—noises like heavy sighings, and with grunts mixed up in them; and sometimes a snoring, far away down—*real* snoring, yet somehow not *honest* snoring, like you and me o'nights, you know!

142

BOY (*Quietly*). *I* know.

FATHER. Of course I was terrible frightened; yet somehow I couldn't keep away. So this very evening, before I come down, I took a cast round by the cave, quietly. And there—there I saw him at last, as plain as I see you!

MOTHER. Saw WHO?

FATHER. Why HIM. I'm a-telling you! He was sticking halfway out of the cave and seemed to be enjoying of the cool of the evening in a poetical sort of way. He was big as four cart horses, and all covered with shiny scales. He had his chin on his paws, and I should say he was meditating about things. Oh yes, a peaceable sort o' beast enough, and not ramping or carrying on or doing anything but what was quite right and proper. I admit all that. And yet, what am I to do? SCALES, you know, and claws, and a tail for certain, though I didn't see that end of him—

I ain't USED to 'em, and I don't HOLD with 'em, and that's a fact!

BOY (*Closes his book, yawns, clasps his hands behind his head*). It's all right, Father. It's only a Dragon.

FATHER. Only a Dragon? What do you mean, sitting there, you and your Dragons? ONLY a Dragon indeed! And what do YOU know about it?

BOY (*Quietly*). 'Cos it IS, and 'cos I DO KNOW. Look here, Father, you know we've each of us got our line. *You* know about sheep and weather and things; *I* know about Dragons. I always said, you know, that that cave up there was a Dragon-cave. Now please, just leave this all to me. I'll go up and have a talk with him, and you'll find it'll be all right. Only, please don't you go worrying round there without me. You don't understand 'em a bit, and they're sensitive, you know!

MOTHER. Oh, he's quite right, Father. As he says, Dragons is his line and not ours. He's wonderful knowing about book-beasts, as everyone allows. And to tell the truth, I'm not half happy in my own mind, thinking of that poor animal lying alone up there, without a bit o' hot supper or anyone to change the news with; and if he ain't quite respectable our Boy'll find it out quick enough. He's got a pleasant sort o' way with him that makes everybody tell him everything. Now, you two come along to bed now! *(She leads the* BOY *off right, followed by the* FATHER.*)*

(The DRAGON *emerges from the cave entrance, looks happily about him, puts his chin on his paws, and purrs blissfully. The* BOY *enters from stage right.)*

BOY. Well, we live and learn! None of my books about Dragons told me that they purred! *(Goes nearer).* Hallo, Dragon!

DRAGON HEAD *(Severely).* Now don't you hit me, or bung stones, or squirt water, or anything. I won't have it, I tell you!

BOY. I've simply looked in to ask you how you were and all that sort of thing; but if I'm in the way I can easily clear out.

DRAGON LEFT PAW. No, no, no, don't go off in a huff. Fact is—I'm as happy up here as the day's long; never without an occupation, dear fellow, never without an occupation! And yet, between ourselves, it *is* a trifle dull at times.

BOY *(Politely).* Going to make a long stay here?

DRAGON RIGHT PAW. Um, can't hardly say at present. It seems a nice place enough; but I've only been here a short time, and one must look about and reflect and consider before settling down. Besides—fact is, I'm

144

such a confounded lazy beggar!

BOY. You surprise me.

DRAGON TAIL. Well, it's the sad truth; and I fancy that's really how I came to be here. You see, all the other fellows were so active and EARNEST and all that sort of thing—always rampaging, and skirmishing, and scouring the desert sands, and pacing the margin of the sea, and chasing knights all over the place, and devouring damsels—whereas I liked to get my meals regular and then to prop my back against a bit of rock and snooze a bit, and wake up and think of things going on and how they kept going on just the same, you know! So when it happened I got fairly caught.

BOY. When *what* happened, please?

DRAGON HEAD. That is JUST what I don't precisely know. I suppose the earth sneezed, or shook itself, or the bottom dropped out of something. Anyhow there was a shake and a roar and a general stramash, and I found myself miles away underground and wedged in as tight as tight. Well, thank goodness, my wants are few, and I had peace and quiet. But time went on, and there was a certain sameness about the life, and at last I began to think it would be fun to work my way upstairs and see what the other fellows were doing. So I scratched and burrowed, and at last I came out through this cave here. On the whole I feel inclined to settle down here.

BOY. What's your mind always occupied about?

DRAGON LEFT PAW *(Bashfully).* Did you ever—just for fun—try to make up poetry—verses, you know?

BOY. 'Course I have. Heaps of it. And some of it's quite good, I feel sure, only

146

there's no one here cares about it. . . .

DRAGON RIGHT PAW. Exactly, it's my own case exactly. Now you've got culture, you have, I could tell it on you at once. I'm awfully pleased to have met you, and I'm hoping the other neighbors will be equally agreeable. There was a very nice old gentleman up here only last night, but he didn't seem to want to intrude.

BOY. That was my Father, and he IS a nice old gentleman, and I'll introduce you someday if you like.

DRAGON TAIL *(Eagerly).* Can't you two come up here and dine tomorrow?

BOY. Thanks awfully, but we don't go out anywhere without my Mother, and, to tell you the truth, I'm afraid she mightn't quite approve of you. You see, there's no getting over the hard fact that you're a Dragon, is there? And when you talk of settling down, I can't help feeling that you don't quite realize your position. You're an enemy of the human race, you see!

DRAGON HEAD *(Cheerfully).* I haven't got an enemy in the world. Too lazy to make 'em, to begin with.

BOY. Oh, dear! I wish you'd try and grasp the situation properly. When the other people find you out, they'll come after you with spears and swords and all sorts of things. You'll have to be exterminated, according to their way of looking at it! You're a direful scourge, and a pest, and a baneful monster!

DRAGON LEFT PAW. Not a word of truth in it. Character'll bear the strictest investigation. And now, there's a little sonnet-thing I was working on. . . .

BOY. I can't stop for sonnets. Do for goodness' sake try and realize that you're a pestilential scourge, or you'll find yourself in a

most awful fix. Good night! *(The BOY waves good-by as he goes off the stage. The DRAGON waves, yawns, and backs carefully into his cave, as the lights dim.)*

(There are a few moments of quiet which mean the night has passed. From different parts of the audience the VILLAGERS come singing to the stage. They carry small stools. They greet each other and settle themselves on their stools in a half circle at stage right.)

FIRST VILLAGER. I say he IS a pestilential scourge!

SECOND VILLAGER. Fancy that! A real live Dragon in the cave on our Downs!

THIRD VILLAGER. Just where we were a-picnicking, peaceful as could be, only last Sunday!

FOURTH VILLAGER. He's as big as four cart horses!

148

FIFTH VILLAGER. And covered from tip to tail with huge SCALES!

SIXTH VILLAGER. In a way, it's a distinction for a village to have a Dragon of its own!

SEVENTH VILLAGER. Not many a village can say the same, that's sure!

EIGHTH VILLAGER. He sits so quiet, he don't behave like a Dragon. . . .

FIRST VILLAGER. Well, that's his own lookout! He IS a Dragon and no denying it!

SECOND VILLAGER. They do say there's a Princess in the cave waiting to be freed!

THIRD VILLAGER. And I do hear tell many a sheep's been stolen o'nights!

FOURTH VILLAGER. It's not only SHEEP! Children too, who have wandered on the Downs alone, have not come back. . . .

FIFTH VILLAGER. Who's a-telling you this?

SIXTH VILLAGER. Never mind, who's a-telling! Anyone knows what a Dragon does.

149

SEVENTH VILLAGER. My great grampa had tales enough in HIS time. Anyone knows what a Dragon does!

EIGHTH VILLAGER. This sort of thing can't go on!

FIRST VILLAGER. The dreadful beast must be EXTERMI-NATED!

SECOND VILLAGER. The country-side must be freed from this pest!

THIRD VILLAGER. Oh, this terror! This destroying scourge!

FOURTH VILLAGER *(Rises).* Who will take sword and spear and free our suffering village?

FIFTH VILLAGER *(Rises).* And rescue that poor captive Princess?

SIXTH VILLAGER *(Rises).* And win deathless fame?

SEVENTH VILLAGER *(Rises).* Who? Who?

EIGHTH VILLAGER *(Rises).* Who? Who? Who?
(They look at each other in silence. There is a pause and then they all sit down again.)

FOURTH VILLAGER. *(He looks straight out at the audience and then rises in great excitement.)* It's all right! He's a-coming!

ALL OTHERS. Who's a-coming?

FOURTH VILLAGER. St. George, of course!
(They see him striding through the audience. They stand on their stools and cheer.)

ALL. St. George! St. George!! St. George!!!

FIRST VILLAGER. He's heard tell of our Dragon. . . .

SECOND VILLAGER. He's coming on purpose just to slay the deadly beast. . . .

THIRD VILLAGER. And free us from his horrid yoke!

FOURTH VILLAGER. My! Won't there be a jolly fight!

FIFTH VILLAGER. It's all up now, Dragon! He's coming!

SIXTH VILLAGER. We'll have a real fight!

SEVENTH VILLAGER. Who'll give me odds on George!

EIGHTH VILLAGER. Let's have a good look at him first!

150

ALL *(Making a path for St. George, as they cheer and wave).* Hail, St. George!

ST. GEORGE. *(Striding through the VILLAGERS, he goes to a stool at the center of the half circle and mounts it. He silences the VILLAGERS with a wave of his hands.)* Dear friends, I have come to rid your village of the dreadful Dragon.

(The VILLAGERS all cheer.)

ST. GEORGE. Tell me all the wrongs which you have suffered, the wrongs which I will avenge.

(There is an awkward silence, in which the VILLAGERS prod each other.)

FIRST VILLAGER. Well, the sheep have been disappearing. . . .

SECOND VILLAGER. And some of the children. . . .

THIRD VILLAGER. And some crops ravished. . . .

FOURTH VILLAGER. And a Princess bound in the cave . . . .

FIFTH VILLAGER. And some folk being murdered all over the place. . . .

151

SIXTH VILLAGER. And thieving and wrongdoing such as would shame your ears to hear and my lips to speak it.

SEVENTH VILLAGER. We dare not even go out of doors for the fear of being snatched alive. . . .

EIGHTH VILLAGER. Or burned to a crisp because of his hot, scorching breath a-blowing on us and a-making waste our countryside.

ST. GEORGE. All will be well now. Sleep tonight, and tomorrow I will slay your foe. But now, good night!

(The VILLAGERS bow to him, and go off in groups. As they go, they look back at him and make bets on the fight. ST. GEORGE watches them go. Then he sits wearily on the stool and puts his head in his hands.)

BOY *(Enters politely)*. May I come in, St. George?

ST. GEORGE *(Kindly)*. Yes, do come in, Boy. Another tale of misery and wrong, I fear me. Well, it shall soon be avenged.

BOY. Nothing of the sort. There's a misunderstanding somewhere, and I want to put it right. *(He moves a stool close to ST. GEORGE and sits beside him.)* The fact is, this is a GOOD Dragon. And a friend of mine. Nobody can help liking him once they know him.

ST. GEORGE *(Smiles)*. I like a fellow who sticks up for his friends. But that's not the question. I've been listening to tales of murder, theft and wrong. This Dragon has to be speedily exterminated.

BOY *(Impatiently)*. Oh, you've been taking in all the yarns those fellows have been telling you. Our Villagers are the biggest storytellers in all the country round. All they want is a FIGHT. I came down the street just now, and they were betting six to four on the Dragon!

152

ST. GEORGE *(Sadly)*. Not six to four on the Dragon! This is an evil world, and sometimes I begin to think that all the wickedness is not entirely bottled up inside the Dragons. And yet— may there not be, at this very moment, some princess within yonder gloomy cavern?

BOY *(Earnestly)*. I assure you, St. George, there's nothing of the sort at all. The Dragon's a real gentleman, every inch of him.

ST. GEORGE. Well, perhaps I've misjudged the animal. But what are we to do? Here are the Dragon and I, almost face to face, each supposed to be thirsting for each other's blood. I don't see any other way out of it, exactly.

BOY. I suppose you couldn't be persuaded to go away quietly, could you?

ST. GEORGE. Impossible, I fear. Quite against the rules. YOU know that.

BOY. Well then. . . . Look here, would you mind strolling up with me and seeing the Dragon and talking it over?

ST. GEORGE *(Rises)*. Well, it's *irregular,* but really it seems about the most sensible thing to do. Perhaps there won't have to be any fight after all.

BOY *(Following him off the stage)*. Oh, but I hope there will, though!
(They circle through the audience, come onto the stage again, and stand before the cave.)

BOY *(Calls out)*. I've brought a friend to see you, Dragon!

DRAGON HEAD *(Coming out of the cave)*. I'm very pleased to make your acquaintance, sir. Charming weather we're having!

BOY. This is St. George. We've come up to talk things over quietly, Dragon, and do let us have a little straight common sense.

DRAGON LEFT PAW *(Nervously)*. Glad to meet you, St. George.

153

You've really been a great traveler, I hear, and I've always been rather a stay-at-home. But if you're stopping here any time. . . .

ST. GEORGE *(Shakes hands with the Dragon).* I think we'd better try to come to some understanding about this little affair of ours. Now don't you think that the simplest plan would be just to fight it out, and let the best man win? They're betting on you down in the

village, but I don't mind that!

BOY *(Delighted).* Oh, yes, DO, Dragon. It'll save such a lot of bother!

DRAGON RIGHT PAW. Believe me, St. George, there is nobody in the world I'd sooner oblige than you and this young gentleman here. But the whole thing's nonsense, and conventionality, and popular thick-headedness. There's absolutely nothing to fight about, from beginning to end. And anyhow

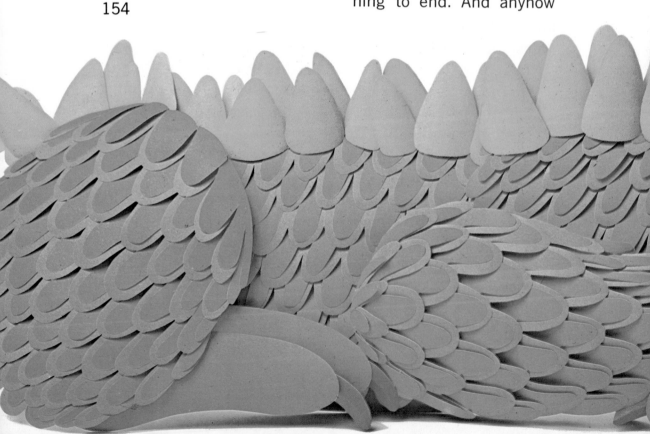

I'm not going to, so that settles it!

ST. GEORGE. But suppose I just make you?

DRAGON TAIL. Well, you can't. I should only go into my cave and retire for a time down the hole I came up. And as soon as you'd gone away, why I'd come up again. For I tell you frankly, I like this place, and I'm going to stay here!

ST. GEORGE (Looking around him). This would be a beautiful place for a fight. These great rolling Downs — and me in my golden armor showing up against your big, blue, scaly coils! Think what a picture it would make!

DRAGON HEAD. Now you're trying to get at me through my artistic sensibilities. But it won't work. Not but what it would make a very pretty picture, as you say.

BOY. You must see, Dragon, that there's got to be a fight of some sort, 'cos you can't

155

want to have to go down that dirty old hole again and stop there till goodness knows when.

ST. GEORGE *(Thoughtfully).* It might be arranged. I MUST spear you somewhere, of course, but I'm not bound to hurt you very much. *(He walks the length of the DRAGON, looking him over.)* There's such a lot of you that there must be a few SPARE places somewhere. *(He prods the DRAGON with his spear in several places. Each time, the DRAGON giggles.)* Here, for instance. Or here! Or here!

DRAGON LEFT PAW. Stop! You're tickling me, George! Those places won't do at all.

ST. GEORGE. Let's try somewhere else, then. Here! *(Points his spear at the back folds of the DRAGON'S neck).* All these folds of thick skin. If I speared you here you'd never even know I'd done it!

156

DRAGON RIGHT PAW *(Anxiously)*. But are you sure you can hit the right place?

ST. GEORGE. Of course I am. You leave that to me!

DRAGON LEFT PAW. It's just because I've GOT to leave it to you that I'm asking.

BOY. Look here, Dragon, I don't see quite where you come in! There's to be a fight, apparently, and you're to be licked; and what I want to know is, what are you going to get out of it?

DRAGON HEAD. St. George, you just tell him, please—what will happen after I am vanquished in the deadly combat?

ST. GEORGE. Well, according to the rules there'll be speeches and things, and I shall explain that you're converted, and see the error of your ways, and so on.

DRAGON TAIL. Quite so. And then what?

ST. GEORGE. Oh, and then— why, and then there will be the usual banquet.

DRAGON RIGHT PAW. Exactly. And that's where *I* come in. I'm bored to death up here, and no one really appreciates me. I'm going into Society, I am, and you'll find I've got all the qualities to endear me to people! So now that's all settled.

ST. GEORGE. Remember, you'll have to do your proper share of the fighting, Dragon! I mean ramping, and breathing fire, and so on!

DRAGON TAIL. I'll do the best I can. *(Yawns).* And now, good night! *(He backs into his cave as the lights grow dim.)*

ST. GEORGE *(As he and the Boy leave).* I knew I had forgotten something. There ought to be a princess. Terror-stricken and chained to a rock, and all that sort of thing. Boy, can't you arrange a princess?

BOY *(Yawns).* I'm tired to death, and I can't arrange a princess or anything more at this time of night. And my Mother's sitting up, and please stop asking me to arrange more things till tomorrow!

(They are now off the stage and there are a few moments of silence. Then VILLAGERS enter from different places in the audience. They are calling out to each other as they come to the stage. They get the stools from the Inn and, as they call to each other in a holiday mood of festivity, they line them up across the back of the stage and stand on them to watch the fight.)

FIRST VILLAGER. Six to four on the Dragon!

SECOND VILLAGER. Wait till we collect on you!

THIRD VILLAGER. Taken—and I'm glad to!

FOURTH VILLAGER. And I'll raise that!

FIFTH VILLAGER. Don't get too near that cave!

158

SIXTH VILLAGER. If the Dragon wins, he'll take us on next!

SEVENTH VILLAGER. If he wins! Sure he'll win!

EIGHTH VILLAGER. Anyway, you keep your distance!

(The BOY, with his MOTHER and FATHER, join the crowd at the right side of the stage. MOTHER and FATHER carry baskets of food.)

BOY. He's coming!

ALL *(Cheer).* St. George! St. George!

(ST. GEORGE, in all his splendor, strides down the center aisle of the audience. He comes to center stage and bows to the cheering crowd. Then he walks, magnificently, to stage far right and poses.)

ALL. Now, then, Dragon!!

(The DRAGON, with great snorts and bellows, comes from his cave. He lashes his tail, claws the ground, and gives a good show of fierceness.)

159

ALL. OO-OO-OO-OO! Oh, well done, Dragon! Well done! (*The DRAGON bows and poses, at stage left.*)

FIRST VILLAGER (*Waving a big banner*). ROUND ONE!

ALL. ROUND ONE!
(*ST. GEORGE lowers his spear and rushes at the DRAGON. The crowd is breathless. The DRAGON snorts, roars, and dodges.*)

ALL. MISSED! MISSED!
(*ST. GEORGE strides back to his place at stage right. He wipes his brow and winks at the BOY.*)

ALL. End of Round One!
(*THE DRAGON gives a ramping exhibit which terrifies the crowd. Then he bows and poses. ST. GEORGE nods that he is ready.*)

ALL. Time! ROUND TWO!
(*ST. GEORGE rushes at the DRAGON, who leaps from side to side whooping like an Indian.*)

All. MISSED! THE END OF ROUND TWO!

(*ST. GEORGE returns to stage right, sighing heavily. He pats the BOY on the shoulder and gives him his spear to hold while the DRAGON entertains the crowd with a little dance.*)

ALL. TIME! ROUND THREE!
(*ST. GEORGE, with spear lowered, advances very carefully. The DRAGON circles. They spar, while the crowd is silent and breathless. Then a quick movement of the Saint's spear pins the DRAG-ON to the earth. ST. GEORGE stands astride the DRAGON.*)

ALL. (*They cheer wildly with great whoops of noise and claps.*) St. George! ST. GEORGE!! ST. GEORGE!!!

FIRST VILLAGER (*Above the cheers*). Bain't you going to cut 'is 'ed orf, master?

ST. GEORGE (*Commanding silence with a gesture*). There's no hurry about that, you know. I have a few

words to say first. *(The crowd listens.)* My friends! I have removed your direful scourge. Now I want to ask the Dragon a few questions. Do you, Dragon, see that there are two sides to everything? *(The DRAGON nods.)* Are you going to be bad any more? *(The DRAGON shakes his head.)* Would you like to stay and settle down here in a peaceful sort of way? *(The DRAGON nods vigorously. ST. GEORGE draws the spear out of the DRAGON'S neck. The DRAGON sits up and shakes hands with ST. GEORGE.)* Now, my friends, I do not want you to be prejudiced any more. You are never to go around grumbling and fancying that you have grievances. And you should not be so fond of fights, because next time you might have to do the fighting yourselves, which is not at all the same thing. And now I think we should have refreshments!

ALL. Refreshment! Celebration! Party! Food! Drink! That's wot we'll have! *(MOTHER and FATHER start passing food and drink to everyone. The crowd sings merrily. When everyone has some refreshment ready to eat and drink, ST. GEORGE pats the happy DRAGON on the head.)*

ST. GEORGE *(Lifts his mug).* And now I give you — your friend from now on — THE DRAGON!

ALL. OUR FRIEND — THE DRAGON! *(The DRAGON bows courteously as they all drink to him. The BOY runs to the DRAGON and hugs him, as the curtain closes.)*

— *Moyne Rice Smith*

162

THINKING IT OVER

1. Tell several ways this dragon was different from most dragons. Did you think he was funny? Why or why not?

2. A villain is a wicked person. Would you call any of the characters a villain? Why? Who was the hero of this story?

3. On page 162 St. George gave advice to the dragon and the villagers. What did he want the dragon to realize? What did he want the villagers to realize?

THOUGHTS AT WORK

1. At first the villagers were interested in the dragon, then they decided he must be killed. How did their discussion on pages 149–150 lead to this decision?

2. When St. George asked the people to name the wrongs they had suffered, there was an "awkward silence." Why?

3. List all the rules and customs St. George and the dragon had to observe in order to have a proper fight.

4. Some words and phrases in the play may have seemed strange to you—such as "them there Downs." Find ten of these expressions and restate them in your own words.

5. On page 150 why do the villagers "all sit down again" after the eighth villager shouts, "Who? Who? Who?"

6. How many actors play the dragon's part? Which of the actors should probably be the tallest?

7. Reread carefully the description of the stage setting on page 141 and draw a sketch showing how it would look. Can you think of another way the stage could be arranged? Draw a second sketch showing your own idea for a stage setting.

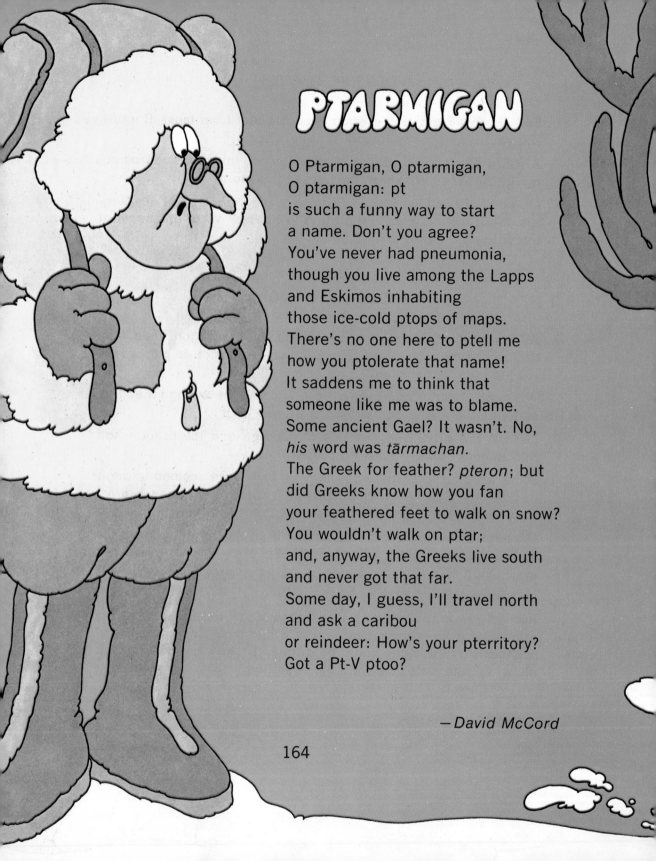

PTARMIGAN

O Ptarmigan, O ptarmigan,
O ptarmigan: pt
is such a funny way to start
a name. Don't you agree?
You've never had pneumonia,
though you live among the Lapps
and Eskimos inhabiting
those ice-cold ptops of maps.
There's no one here to ptell me
how you ptolerate that name!
It saddens me to think that
someone like me was to blame.
Some ancient Gael? It wasn't. No,
his word was *tārmachan*.
The Greek for feather? *pteron*; but
did Greeks know how you fan
your feathered feet to walk on snow?
You wouldn't walk on ptar;
and, anyway, the Greeks live south
and never got that far.
Some day, I guess, I'll travel north
and ask a caribou
or reindeer: How's your pterritory?
Got a Pt-V ptoo?

—*David McCord*

164

In the hundreds of folktales from around the world a trickster often appears. He is a humorous character because he outwits others with his pranks and at the same time exposes their weaknesses. Here is one of many stories from West African folklore about a trickster named Anansi. What kind of trick could he have played on a fishing expedition?

166

ANANSI'S FISHING EXPEDITION

In the country of Ashanti,[1] not far from the edge of the great West African forest, there was a man named Anansi,[2] who was known to all the people for miles around. Anansi was not a great hunter, or a great worker, or a great warrior. His specialty was being clever. He liked to outwit people. He liked to live well, and to have other people do things for him. But because all the people of the country knew about Anansi and had had trouble with him he had to keep thinking of new ways to get something for nothing.

One day Anansi was sitting in the village when a man named Osansa[3] came along.

"I have an idea," Anansi said. "Why don't we go and set fish traps together? Then we shall sell the fish and be quite rich."

¹ Ashanti (ə shant'ē)   ² Anansi (ə nan'sē)   ³ Osansa (o san'sə)

But Osansa knew Anansi's reputation very well, and so he said:

"No, I have as much food as I can eat or sell. I am rich enough. Why don't you set your fish traps by yourself?"

"Ha! Fish alone? Then I'd have to do all the work!" Anansi said. "What I need is a fool for a partner."

Osansa went away, and after a while another man named Anene [1] came along.

"I have an idea," Anansi said. "Why don't the two of us go and set fish traps together? Then we shall sell the fish and be quite rich."

Anene knew Anansi very well too, but he seemed to listen thoughtfully.

"That sounds like a fine idea," he said. "Two people can catch more fish than one. Yes, I'll do it."

The news went rapidly around the village that Anansi and Anene were going on a fishing expedition together. Osansa met Anene in the market and said:

"We hear you are going to trap fish with Anansi. Don't you know he is trying to make a fool of you? He has told everyone that he needs a fool to go fishing with him. He wants someone to set the fish traps and do all the work, while he gets all the money for the fish."

"Don't worry, friend Osansa, I won't be Anansi's fool," Anene said.

Early the next morning Anansi and Anene went into the woods to cut palm branches to make fish traps.

Anansi was busy thinking how he could make Anene

[1] Anene (ə nē′nē)

168

do most of the work. But when they came to the place where the palm trees grew, Anene said to Anansi:

"Give me the knife, Anansi. I shall cut the branches for the traps. We are partners. We share everything. My part of the work will be to cut branches, your part of the work will be to get tired for me."

"Just a minute, let me think," Anansi said. "Why should I be the one to get tired?"

"Well, when there's work to be done someone must get tired," Anene said. "That's the way it is. So if I cut the branches the least you can do is to get tired for me."

"Hah, you take me for a fool?" Anansi said. "Give me the knife. I shall cut the branches and *you* get tired for *me*!"

So Anansi took the knife and began cutting the branches from the trees. Every time he chopped, Anene grunted. Anene sat down in the shade and groaned from weariness, while Anansi chopped and hacked and sweated. Finally the wood for the fish traps was cut. Anansi tied it up into a big bundle. Anene got up from the ground holding his back and moaning.

"Anansi, let me carry the bundle of wood now, and you can get tired for me," Anene said.

"Oh, no, my friend Anene," Anansi said, "I am not that simple-minded. I'll carry the wood myself, and you can take the weariness for me."

So he hoisted the bundle to the top of his head and the two of them started back to the village. Anene groaned all the way.

"Oh, oh!" he moaned. "Take it easy, Anansi! Oh, oh!"

When they came to the village, Anene said:

"Let me make the fish traps, Anansi, and you just sit down and get tired for me."

"Oh, no," Anansi said. "You just keep on as you are." And he made the fish traps while Anene lay on his back in the shade with his eyes closed, moaning and groaning.

And while he was making the traps, working in the heat with perspiration running down his face and chest, Anansi looked at Anene lying there taking all his weariness and sore muscles for him, and he shook his head and clucked his tongue.

"Anene thinks he is intelligent," he said to himself. "Yet look at him moaning and groaning there, practically dying from weariness!"

When the fish traps were done Anene climbed to his feet and said, "Anansi, my friend, now let me carry the fish traps to the water, and you can get tired for me."

"Oh, no," Anansi said. "You just come along and do your share. I'll do the carrying, you do the getting-tired."

So they went down to the water, Anansi carrying and Anene moaning. When they arrived, Anene said to Anansi:

"Now wait a minute, Anansi, we ought to think things over here. There are sharks in this water. Someone is apt to get hurt. So let me go in and set the traps, and should a shark bite me, then you can die for me."

"Wah!" Anansi howled. "Listen to that! What do you

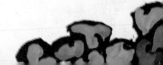

take me for? I'll go in the water and set the traps myself, and if I am bitten, then *you* can die for *me!*" So he took the fish traps out into the water and set them, and then the two of them went back to the village.

The next morning when they went down to inspect the traps, they found just four fish. Anene spoke first.

"Anansi, there are only four fish here. You take them. Tomorrow there will probably be more, and then I'll take my turn."

"Now, what do you take me for?" Anansi said indignantly. "Do you think I am simple-minded? Oh, no, Anene, you take the four fish and I'll take my turn tomorrow."

So Anene took the four fish and carried them to town and sold them.

Next day when they came down to the fish traps, Anene said:

"Look, there are only eight fish here. I'm glad it's your turn, because tomorrow there doubtless will be more."

"Just a minute," Anansi said. "You want me to take today's fish so that tomorrow you get a bigger catch? Oh no, these are all yours, partner, tomorrow I'll take my share."

So Anene took the eight fish and carried them to town and sold them.

Next day when they came to look in the traps they found sixteen fish.

"Anansi," Anene said, "take the sixteen fish. Little ones, too. I'll take my turn tomorrow."

"Of course you'll take your turn tomorrow, it's my

turn today," Anansi said. He stopped to think. "Well, now, you are trying to make a fool out of me again! You want me to take these sixteen miserable little fish so that you can get the big catch tomorrow, don't you? Well, it's a good thing I'm alert! You take the sixteen today and I'll take the big catch tomorrow!"

So Anene carried the sixteen fish to the market and sold them.

Next day they came to the traps and took the fish out. But by this time the traps had rotted in the water.

"Well, it's certainly your turn today," Anene said. "And I'm very glad of that. Look, the fish traps are rotten and worn out. We can't use them any more. I'll tell you what—you take the fish to town and sell them, and I'll take the rotten fish traps and sell them. The fish traps will bring an excellent price. What a wonderful idea!"

"Hm," Anansi said. "Just a moment, don't be in such a hurry. I'll take the fish traps and sell them myself. If there's such a good price to be had, why shouldn't I get it instead of you? Oh, no, *you* take the fish, my friend."

Anansi hoisted the rotten fish traps up on his head and started off for town. Anene followed him, carrying the fish. When they arrived in the town Anene sold his fish in the market, while Anansi walked back and forth singing loudly:

"I am selling rotten fish traps! I am selling wonderful rotten fish traps!"

But no one wanted rotten fish traps, and the towns-people were angry that Anansi thought they were so

stupid they would buy them. All day long Anansi
wandered through the town singing:

"Get your rotten fish traps here! I am selling wonderful rotten fish traps!"

Finally the head man of the town heard about the
affair. He too became very angry, and he sent messen-
gers for Anansi. When they brought Anansi to him he
asked indignantly:

"What do you think you are doing, anyway? What kind
of nonsense is this you are trying to put over the
people of the town?"

"I'm selling rotten fish traps," Anansi said, "very
excellent rotten fish traps."

"Now what do you take us for?" the chief of the
town said. "Do you think we are ignorant people? Your
friend Anene came and sold good fish, which the
people want, but you come trying to sell something
that isn't good for anything and just smell the town
up with your rotten fish traps. It's an outrage. You
insult us."

174

The head man turned to the townspeople who stood near by, listening.

"Take him away and whip him," he said.

The men took Anansi out to the town gate and beat him with sticks. Anansi shouted and yelled and made a great noise. When at last they turned him loose, Anene said to him:

"Anansi, this ought to be a lesson to you. You wanted a fool to go fishing with you, but you didn't have to look so hard to find one. You were a fool yourself."

Anansi nodded his head.

"Yes," he said thoughtfully, rubbing his back and his legs where they had beat him. And he looked reproachfully at Anene. "But what kind of partner are you? At least you could have taken the pain while I took the beating."

—Harold Courlander
and George Herzog

THINKING IT OVER

1. At the beginning of the story the author said that Anansi was clever, but at the end Anene called him a fool. How could he be both clever and foolish?

2. Folktales usually contain a thread of truth about human nature. What did you learn about human nature from this story?

3. Who do you think was the cleverest man in the story? Anansi? Osansa? Anene? Why?

THOUGHTS AT WORK

1. Do you think Anansi deserved the beating? Why or why not?

2. Why didn't Anene groan and yell when Anansi was beaten?

3. List in proper order the jobs that must be done in trap fishing.

4. What do you think Anansi meant when he said, "At least you could have taken the pain while I took the beating"?

5. Can you think of other folktales in which someone was tricked? "The Three Little Pigs" is one example.

FISH STORY

Count this among my heartfelt wishes:
To hear a fish tale told by fishes
And stand among the fish who doubt
The honor of a fellow trout,
And watch the bulging of their eyes
To hear of imitation flies
And worms with rather droopy looks
Stuck through with hateful, horrid hooks,
And fishermen they fled all day from
(As big as this) and got away from.

—Richard Armour

A successful actor gets curtain calls. After the last act the audience claps so loudly and so long that the curtain rises and the actor bows. But "curtains" is also used in another sense. It may mean the end of a career for an actor.

As you read this comedy of errors, think about Joey's performance. Did he deserve a curtain call or curtains? Or did the author have still another idea when he chose the title for his story?

CURTAINS FOR JOEY

Joey and his friend Steve usually ended the school day by having to stay after school. It wasn't that Miss Rafferty was mean or that they were particularly bad. Without ever really trying to, Joey and Steve simply drifted into one hilarious scrape after another. The only trouble was, Miss Rafferty wasn't always amused.

The day this story begins was very much like the others during this school term except for one important difference. This time Miss Rafferty didn't tell Joey and Steve to stay; she invited them to do so. They knew right away that something was up.

Here is what happened in Joey's own words.

179

First, Miss Rafferty told us the Mother's Club was going to put on a play. Then she told us Mr. DeZell (the one who works for the railroad) was going to be the stage manager. *Then* she said he'd asked her to pick out two boys to be stagehands, and we were the ones. Here was our chance to learn all about acting.

Miss Rafferty called a meeting of all the mothers who wanted to be in the play. It was on a Friday night in the fifth-grade room. When everybody got there— there must have been at least twenty—she called the meeting to order. It sure smelled perfumy. Me 'n' Steve and Mr. DeZell took seats in the back.

Three of the smallest ladies sat down. The rest stood up around the room. Miss Rafferty invited them to sit down too, but they didn't seem very anxious. She invited them again. A couple of them squeezed into seats. The others watched, saw what tight fits the seats were, and pretended they were busy, flicking spots off their coats, blowing their noses, and cleaning their glasses. Me 'n' Steve started to laugh but shut up quick when Miss Rafferty made a face at us. We knew why the rest of them didn't sit. Then Miss Rafferty looked up at the windows (which were all closed tight), just as if she were trying to figure something out.

"I'm afraid it's going to be too drafty in here," she said. "I think we'll retire to the cafeteria."

The ladies nodded and said they thought that was a splendid idea. Except the last two that sat down. One of them said she felt kind of faint, and would Miss Rafferty mind if she just sort of sat there for

a moment until her strength came back? The other one said she felt exactly the same way. I winked at Steve. We knew they didn't want anybody to see them trying to get out of those seats.

While the other ladies were filing out to the cafeteria, Miss Rafferty whispered to us to please find a screwdriver or something and loosen the seats from the desks the two ladies were sitting in. So they could get out. We did. While we were loosening them, one of the ladies said she remembered clearly that those seats had always been tight like that, even when she was a little girl. The other lady said the first one was so right. I guess you could call that our first job as stagehands.

When we finally got to the lunchroom, the ladies sat down. On the benches. Miss Rafferty stood up in front of us and explained the play that was going to be put on, for two nights.

"Of course," she said, "we all know the story of *Romeo and Juliet*, but everyone who puts on a play always reads it at the first meeting of the cast."

Most of the ladies smiled at each other. You could tell they were anxious to be casted. By the way some of them looked, though, me 'n' Steve weren't the only ones who didn't know what *Romeo and Juliet* was all about. Miss Rafferty explained as she read. . . .

It seems there were two rich Italian families in Verona [1] who didn't get along. Every time they met each other, they fought. With swords. Even the servants. One of the families was the Capulets. [2] The

[1] Verona (və rō′nə)   [2] Capulet (kap′yə lət)

other was the Montagues.[1] Juliet's father, who was a Capulet, wanted her to marry another Capulet, who was a nobleman named Paris. She didn't think much of the idea. Then she met Romeo, who was a Montague man. At a dance. And fell in love with him. They were married in secret. That's when the trouble started. Romeo's friend was killed by Juliet's cousin. Then Romeo killed *him*. Juliet's friend who had a drugstore, said he'd cook up something to make her sleep like a log. That way, everybody'd think she was dead, so after the burial, which would be in a vault, he'd wake her up and she could run away with Romeo.

The only thing was, Romeo wasn't told about the deal until after he'd killed himself with sorrow. And poison. He killed Paris, though, before he died. Then Juliet woke up and stabbed herself because Romeo was really dead. The moral of the story was that both families felt so bad about all the dead ones, they made up. . . .

By the time Miss Rafferty finished reading, all the ladies were wiping their eyes and looking real sad. Me 'n' Steve hoped all the rehearsals wouldn't be like this. Before she broke up the meeting, Miss Rafferty said they would have to practice twice a week for at least a month and a half. And everybody would have to work very hard. Mr. DeZell said we would have to be there for all the practices, to kind of get the hang of it.

The next three meetings they used up trying out for parts. They took turns reading in front of everybody. I guess they liked the idea of stabbing themselves for love in front of a crowd—they all wanted to be Juliet.

[1] Montague (mänt′ə gyü)

183

Me 'n' Steve made a list of everything we would need: furniture, pictures, flowers, drapes, books, ornaments, and stuff like that. Mr. DeZell was a lot smarter than we thought; he knew all about sound effects and lighting. He even knew how to make stage sets. The three of us worked on scenery and made a dandy portable balcony for Juliet. Steve wanted to know about refreshments, but Mr. DeZell said we'd do something about that after the show.

Miss Rafferty told the ladies to practice talking like they would in the show, every chance they got. In case they had to fill in for somebody who was sick. Or out of town. She didn't tell me 'n' Steve, but we did anyway.

Both our mothers were going to be in it. They were soldiers. They talked "stage" talk even if they didn't have main parts. One night when I came home after school, Mom was on the phone. She didn't hear me come in. For a change.

I heard her say, "Verily, younger than she are happy mothers made."

Then, whoever was on the other end of the line — Aunt Laura, I think — must have said something about fathers, because Mom said, "You would have me speak ill of him that is my husband?"

I sneaked back to the door and closed it real hard so Mom would hear it. Then I walked in just as if nothing was up. She didn't catch on, I don't think. It was hard to keep a straight face, but I did. I didn't want to make her feel embarrassment.

All this time, the play practices were going on. Twice a week. When me 'n' Steve took the job as stagehands,

184

Miss Rafferty made us promise it wouldn't interfere with our homework. Promises are sure easy to make. Right after that, she kept some of us kids who weren't at the head of the class after school and gave us a bawling out for not doing better. Didn't Steve's conscience bother him when he didn't do his homework? she asked. Like last night, for instance?

He said, "Madam, before the worshiped sun peered forth, a troubled mind drave my booted feet to walk abroad."

"From now on," Miss Rafferty said, "your troubled mind had better drive you to do your homework."

We thought she was finished and started edging out.

"Nay, gentlemen," she tells us, "let ye prepare not to be gone!"

Then she gave it to us good for a couple of minutes more, not exactly Shakespeare talk either, and let us go. We made a dive for the door.

"Wisely and slow," she said. "They stumble that move with haste."

When I got home, Mom says, "What sadness doth lengthen Joey's hours?"

See what I mean? When ladies do something, they *really* do it!

By this time, they knew their lines pretty well. 'Course, they'd had about ten practices. Then came dress rehearsal—without anybody in the seats. After that, a full dress-up practice was put on for the kids in the school. It was pretty good, but kind of dry. The only reason the kids paid attention was that most of their mothers were in it. And they were surrounded

185

by teachers. Mr. DeZell took time off from his railroad job so he could be there. He told us what to do. It didn't go too bad. The kids clapped when the teachers did. It was better than being in class.

The day of the first night of the play, Mom was sure jumpy. Most of the time she was on the telephone telling other mothers not to be nervous. She burned the potatoes for supper and forgot to put coffee in the coffee. Dad said that when the show was over, they oughta get all the fathers up on the stage and decorate them for all the sacrifices they had made. He was just kidding Mom, of course, to make her forget her nervousness and how bad she felt because she hadn't sold all her tickets. He was really proud of her and told me if anybody sitting by him didn't clap, they'd be sorry. He didn't say what he'd do.

That night everybody got there early. But not as early as me 'n' Steve. We played a couple of sound-effects records while we were waiting. When they got there, the ladies sure were excited. Man, you never saw so much fussing and hankie wringing! Steve brought a lunch for us. Sandwiches. Out of baloney and cheese and bread. He even brought salt and pepper, folded up in paper.

I was getting used to seeing the ladies in costume, but they still looked funny. Especially the ones taking men's places. They sure had to use a lot of padding to make the shoulders the widest part. Romeo, who was really Mrs. McNovis, was smaller than Juliet, who was Mrs. Amaturzio.[1] I think she got to be Romeo

¹ Amaturzio (am ə tėr′ zē ō)

186

because she was the only one who could climb the balcony.

They sure dressed funny in those days. There was enough cloth in Juliet's dress to make a pup tent. She wore big white beads around her waist. Too heavy for her neck. I guess. Her hair was long and black, and her hat was made out of—guess what?—more beads! They must have been real cheap in those days. Mom said the dress was very modest. It sure looked expensive, though. About her feet, she might have been barefoot, for all I know. I couldn't see them.

Romeo was worse. For a man, that is. You should have seen the long, pointed slippers and the even longer yellow stockings. And I mean long! Above them, he wore short pants and kind of a gold half-coat, half-jacket that looked like he'd worn it on an overnight hike and got caught in the rain. It was that short. I'm sure glad civilization brought in long pants for men. Would I ever hate to wear those long stockings! Except at Christmas.

All the ladies seemed to enjoy scaring themselves. They'd peek out the side of the curtain, which was rolled down, and say, "Oh, dear! Just *look* at that crowd!" It didn't look like anyone would have to stand up to see the show, though.

Backstage it was getting warmer and warmer. From nerves, I guess. And all the crowding around in such a small space. I told Steve we ought to eat the cheese sandwiches, which were pretty strong. The ladies asked Miss Rafferty if we could turn on the fan to kind of refresh the air. She said we most certainly could; in fact, it might even help the actors to have a little breeze on the stage.

Me 'n' Steve and Mr. DeZell were plenty busy getting everything ready. We had a big ball of cellophane ready to crumple in our hands to imitate a roaring fire; a coconut sawed in half, with each half having a piece of leather fastened to the outside for a handle, so we could make horses' hoofbeats by pounding them on a wooden box; a big sheet of tin hanging up to shake for thunder; a vacuum cleaner to run to make the sound of wind; and a canvas bag filled with tin and rocks to shake for a loud crash. We also had a pail of dried peas to drop on some paper stretched over a box to sound like rain. Besides all that, we had a bubble pipe and a fruit jar of water to go with it so we could make the noise of somebody drowning.

We had marked all the light switches with pasted slips of paper so we wouldn't turn on the wrong one. We did the same thing with all the scenery ropes, even the ones we used to pull the balcony on and off the stage. Also, the moon and the sun. We were sure glad Mr. DeZell was there to kind of overseer the whole thing. Then, of course, we had the record player. With records of different crowd noises like at a football game, traffic jams, and stuff.

When Miss Rafferty peeked out, she said, "Maybe we should have planned on giving the show just one night instead of two. Then there would be more full seats. However, it's too late to do anything about that now."

At eight o'clock, she "sh-h-hed" everybody and went out in front of the curtain to welcome the people who

188

did come. Mostly relatives of the ladies in the program. She, Miss Rafferty, I mean, was dressed in regular clothes and explained a little about the play. And how the ladies had worked hard. Then she bowed, walked off the stage very slow and dignified (so everyone could get a good look at her new red dress) and we cranked up the curtain. Those that were there clapped.

It went pretty good. There were a couple of mistakes, but not bad. Mrs. Blimpnic, who was Benvolio,[1] got kind of mixed up. She said, "Put up your fools, you swords!"

Another time, Romeo said, "Go in and tell thy fair lady I am goon!"

The worst thing was when Juliet was up in the balcony looking down at Romeo, who was making eyes at her, and all of a sudden the balcony starts to sink. It just kind of floated down to the floor real easy, until Juliet was standing right in front of Romeo. Nobody got hurt, though, and Romeo kept right on shouting his words up in the air, just as if Juliet was still up there. The people were very polite and didn't laugh out loud. In between acts, the lights were turned on in the hall to kind of wake up the crowd. So they could listen to music by the school band.

Mr. DeZell was called to the phone just as Act Four was finishing. By the time he got back, we had the curtain down and the band was playing "Brahms'[2] Lullaby." In between bites of the sandwich we were sharing, Steve says, "They oughta play 'Macnamara's Band.' At least they'd be awake *between* the acts!"

That was when Mr. DeZell said he'd have to leave

[1] Benvolio (ben vō′lē ō)   [2] Brahms (brämz)

189

for a little while, and could me 'n' Steve handle it? Something wrong on the job, he said. We said O.K. but to hurry back in case we had a question. He should have whispered that he was going; it wouldn't have upset the ladies so much. They didn't seem to think they could trust us. I heard Mrs. Tyrose[1] say, "Oh, no!"

I watched the people in the audience while we were cranking the curtain up for Act Five. Most of them slumped down in their seats like they were expecting a collection. Or were going to take a nap. It seemed they were even too tired to clap the way they did when the other acts started.

Soon as we got the curtain up, we got ready for Romeo's entering. Steve squatted down in front of the wooden sound box on the floor. He grabbed the coconut halves and made like a horse's *clippety-clop*. He did it fine too. Except that he kept up the galloping after Romeo had tied his horse outside and walked in. I guess it kind of upset Balthasar.[2] She—I mean, he— was supposed to go on the stage when Romeo said, "Love's shadows are so rich in joy," but his robe got caught on the hunk of tin we used for making thunder.

Romeo said it again, a little louder. "Love's shadows are so rich in joy!"

Still no Balthasar. We finally got his cloak tore loose and pushed him out on the stage. Just as Romeo yelled, *"Love's shadows are so rich in joy!"*

What Balthasar had lost of his costume didn't show much. Except that it was kind of uneven. You could see the back of his knees.

[1] Tyrose (tī'rōz)   [2] Balthasar (bal'thə zär)

190

When Romeo was told about Juliet's dying, he stopped crying long enough to tell Balthasar to get some horses. This time, Steve did it better. He waited until Balthasar was almost all the way off the stage before he started making hoofbeats.

By this time, Steve's squatting down had put his leg to sleep. He tried to stand. Couldn't. He grabbed the nearest rope—and down came the curtain! It was sure a short act. Everybody was getting jumpy. Even the customers seemed more awake. Miss Rafferty tried to calm down the ladies, but they kept getting nervouser. We finally got the curtain rolled up again.

This was the part where Romeo says he will go to the drugstore and get a bottle of poison. With which to kill him. He walked over to the side of the stage where somebody was supposed to hand him the bottle. Only nobody could find it. Steve saved the day. He handed Romeo the fruit jar with the water in it for blowing bubbles. You know, for imitating drowning. Romeo was kind of surprised, but didn't say anything. The curtain came down then anyway, so it was O.K.

All the ladies felt pretty good because it was almost over. They cheered each other up, saying what a wonderful job everybody else was doing. Even if they weren't making enough to pay for the tickets they'd printed. They patted me 'n' Steve on the head and said we were regular little men.

Just then somebody bumped into the fan and knocked it over on top of Steve's lunch. Which was still open. It blew everything all over, salt and pepper too, until somebody shut it off. Everybody started sneezing. Miss Rafferty was in a panic. She asked Mom and Steve's mother—since they were soldiers and would be on the stage during the last scene—to get in front of any of the dead ones that might have to sneeze. So the patrons wouldn't notice.

When we cranked up the curtain for the last time, hardly anybody in the hall was sleeping. Some of them even clapped. Romeo and Paris put on a good fight with their swords. Of course, they were only wood. Me 'n' Steve made the noise for them off stage, by dueling with a couple of short pieces of iron pipe. Man, was it ever fun! We danced around and really put on a duel. I didn't know part of me had backed out on the stage, until Miss Rafferty yelled.

When Romeo wounded Paris in the mortality, he fell down quite a ways from Juliet. Where he wanted to die. Romeo had to drag him over. Like he'd promised. It wasn't easy. Then Romeo staggered over and picked up the fruit jar of poison. Talking all the while. He must have been tired from dragging Paris, because he couldn't get the cover off the jar. He tried everything. Putting the jar between his knees and wrestling with it. Banging it on the floor. We all sweated and watched from the side of the stage, hoping he'd make it. All of a sudden, Steve ran out on the stage, grabbed the jar, and opened it. He quick handed it back to Romeo and ran off again. The people in the audience couldn't help laughing.

Everything got serious again when Romeo drank the poison. Somebody in the crowd yelled, "Don't!"

Only it was too late. He died. By then, it was getting

pretty crowded on the stage. The friars were all there. And the soldiers. And the victims. That's when Juliet woke up. She was a little early, but I guess she had to sneeze and figured it would look better if she wasn't sleeping. Then she kissed Romeo and looked for the knife. It was there, but she couldn't find it. So she took poison. There was plenty in the jar for them both.

That was the sign to start the record player, for crowd noises outside the graveyard. I quick set the needle to start it, then beat it back to help Steve with the lights. I should have checked the record closer— out came "On, Wisconsin." The paste we'd put on the paper slips for the light switches dried and the slips fell off. Steve didn't know which switch was which.

By that time, the whole cast was on the stage, the lights flashing red, white, green, and blue. Everybody around us was trying to help, pulling this and pushing that. The sun and the moon were bobbing up and down, the football song was blaring, and the soldiers on stage were jumping around trying to cover up the sneezers. The school band thought it was all over for sure and started playing "The End of a Perfect Day!"

"The curtain!" Miss Rafferty yelled. "The curtain!"

Me 'n' Steve were buried under a mob trying to get the curtain down. They did. Us too. Then they rushed out on the stage again. We jumped up as quick as we could and pulled up the curtain, to give the people a chance to clap some more. Like we'd been told. Maybe we shouldn't have. Romeo and Juliet were staggering around like they really *had* been poisoned. Paris too. When they saw the curtain going up, they quick fell dead again. In a pile. The people yelled and clapped and whistled. And stood up and cheered—a real terrific racket!

Mom pulled me 'n' Steve aside. "C'mon, boys," she said, "we had better get you out of here. In a hurry! Hurry!"

When we got outside, she told us it might be best if we went right home. And gave the ladies a chance to cool off. Till it kind of blew over. Steve wanted to know where the Foreign Legion office was. So we could sign up.

There wasn't any school next day, and I slept late. Until Mom came busting into my room—and almost scared me to death! She was laughing and crying, all at the same time. She threw her arms around me and gave me a big hug. I knew she was gone. And it was all my fault.

"Joey," she said, "the phone's been ringing all morning! Mr. Nostrum down at the drugstore wants more tickets for tonight's show. All the ladies have been getting calls. Everybody that was there has called to say how much they enjoyed it. Most of them are coming back to see it again. And Miss Rafferty wants to know if you and Steve can do it exactly the same tonight."

—*Roy O. Brotherton*

195

THINKING IT OVER

1. What events in the story made you smile, chuckle, or laugh aloud? Which did you enjoy the most? Why?

2. Stuart Little was described as a "typical American boy." Were Joey and Steve typical—that is, like boys you know?

3. How did Joey and Steve make the play a success?

THOUGHTS AT WORK

1. List the jobs Joey and Steve did as stagehands. Which ones caused the trouble when the play was presented?

2. Find the sentences written in Shakespearean language and put them into your own words.

3. Mrs. McNovis, Mr. Nostrum, and Mrs. Blimpnic were characters in the story. Find *novice* and *nostrum* in your glossary and then tell why these names were appropriate. What do you think Mrs. Blimpnic looked like?

4. Joey told this story in his own words. How would Miss Rafferty have described the first night the play was presented?

5. Why do you think Joey's mother hurried the boys out at the end of the play?

6. Why do you think the audience wanted to come back to see the play again?

7. Which of the stories in this unit did you think was the most amusing? Why? What kind of humor do you enjoy most?

BIBLIOGRAPHY

Two Are Better Than One, by Carol Ryrie Brink.
   The amusing adventures and misadventures of Chrystal and Cordy, growing up together at the turn of the century.

Tall Tales from the High Hills, by Ellis Credle.
   Twenty amusing old tales from the mountains of Tennessee.

The Wonderful Flying-Go-Round, by Dana Faralla.
   There is fun and fantasy in the Dump Yard when it is turned into a marvelous playground.

John Henry and His Hammer, by Harold W. Felton.
   This American folk hero and superman competes with a steam hammer to build a railroad tunnel.

By the Great Horn Spoon, by Sid Fleischman.
   There is great fun when a boy and a butler stow away on a sailing ship bound for California and the Gold Rush.

The Reluctant Dragon, by Kenneth Grahame.
   The play about the most untraditional dragon is based on this story.

Phoebe Snow, by Elizabeth Hall.
   Lucy fools the new preacher when he comes to call and then uses the joke for another very funny escapade.

Anansi, the Spider Man, by Philip M. Sherlock.
   When trouble threatens, Anansi can change into a spider. Amusing tales from West Africa that were carried to Jamaica and became part of Jamaican folklore.

Mr. Smith and Other Nonsense, by William Jay Smith.
   Imaginary birds and beasts, unusual people, and limericks too.

TALES FROM ANCIENT GREECE

In Greek mythology the gods ruled supreme over the heavens and the Earth, controlling the lives of men and the forces of nature. In many of the myths the gods walked the Earth, appearing in different disguises to test the character of mere mortals. Some myths explained natural phenomena that puzzled the Greeks, such as the rising and setting of the sun and the changing seasons of the year. Others told of legendary heroes and their daring deeds.

Through mythology the Greek people developed and handed down, from one generation to another, their ideals. Some of those ideals are as real and important today as they were in ancient Greece centuries ago.

199

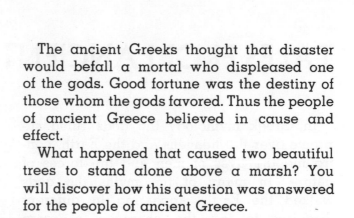

The ancient Greeks thought that disaster would befall a mortal who displeased one of the gods. Good fortune was the destiny of those whom the gods favored. Thus the people of ancient Greece believed in cause and effect.

What happened that caused two beautiful trees to stand alone above a marsh? You will discover how this question was answered for the people of ancient Greece.

BAUCIS AND PHILEMON

On a certain hill in the pleasant land of Greece, there stand a linden tree and an oak. A low wall circles them. Not far from this spot is a marsh. It was once good, fertile land, but now it is fit only for marsh birds and cormorants. This is a tale the ancients told of how that marsh and those two trees came to be.

200

Once upon a time, Zeus[1] visited this country along with his son Hermes.[2] Pretending to be weary travelers, they presented themselves at many a door, seeking rest and shelter. It was late and all the doors were closed. And though the gods banged and called, the sleepy families inside would not bother to leave their beds and let the travelers in.

So Zeus and Hermes wandered on until a bit beyond the fine town, they came to a very humble little cottage. It was small with a thatched roof and a door so low that Zeus had to stoop to knock upon it.

"Who's there? Who's there?" called a voice from within.

"Weary travelers wanting food and a bed," cried Hermes, who was very tired and hungry by this time.

Almost at once the door was flung open and an old man stood peering out at the two strangers. "Come in," he said, "you are welcome here."

Zeus and Hermes, stooping, entered the little cottage. A soft light greeted them from the fireside where an old woman was stirring the embers to make the flames spring up again.

"Here are two weary travelers wanting food and bed," her husband said to her.

[1] Zeus (züs)   [2] Hermes (hêr′ mēz)

"Can we manage to put something before them?"

The wife came hurrying over. She spread a rough cloth on the one bare table. Then on it she placed black bread and cheese. The husband reached down a piece of bacon hanging from the roof rafters and the old wife cut it up and put it over the fire to boil. Then she brought water in a basin so that the travelers could refresh themselves before eating.

When the bacon was ready, the old man bade Zeus and Hermes to come at once to the table. He made no apologies for the very simple supper, for it was what he ate every day. He was only sharing what food he had.

The gods seated themselves and began to put the cheese and the bacon onto the wooden plates before them. They reached for the earthen pitcher to pour the goats' milk into their earthen mugs.

Then a strange thing happened. As Zeus picked up a piece of the coarse black bread, it became fine-grained and as white as snow. The wooden plate began to glow in the firelight as if it were made of gold. Indeed, it was suddenly changed to pure gold. The goats' milk turned into red wine and the earthen mug was changed to clearest crystal.

202

At sight of this, the old man, whose name was Philemon,[1] flung himself down on his knees, for now the travelers had revealed themselves as gods. The whole cottage shone with their glory. Baucis,[2] the wife, also fell to her knees, and both old people trembled with terror. With clasped hands they begged their guests to forgive the humble food which was all they had to put before them.

"I will kill the goose," declared Philemon. "I was saving it to celebrate our marriage date, but you shall have it."

"Yes, yes," cried old Baucis.

They started after the goose which they kept in the cottage at night to protect it from wolves and foxes. But the goose,

[1] Philemon (fə lē′ mən)   [2] Baucis (bô′ sis)

203

startled out of its sleep, flapped its wings and ran around the room, at last taking shelter on the crude bench between the two gods.

Zeus put his hand upon the goose and quieted it. "No, you shall not kill the goose. Keep it to celebrate the feast of your marriage date. We are gods indeed. I am Zeus and this is my son, Hermes." He rose from the bench. "Now come with us to the top of the hill just beyond here."

The old couple followed the gods out of the cottage and into the night. Slowly they began to climb the hill. When they neared its top, Zeus said, "Look below."

Baucis and Philemon turned. What a sight met their eyes! The moon had risen and they could see plainly. Where once the fair town had stood there was now only water with marsh grasses growing around its edge. The only building in sight was their own humble little cottage.

While they stood, wondering and sad at the terrible fate of their neighbors, suddenly they saw their cottage change. Its thatched roof rose, then disappeared, and shining tiles shone in the moonlight. White pillars appeared where once the low door had been. Their cottage was transformed into a *temple*. A temple of the gods!

Then Zeus spoke in a gentle tone. "Kindly old man, and woman fit for such a husband, tell us what your wishes are. Ask anything you want, and it shall be granted to you."

The old couple whispered together for a moment and then Philemon spoke. "We ask to be priests and guardians of this, your temple. And since we have passed our lives together in love and peace, we desire that we may die at the same moment. Let our graves be side by side."

Their wish was granted. Baucis and Philemon lived out the rest of their lives tending the temple which had been raised where their humble dwelling had stood.

205

Then one day, as they stood on the steps of the temple, Baucis saw Philemon begin to put out leaves. Philemon saw Baucis changing in the same way.

"Good-by, my dear wife," whispered Philemon.

"Good-by, dear husband," she whispered back.

Suddenly two beautiful trees appeared, one an oak, the other a linden.

Thus did two great gods reward the kindness of two good people.

206

THINKING IT OVER

1. According to the first paragraph, what is one purpose of this story? What might another purpose be?

2. Greek gods had human qualities as well as godly ones. What human qualities did they show? What godly ones?

3. Why did the gods punish the townspeople? Why did they reward Baucis and Philemon?

THOUGHTS AT WORK

1. Why do you think Zeus and Hermes pretended to be weary travelers seeking rest and shelter?

2. Why do you think Philemon answered the knock at his door? Why did the townspeople ignore it?

3. For what things did the old couple wish? Why?

4. Pretend that you were a visitor at the temple when Baucis and Philemon changed to trees. Describe what you saw.

5. Do you think Baucis or Philemon was the oak tree? Which one was the linden? Explain your answer.

6. Did the ending of the story please you? Why or why not?

7. Zeus and Hermes were important Greek gods. Look in reference books to find more information about them.

Athena, for whom the city of Athens was named, was the goddess of wisdom and such fine arts as weaving. She demanded the highest respect from earthbound mortals. According to Greek mythology, Athena gave help and gifts to those who worshiped her.

But then came Arachne! What natural phenomenon does her strange fate explain?

ARACHNE

In very olden times, there lived in Greece a girl named Arachne.[1] She was known through all the land because of her great skill at weaving. No person on earth, it was said, could weave as skillfully as she. There were some who said not even Athena, goddess of wisdom and the household arts, could weave as well as Arachne. Among those who boasted arrogantly was Arachne herself.

No, this girl was not modest about her skill. She was foolishly proud of it and even made fun of the work of girls less gifted than she. But then, one had to admit it was a wondrous sight to see her fingers moving lightly and swiftly back and forth across her loom. Her designs were intricate and beautiful, and she wove the colors of her threads with the ease and smoothness of an artist working with brush and paint. So graceful was she in all her motions that often the wood nymphs left their shadowy hiding places to watch her at work.

In time Arachne's fame and her boasting reached the ears of Athena, and the goddess decided to draw the girl into a contest that would cure her arrogant pride. So one day when Arachne was weaving in a pleasant grove, there suddenly appeared

[1] Arachne (ə rak′nē)

209

beside her a bent old woman. She gazed for a moment at Arachne's loom, then said, "That is a pretty piece of weaving, my dear, and yet I have seen the time in my youth when I could have done as well."

At this Arachne threw up her head and said in a scornful tone, "Never did any mortal weave as I am weaving now, old woman."

"Those are rash words," said the old woman, and a strange angry light came into her gray eyes, which were exceedingly youthful for one so bent with years. "It is foolish to take too great pride in what one can do, for surely there is always someone who can do the task even better."

"Not so," cried the angry girl. "There is no one who can weave better than I."

The old woman smiled and shook her head doubtfully. "Allowing that no mortal

can weave as well as you, at least among the immortals there is one who can surpass you in the art."

Arachne left off her weaving to stare at the old woman. "And who is that, pray?" she asked.

"The goddess Athena," replied the old woman.

Arachne laughed scornfully. "Not even Athena can weave as well as I."

At these words, the wood nymphs, who had on this occasion as on so many others come to watch Arachne, began to whisper among themselves. They were very frightened, for it was highly dangerous for any mortal to set himself above the gods in anything. Foolish Arachne!

On hearing the boastful words, the old woman's eyes again flashed angrily. But in a moment they softened, and she said,

211

"You are young and have spoken foolishly and in haste. Surely you did not mean what you said. I will give you a chance to take back your words."

But Arachne again flung up her head defiantly. "I did mean what I said, and I shall prove it."

"Prove it then," cried the old woman in a terrible voice. In the next instant, a cry went up from the circling crowd, and Arachne's face turned as white as a cloud bank. For the old woman had vanished and in her place stood the shining form of the goddess Athena.

"For long," she said, "I have heard your boastings and have watched your growing vanity. Now it has led you to defy the very gods. It is time you received a lesson from which other mortals as foolish and vain as you may profit. Let the contest begin."

Another loom was set up in the pleasant grove and Arachne and the goddess began to weave. News of the contest spread through the quiet meadow and up the mountain heights. Soon a large crowd of shepherds drew near to watch the weavers. What they saw was worth coming far to see.

Athena wove upon her loom a bright tapestry which told the story of other

foolish mortals who had thought themselves greater than the gods and who had
been punished for their pride. Arachne
pictured on her loom the stories which
told of the foolish acts of the gods themselves, for it was well known among
mortals that the gods did not always
behave wisely.

The colors used by the two weavers were
so bright they might have been plucked
from the rainbow. The weaving was so perfect that the figures on each loom seemed
to be alive and breathing. The watchers
marveled that such skill could be on earth
or in heaven.

214

At last the tapestries were finished and the two contestants stood back to see what each had wrought upon her loom. At the sight of Arachne's finished work, Athena was so angered by what the girl had dared to picture there, that she struck the tapestry with her shuttle, splitting it in two. Then she struck Arachne on the forehead. Immediately there swept over the girl a deep sense of her vanity in setting herself above the very gods. So great was her shame that she went at once and hanged herself. But when Athena beheld her lifeless body, she took pity upon the foolish Arachne.

"Live," she said, "but never must you be allowed to forget the lesson you have learned today. Though you may live, you must hang throughout all eternity—you and all who come after you and are of your flesh and blood."

With that, she sprinkled Arachne with bitter juices. At once her hair and ears and nose disappeared. Her whole body shrunk up, her arms and legs too. Her head grew small, and she took the shape of what we now call the spider. From her body she drew the thread with which she spun her web. And often we come upon her hanging by that thread just as Athena said she must hang throughout all eternity.

215

THINKING IT OVER

1. Which character did you admire more — Arachne or Athena? Why?

2. Do you think Arachne deserved her punishment? Why or why not?

3. What did this myth explain about nature?

THOUGHTS AT WORK

1. What were Arachne's good qualities? What were some of her bad qualities?

2. What was the one flaw in Athena's disguise?

3. Was Athena's tapestry better than Arachne's? Explain your answer.

4. Name the ways in which Arachne insulted the gods. Why do you think she did this?

5. Why did Athena think that a contest would teach Arachne a valuable lesson?

6. Look up the name Arachnida and tell what it means. How is it related to this story?

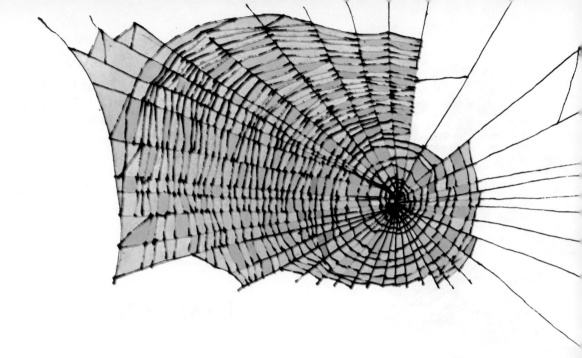

DEW ON A SPIDER WEB

Two twigs acting as a loom
Hold a wonderful weaving.
Silver threads, simple but beautiful against
    the bright blue sky.
Who would ever think this was woven by an ugly
    old spider?
How I would like to have a wonderful weaving
    like that.
My one would never fade away.

                  — *Michael Stone, age 10*
                        (New Zealand)

The ancient Greeks believed that the great Sun-god, Phoebus Apollo, drove his fiery chariot across the sky from dawn to dusk. Here again a myth explained the wonders of nature which fascinated and puzzled the Greeks. It also told about Phaethon, son of Phoebus Apollo, and the awful request he made of his father. What terrifying thing happened as a result of this request? Read the myth to find the answer.

PHAETHON

The Greeks believed their gods dwelt on the top of a high mountain called Olympus.[1] Among them was Phoebus Apollo,[2] god of music and medicine as well as god of the sun. He it was who drove the fiery chariot, drawn by four winged horses, across the sky each day. Every morning, heading out from the Gates of Dawn, Phoebus drove his chariot up into the sky and straight across the heavens, until at last he reached the spot where his course descended into the western ocean and Night arrived.

The Sun-god's palace was a splendid dwelling. Its golden walls dazzled the eyes. Its lofty columns were of glowing bronze, and its doors of gleaming silver.

[1] Olympus (ō lim′pəs)   [2] Phoebus Apollo (fē′bəs ə pol′ō)

218

Now, to this shining palace there came one day a youth named Phaethon.[1] He approached the silver doors slowly, pausing frequently to clear his eyes which were dazzled by all the brilliance. Still he pressed on because he had a question to put to the Sun-god. His mother, a mortal named Clymene,[2] had told Phaethon that Phoebus Apollo was his father. But when the boy boasted to his playmates that his father was a god, they scoffed at him and said, "Prove it."

And thus Phaethon was standing in the very throne room of the great palace where the god Phoebus sat, his radiant crown upon his head. Around him stood his attendants ranged in appointed order. Here were the Days, the Months, the Years, and, at regular intervals, the Hours. The Seasons were present too: Spring in a garland of flowers, Summer cradling a sheaf of wheat, Autumn with wine-stained feet, and Winter wearing a hoary cap of ice.

The Sun-god, who sees everything, soon noticed Phaethon standing there, his sight almost blinded by the splendor.

Phoebus looked kindly upon the boy and asked, "What has brought you here?"

And Phaethon answered boldly, "I have come to ask if you are in truth my father.

[1] Phaethon (fā′ə thon)   [2] Clymene (klī′mə nē)

219

My mother, Clymene, has told me so, but my friends laugh when I claim you. And so I have come to ask you if it be true and if so, to grant me proof."

As Phaethon spoke, Phoebus removed the glittering crown from his head so that the boy might more easily gaze upon him. Then, reaching out, he took Phaethon tenderly into his arms and drew him close.

"Phaethon, Clymene, your mother, has spoken the truth. I am indeed your father and to prove it, ask anything of me and I swear by the river Styx your wish will be granted you."

Now, no god could swear by the river Styx and go back upon his oath. It was the highest vow a god could take. And Phoebus had taken this great oath to grant Phaethon anything he wished, whatever it might be.

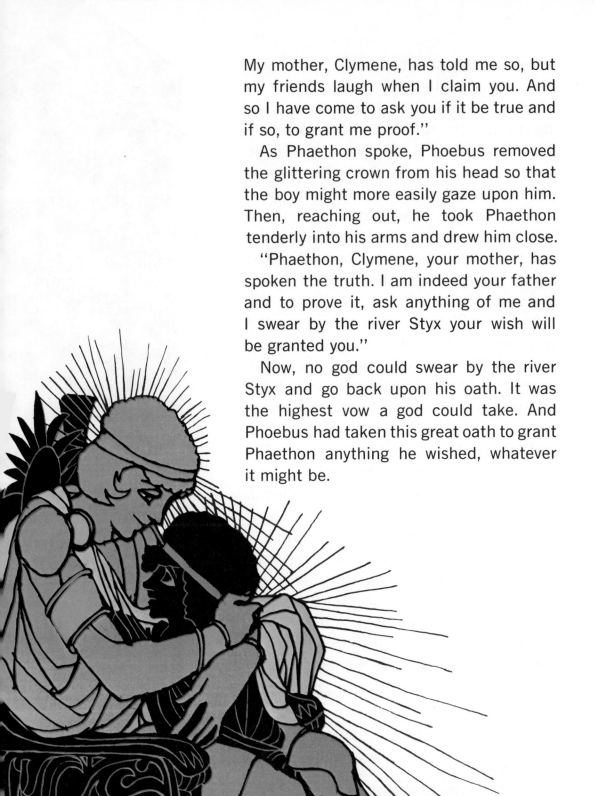

Phaethon had his answer ready. He knew of the Sun-god's journey each day across the sky. He knew well how all peoples of earth counted upon seeing the fiery chariot and its galloping horses as they cleared the Gates of Dawn, sending light and warmth to the earth below.

So now Phaethon cried, "I choose to take your place, Father. For this one day let me drive your winged chariot across the sky. Just this one day."

Too late, Phoebus realized his own folly. Fear and sorrow shadowed the god's shining face. Why had he made a reckless promise and bound himself to grant whatever foolish wish might enter a boy's rash young head?

At last he said, "Dear lad, this is the only wish I would have refused you. If I could only take back my promise! For you have to do what no one can achieve but me. Not even Zeus, hurler of thunderbolts, can drive my chariot. And no one is as powerful as he. Let me tell you of the danger you face. The road is steep, so steep the horses can hardly climb it though they are fresh in the morning. It runs high across the middle heavens, so high that even I am frightened when I look down and see the earth and sea beneath me. At last it descends as sharply

221

as it rose in the beginning. I must hold
the horses on a tight rein. Adding to all
this, the sky is always spinning and the
stars whirl with it. I can drive successfully
against all this. What would you do? Suppose I should lend you the chariot. Could
you keep the course while the world was
whirling under you?

"Besides all this, the road runs through
the midst of frightening monsters, the
Bull, the Lion, the Scorpion, and the Crab.

"Call back your wish while you can. Do
you want proof that you are my son? I
give you that proof in my fears for you.
Look at my face. I would you could see into
my heart and could there see a father's
fears.

"Look around the world. Choose whatever you will of what earth and sea contain. It shall be yours. I swear it. Only do
not ask what you have asked."

He ended. But the youth held to his
demand.

Phaethon pled with his father, remind-
ing him that he had sworn the most sacred
oath even a god could take. Phoebus
Apollo was forced to consent to the lad's
mad wish. Sorrowfully he took Phaethon's
hand and led him to where the shining
chariot waited.

222

While Phaethon stood admiring the great beauty of its craftsmanship, Dawn woke in the east and flung wide her doors. The stars faded. The Sun-god watched as the moon vanished from the sky. Then he ordered the Hours to harness up the horses. They obeyed, leading the animals from their stalls. Then the harness was put in place and the Sun-god annointed his son's face so he could endure the chariot's heat. Next Apollo placed the dazzling crown upon young Phaethon's head.

"My son," he said, "listen to a last few words of warning and heed them. Use the whip seldom and hold tight the reins. These horses go fast enough on their own. Your work will be to hold them in. You will see the marks of the wheels and they shall guide you. Go not too high or low. The middle course is the safest and the best. Now I leave you to your own luck.

223

May it plan better for you than you have done for yourself."

While he was talking, Phaethon leaped into the chariot. He grasped the reins with delight, pouring out thanks to his reluctant father.

The moment for starting had come. The doors were flung open and the horses rushed upon the sky, swinging the chariot aloft behind them. Their galloping hoofs parted the morning mist and outran the morning breezes which had sprung up in the east.

Suddenly the horses became aware that all was not as it usually was. The load in the chariot was lighter. The feel of the reins was different too. The horses soon realized that another driver was trying to control them. They began to run where they wished, up and down, here and there, leaving the traveled road. Phaethon, frightened, did not know how to guide them. Even had he known, he did not have the power to force his will on them.

When the unlucky boy looked down upon the earth now spreading beneath him, he grew pale. His knees shook with terror and his eyes grew dim. He wished he had never touched his father's horses. What should he do? Much of the road lay behind him, but more remained before. His courage

224

OMNE AES FENESTRAE
NON OMNE POTEST AETHERA
VNDE IOVIS VARIETVR
PONDER.E FLAMMIS

gone, Phaethon let the reins fall from his hands. The horses, feeling the reins loose upon their backs, dashed headlong into unknown regions of the sky. Now they were high in the heavens, now down to earth. The clouds smoked and the mountaintops caught on fire. The very rivers began to dry up from the fierce heat. The sea shrank up. Phaethon, surrounded by the fire and smoke, with the floor of the chariot burning his feet, longed to be rid of this terror.

At last Earth herself sent up a plea to Zeus. "Save us, Father," she cried. "Save what remains to us."

Zeus heard her plea and seizing his thunderbolt hurled it at the young driver. Phaethon, his hair on fire, fell headlong like a shooting star which marks the heavens with its brightness as it falls.

A great river received his burning body and put out its fire. And the river nymphs buried him, marking his grave with a stone which bore these words:

Phaethon rests beneath this stone.
He tried to drive his father's chariot,
And though he failed,
Yet brave was his try.

THINKING IT OVER

1. This myth explained things in nature which the ancient Greeks found hard to understand. Be ready to discuss how the story explained these matters. How does modern science explain them?

2. Do you agree with the last line the river nymphs wrote on Phaethon's grave stone? Why or why not?

3. What did Apollo mean when he said to Phaethon, "Now I leave you to your own luck. May it plan better for you than you have done for yourself"?

THOUGHTS AT WORK

1. If Phaethon had not boasted to his friends, would this story have happened? Why or why not?

2. How did Phoebus Apollo prove that even a god could make mistakes?

3. Describe in your own words Phoebus Apollo's daily trip across the sky. Be sure to include its three stages.

4. What dangers did Phoebus face on his daily journey? What additional dangers did Phaethon face?

5. Why do you think Phaethon lost his courage? Give two reasons.

6. Tell about a time when your parents refused to let you do something because they felt it was dangerous. Tell why they were right or wrong.

7. Phoebus Apollo, like Athena, Hermes, and Zeus, was an important Greek god. Try to find additional information about him.

THE STORY OF PERSEUS

In Greek mythology one of the great heroes was Perseus, son of Zeus, the ruler of all the gods, and Danae, a mortal woman. The name Zeus was sometimes spelled Seus. In the Latin language the prefix *per* means *through*. So Perseus was a son through Zeus. The story which follows tells about the great and daring deeds of this mortal son as he searched for terrible Medusa, whose hair was curling ringlets of snakes.

228

Danae and the Shower of Gold

In the days of the gods, there lived in Greece a king named Acrisios.[1] He was rich and powerful, but still a most unhappy man. An oracle had foretold that King Acrisios would one day be killed by his own grandson.

At the time of this oracle, Acrisios did not have a grandson. But he did have a beautiful daughter named Danae.[2] She was so lovely that many men had already sought her hand in marriage. The possibility that Acrisios would someday have a grandson was all too real, and so the frightened king took steps to prevent this.

He built a strong tower of brass and had poor Danae shut up inside it along with her waiting-women, and he allowed no one else to go in.

This was a cruel fate, and Danae was very unhappy. But what could she do? No one dared to come in, and the attendants and guards were too much afraid of the king to allow anyone to visit her.

But Zeus, ruler of the gods, who sees all things, saw Danae in her tower. And as she was beautiful, Zeus fell in love with her, resolving to make her his wife. It was easy enough for him, but he did not march up to the door and demand admittance. He made another plan, quite a new one.

So it happened that one day as Danae sat melancholy in her chamber at the top of the tower, she saw the air become thick with a kind of mist. Soon the mist grew into soft flakes of gold, like a golden snow, and

[1] Acrisios (ə kris′ē əs)   [2] Danae (dan′ə ē)

fell all over the room. The flakes gathered up into a solid shape. And she saw standing before her what she thought was a noble young man, and his body was covered with bright clothing that shone like gold.

"Who are you?" said Danae, astonished.

"Do not fear me," said he, "for I have heard of your sad fate, and I have come to comfort you if you will be my wife."

Danae was delighted to have so noble a husband when she expected none at all, not even an ugly one. So after that, Zeus would often come and visit her in a shower of golden snowflakes, unknown to all, and after his visit he would melt into golden snowflakes again and pass away on the wind.

Acrisios knew nothing of all this. And what was his amazement one day when a messenger came panting before him, and said:

"Sir, your daughter has borne a son!"

"What!" cried Acrisios. "Did I not forbid you to let anyone go in?"

"Sir," he answered, "we have let no one go in. We know nothing about it! Do not blame us, we have done our duty, I swear it."

Then Acrisios was angry and frightened at once. Whatever the cause, there was his grandson, and the oracle said he was to kill Acrisios one day. Acrisios did not like to murder his daughter and the baby outright. But he quieted his conscience by saying that they should have a chance. So he put them into a large chest and fastened the cover, with holes to let in the air. And then he set them adrift on the sea.

The winds blew and the waves rose, and the foam drenched the mother and her son as they lay in the chest. The tears ran down her cheeks, and she threw her arms about the boy and said, "Ah, my baby, what sorrow is yours! And yet you weep not. You sleep quiet like a suckling babe in this dark chest. You care not for the salt foam on your hair nor for the whistling wind as you lie in your purple wrappings with your soft cheek against mine. If you knew your danger, you would open your little ear to my words. Sleep on, my babe, and may the sea sleep, and may Zeus your father send us help!"

Perseus and the Gorgon Medusa

Zeus heard the mother's prayer. The chest was washed up on the shore of a little island named Seriphos.[1] A man of the island came by and saw the chest which was richly carved, and he thought it a great find. But when he prized off the lid, what was his surprise to see Danae and the baby inside! He was a kind man, and took them in, and they lived in his house while the boy grew up.

The boy's name was Perseus;[2] and he grew up to be strong and brave and handsome, and he won prizes in the athletic games of the island. So he was noticed by the king, Polydectes.[3] Before long the king caught sight of Perseus's mother, Danae, and determined to make her his wife.

But Danae would not hear of it. She, the wife of the immortal Zeus, to give herself to the petty chief of a small island! The king persecuted her, but he was afraid of Perseus; and he soon saw that Perseus must be got out of the way.

Accordingly, he pretended to flatter him on his success in the games. "You are a fine boy," Polydectes said. "You can beat everyone in this island at running and boxing and wrestling. In fact, you are wasted in a small place like this. You ought to try some great task and make a name in the world, like the real heroes." You see, he did not know that Perseus was a real hero, being a son of Zeus. Danae kept that secret to herself.

[1] Seriphos (sə rē′fəs) [2] Perseus (pėr′ sē əs) [3] Polydectes (pol ə dik′tēs)

232

"What do you mean, sir?" asked Perseus. "Just tell me something worth trying for."

"I will," said the king. "Go and bring me Medusa's[1] head."

Perseus asked, "Who is Medusa?"

The king said, "There are three awful sisters, the three Gorgons.[2] Two of them are ugly things, but the Gorgon Medusa is the most beautiful creature in the world. I want her head, never mind why."

"Where can they be found?" asked Perseus.

The king said, "Far away in the west, in the land of darkness. You must find your own way, for I do not know any more about it."

This fired the ambition of Perseus, and he determined to fetch Medusa's head.

The gods knew all this, of course, and as Perseus was thinking what to do, suddenly Athena appeared to him.

"Perseus, do you know me?" she asked.

"Indeed I do!" said Perseus. "You are the great goddess Athena."

[1] Medusa (mə dü'sə) [2] Gorgon (gôr'gən)

"Well," said Athena, "we gods are going to help you. First of all, look at this," and she showed him the image of a head. The face was very beautiful, but cruel and cold and unhappy. Instead of hair, it had curling ringlets of snakes all round. "That is the Gorgon Medusa," Athena said. "But if you look at the real face, you will be turned into stone."

"Then how can I get the head?" asked Perseus.

"Take this shield," and she gave him a shield, smooth and shining like a mirror, "and when you come to Medusa, keep your back to her and see her image in the shield, so as to strike back over your shoulder. Then cut off her head and put it in this bag," and she gave him a large bag of leather. "Be careful to leave her sisters alone, for they are immortal. Medusa alone is mortal, and she can be killed."

"But how shall I find the way?" he asked.

"Wait a moment," said Athena, and then all of a sudden, there were Hermes and Hades,[1] who appeared out of nothing, as the gods can do. But Hermes said, "See here, I lend you my winged shoes. Put them on your feet, and you will fly through the air like a bird. And here is a sharp sickle to cut off Medusa's head." Then Hades said, "And I lend you my cap of darkness. When you wear it, you will be invisible, and no one will see you."

"And now," said Athena, "you must fly away to the west until you come to the Three Old Hags, who alone know the way to the Gorgons. They have only one eye between them, and one tooth, which they lend about

[1] Hades (hā' dēz)

234

as they want them. They live in the west beyond the sun and moon, and you will have to persuade them to tell you the way."

This did not sound hopeful, but there was no more to be done, as the three gods had disappeared.

So Perseus slung the shield and the sickle about his shoulders and hung the bag over his back. He put on the cap of darkness and fastened the winged shoes to his feet. Then he rose into the air. For a few moments

he ran along the air trying out the shoes, and his feet felt light and tireless and he smiled with joy to be running along the air. Then he started out to find the Three Old Hags.

On and on he flew, over land and sea, over mountain and forest, beyond the sun and the moon into the dark regions of the west. No doubt the winged shoes guided him, for he came straight to the place where the Three Old Hags had their dwelling.

One said to her sister, "I hear a noise in the air. What is it?"

The second answered, "Give me the tooth, and let me bite it." So the tooth was passed to her, but she could see nothing as the eye was in the socket of the third.

The first asked, "Sister, what can you see?"

And she answered, "I can see nothing at all, but I hear a shivering in the air." For the cap of darkness made Perseus invisible.

"Pass me the eye!" said the first sister. "You are as blind as a bat!" She put the eye into her own socket but saw nothing. Then the second sister said, "Pass it here, will you?"

But as the first sister took out the eye and held it towards the other, Perseus neatly swooped in between them and caught it. "Now then," said the first sister, "can you see anything?" for she thought her sister had taken the eye.

They quarreled back and forth until at last the second sister said, "Here, take the tooth and give her a nip."

But as she held out the tooth, Perseus swooped down quickly and caught it. Then there was a frightful quarrel

236

as each Old Hag thought the others were playing a trick on her. In the midst of it, Perseus called out:

"Fear nothing, mighty beings, the eye and the tooth are safe. I hold them in my hand."

There was a sudden silence. Then they all cried out at once, "Who is that?"

He replied, "I am Perseus, and I come to ask you the way to the place where the Gorgons are."

"We will not tell you," they all cried out.

"Then I will not give you back the eye and the tooth. Good-by," and he made as if to go.

"Wait, wait, wait!" they cried. They did their best to persuade Perseus to give back the eye and the tooth, but he was firm, and in the end they had to tell him the way to go. Then he flew off saying, "When I come back, you shall have your eye and your tooth safe and sound."

Thus the Three Old Hags could not defend their sisters, the Gorgons, and Perseus came to the place where they were.

He found the Gorgons asleep. Two of them had golden wings and bronze claws and enormous teeth. They would have made short work of Perseus if they had caught him, but he was careful to be quiet. Approaching Medusa backwards, he looked at her image in the bright shield and struck a blow behind him and killed her. Then he cut off the head and put it into his bag. The two sisters awoke and tried to catch Perseus in their claws. But he was too quick for them. He flew back to the Three Old Hags and gave them the eye in turn and let them have a look at him when he took off his cap. He gave back the tooth, but took care to give it back just as he was about to fly away. And he gave it to the one who had not the eye at that moment.

Perseus and Andromeda

The journey back was more of a roundabout. No doubt Perseus thought he would never have a better chance of seeing the world. He seems to have flown over Africa and Asia, and he even visited the people who lived behind the North Wind. These were a very happy people, who had a kind of earthly paradise, almost as good as the Islands of the Blest where all the great heroes went and lived forever at peace.

As he passed over Africa, he saw a huge figure with its head in the clouds, and when he looked close, it was old Atlas the Titan,[1] holding up the heavens upon his shoulder.

Old Atlas hailed him and said, "Stranger, you must be the hero Perseus who, according to the oracle, will set me free. Show me the Gorgon's head!" He was weary of holding up the heavens. Perseus took the head out of his bag and held it out towards Atlas, but

[1] Titan (tī′ tn)

239

he was careful to turn his own head away. Then he put it back in the bag. And when he looked at Atlas, he saw that his body had changed into a great rock. His hair and beard were changed into forests. So Atlas rested at last from his long labor. If you look on the map, there you will see the Atlas Mountains still, and they hold up the heavens quite as well as the old Titan did.

As Perseus came nearer to home on a bright, sunny day, he looked down. There on the coast of Palestine, near the port of Joppa,[1] he saw a long procession of people moving towards the sea. They were leading a beautiful maiden and soon they bound her fast with chains to a rock and went away weeping and wailing.

The maiden was named Andromeda[2] and she was daughter to the king of that place. Her mother was a vain and foolish woman and she had boasted that her daughter was more beautiful than all the nymphs of the sea. Accordingly, the god of the sea, Poseidon,[3] the father of these nymphs, was very angry. He flooded the coast and sent a sea monster to devour anyone he could catch. At last, after many prayers, he consented to spare the people if the king would give his daughter for the sea monster to devour. That was why they left her chained to a rock and went away.

Perseus did not know this. He only saw the maiden chained to a rock and an ugly monster swimming in from the sea. The maiden stared at the monster, her eyes full of horror. The monster lashed the sea with his tail, and his green sides shone in the sunlight

[1] Joppa (jop'ə)　　[2] Andromeda (an drom'ə də)　　[3] Poseidon (pə sīd'n)

240

with scales of hard horn. His mouth opened and showed
a red throat and sharp rows of teeth. Neither he nor
Andromeda looked up to see a new kind of bird swoop
down from the sky. Down came Perseus, like an eagle,
holding the sickle of Hermes which had cut off the
Gorgon's head. He attacked the monster from behind
and gave him a deep cut on the neck. Then there was
a terrible fight. But the monster could not reach
Perseus and Perseus flew in and out like an eagle,
cutting under the monster's scales, until at last he cut
its throat and the body fell back lifeless upon the sea.

You may imagine how glad Andromeda was and how Perseus loosed her chains and led her back to her father. And how glad her father was and how willingly he consented when Perseus asked him if Andromeda might be his wife. Had he not well earned the prize?

There was only one difficulty. The king had promised her to someone else. This was a man named Phineus,[1] who came up in a rage and said, "Where is my bride?"

Perseus asked, "Where were you when the sea monster was going to devour your bride?"

Phineus replied, "I could not help her. Why should I be swallowed too?"

Perseus said, "If you did not care enough for your bride to strike a blow for her life, you have no claim."

"We will see about that," Phineus said. "Here, you men!" and he called to his bodyguards, who stood under arms, with threatening looks. But Perseus did not wait for more. He took out the Gorgon's head and showed it to them. There they stood, turned into stone.

There was a grand wedding and high rejoicings. But Perseus had to leave his bride for the time being because he must go back to Seriphos and hand over the Gorgon's head to Polydectes.

When he came to Seriphos, he put off his winged shoes and walked to the town. But he could not find his mother. The fact was, King Polydectes had persecuted her and told her she must be his wife whether she liked it or not. He knew only that Perseus had gone, but he did not know how and he felt sure he would never come back. Then Perseus found his

[1] Phineus (fin′ ē əs)

242

mother in the temple where she had fled for refuge. With her was the kind man who had brought him up.

When Danae saw Perseus, she cried, "Oh, my son! You have come back, and I thought you were dead!"

"What are you doing here?" he asked.

She said, "The king was so violent and threatening that I have fled to this temple for refuge. But I am afraid even here, for he says he will come and fetch me out. And there he is!"

Indeed there he was, with his bodyguard of soldiers, come to drag Danae from the temple.

"Come out!" he cried. "My patience is at an end—But who is this? Never Perseus, returned from his journey? Welcome, dear boy!" for he began to be afraid now.

Then Perseus said, "Do not call me dear boy when you want to lay violent hands on my mother."

"Nonsense," he answered, "but tell me about your journey. Did you get the Gorgon's head?"

"Oh yes," said Perseus, "would you like to see it?"

"Indeed I should," said the king.

Then Perseus whispered to his mother, "Turn your head away," and as she turned away, he drew out the Gorgon's head and turned it towards Polydectes.

As Polydectes looked at it, a shiver ran through him, and in a moment he was a statue of stone with the smile still on his false lips. His men also turned into stone, as many as looked upon the Gorgon's head.

Perseus put the head back and led his mother to her home. The kind man who had helped them became king, and all was well.

The three immortals appeared once more to Perseus. Athena said, "I see you have got the head of Medusa, and come back safe. I am very glad to see it, and now you must return to us what we lent you."

Perseus thanked them all for their help. Then he gave the bag and the shield to Athena, and the cap to Hades, and to Hermes the sickle and winged shoes. But the head of Medusa he gave to Athena, and Athena fixed it upon her shield. Ever after she bore the shield with the Gorgon's head. And if she showed it to her enemies, they turned into stone.

Perseus sent for his bride and they lived a happy life. But there is one more thing you need to know about him.

There used to be games in the island of Seriphos and once Acrisios came to attend them. Perseus had to throw a quoit at the games. It went a little to one side where Acrisios was craning his head forward to look on. The quoit caught his head and killed him. So the oracle was fulfilled which had made Acrisios so cruel to Danae.

—W. H. D. Rouse

244

THINKING IT OVER

1. Explain how the oracle who spoke to King Acrisios was an important part of this story.

2. In Greek mythology, a hero could use trickery honorably if necessary. What tricks did Perseus play in order to obtain Medusa's head?

3. Often the characters in mythology are either good or evil. Using the headings below, (1) write the name of each character in the story, (2) tell whether he was good or evil, (3) give reasons for your judgment.

Character　　　　*Good or Evil*　　　　*Reasons*

THOUGHTS AT WORK

1. Do you think King Acrisios was right to lock Danae in the tower? Why or why not?

2. Why did King Polydectes ask Perseus to bring him the Medusa's head?

3. List in order the tasks Perseus completed in carrying out his mission. In each case, what danger did he face?

4. Why did Perseus return home a roundabout way? What experience would he have missed otherwise?

5. What good deed did Perseus do as he flew over Africa on his way home? What work of nature does this part of the story explain?

6. Recall what happened to Polydectes when Perseus returned home. Explain why you think he did or did not deserve this fate.

7. Think about the four Greek myths you read in this unit. How were they alike? Choose two and tell what lessons they teach.

ANCIENT HISTORY

I hope the old Romans
Had painful abdomens.

I hope that the Greeks
Had toothache for weeks.

I hope the Egyptians
Had chronic conniptions.

I hope that the Arabs
Were bitten by scarabs.

I hope that the Vandals
Had thorns in their sandals.

I hope that the Persians
Had gout in all versions.

I hope that the Medes
Were kicked by their steeds.

They started the fuss
And left it to us!

— *Arthur Guiterman*

BIBLIOGRAPHY

Words from the Myths, by Isaac Asimov.
> You will be surprised to discover how many words we use every day straight out of mythology.

Norse Gods and Giants, by Ingri and Edgar Parin d'Aulaire.
> Let your imagination soar as you look at the beautiful illustrations and read the stories from Viking mythology.

The Children of Odin, by Padraic Colum.
> Stories that the Vikings told about their gods and heroes.

The Golden Fleece and the Heroes Who Lived Before Achilles, by Padraic Colum.
> The people of Greece told these stories hundreds of years before Hector and Achilles fought upon the Plains of Troy.

Heroes of Greece and Troy, by Roger Lancelyn Green.
> These myths and hero tales are good to read aloud.

Mythology, by Edith Hamilton.
> If you have some questions about Greek and Norse myths, this book will answer most, if not all, of them.

A Wonder Book and Tanglewood Tales, by Nathaniel Hawthorne.
> One of the most famous retellings of the Greek myths.

Gods, Heroes and Men of Ancient Greece, by W. H. D. Rouse.
> Those were lucky boys who first heard these stories told by the author in their classroom.

The Clashing Rocks, by Ian Serraillier.
> About the adventures of Jason and his Argonauts as they search for the Golden Fleece.

THE WEB OF LIFE

Unhappily the story of man includes the careless killing of wildlife, the pollution of streams, the draining of salt marshes, and the stripping of forest lands. But man is slowly learning that his survival depends upon the way he treats his environment. The selections in this unit explain how man and all things around him, living and nonliving, affect each other every minute of every day.

Remember as you read that you are a part of the environment, helping to determine man's future on the earth and in space.

249

TO LOOK AT ANY THING

To look at any thing,
If you would know that thing,
You must look at it long:
To look at this green and say
"I have seen spring in these
Woods," will not do—you must
Be the thing you see:
You must be the dark snakes of
Stems and ferny plumes of leaves,
You must enter in
To the small silences between
The leaves,
You must take your time
And touch the very peace
They issue from.

—John Moffitt

As the scientist studies life in the forest, he must step softly, sit quietly, look and listen in silence. If you could watch him, you would think he was alone, but how wrong you would be! As you read, you can quietly join him and discover the secrets of timid creatures that have a town all their own in the forest.

TOWN IN THE FOREST

Every town has its secrets. And a passing stranger may wonder: Who lives here? How do the residents make their living? Why did they choose this place?

The town may be one of the man-made towns, strung out like knots that tie together a fishnet of country roads.

Or the town may be deep in the forest. Its exact location may be a bog, or a cave, or a small hill, or a hollow log.

A dead log may, in fact, be rich with life. Here a thousand varied creatures live, making up a community. In some brisk autumn dawn, these log-dwellers stir. Black crickets and green-gold beetles search busily for food. The last wildflowers of the year strain toward the dwindling sun. A crab spider scurries out of the range of a passing lizard, back to its web.

Within a hive in the log, an aging queen of bees is already in winter sleep, full of the eggs she will lay in the spring. A caterpillar wraps itself carefully into a cocoon. And the log rot gives slow growth to living molds and mosses.

In the burrow formed when the falling oak tore itself from the earth, a chipmunk family breakfasts on a windfall of seeds and berries.

This is the Logtown community. Here a toad shares citizenship with a toadstool. The redbud is neighbor to a green snake curled against the warmth of the decaying log. Countless other creatures live here that are visible only through a magnifying lens.

From the eye level of an insect, this community bustles with life. Like the human community, it has its share of quarrels, its small tragedies, its daily rhythm of food-gathering, resting, mating, homemaking, family-raising.

The inhabitants of the log are not as separate as they may seem. They are each and all members of a real community, bound to one another in countless ways. Their town has a clear-cut form and pattern.

The forest is filled with such towns, all parts of the wider woodland community. And just as there are

towns in the forest, so there are cities in the sea and villages on the prairie. Of all the communities on this planet, only the smallest number is peopled by human beings.

A wide range of animals may share lightless lives in the never ending darkness of a deep cave—all of them whitish and blind. Strange bedfellows may be found living in a sea sponge. An interesting group of creatures may make their home together on some rocky crag. The communities in the rain forest harbor a rich variety of living things. And still another type of community is the tiny sea island where assorted beings live in the shadow of a smoldering volcano.

Wherever such wildlife communities appear, they stir the same haunting questions: Who and how and why? These towns in nature are webbed with a thousand mysteries.

But the questions are not idle ones for human beings to ask. Our own lives are woven deeply into the answers.

Nature withheld few secrets from the American poet-naturalist Henry David Thoreau.[1] He was a Harvard graduate, class of 1837. Some of his classmates went into law, others into the ministry. Thoreau took to the woods.

"Many a forenoon have I stolen away," he recounted, "preferring to spend thus the most valued part of the day; for I was rich, if not in money, in sunny hours and summer days, and spent them lavishly."

[1] Thoreau (thə rō′)

He described himself as a self-appointed inspector of rainstorms, surveyor of forest paths, and keeper of the wildstock. He roamed Indian-style through the woods. His pockets bulged with the gear of the naturalist—a spyglass, a jackknife, twine, and a small microscope. He carried an old music book for pressing plants, and a notebook in which he captured the sights and sounds of the wildlife in soaring poetry or in singing prose.

Thoreau built a tiny cabin on Walden Pond near Concord, Massachusetts. There he enjoyed the company of woodsmen and woodchucks. And there he observed nature in a special way.

"You only need sit still long enough in some attractive spot in the woods that all its inhabitants may exhibit themselves to you by turns," he wrote.

It was in this fashion that Thoreau became a part of the natural community.

He was not an expert in any species, nor was he a great collector or experimenter. He had no laboratory other than the "sweet wild world" of the woodland itself.

He was an eyewitness of the order and life in the natural community. He could look at a neighbor's field, and then remark as he did once, "I had no idea that there was so much going on in Haywood's meadow."

Many of nature's secrets are discovered only in this kind of broad view. Some of the most puzzling events of the woodland are explained only as plants and animals are observed living together against the natural setting of the soil and the season. Certain

facts about species can be learned only by watching the free-flowing life of the natural community.

On a spring night in the year 1842, Thoreau found himself on a strange woodland adventure. As he poled his boat gently across a silent New England pond, his pine torch lit up the scene below. To his delight, the crystal depths appeared like a living city, its roofs raised to reveal the private community of the fishes.

"There they lie in every variety of posture," he later wrote, "some on their backs with their white bellies uppermost, some suspended in mid-water, some sculling gently along with a dreamy motion of the fins, and others quite active and wide awake—a scene not unlike what the human city could present. . . ."

Thoreau's genius was in seeing life whole. One can learn much about a clock by taking it apart—but not find its tick. Thoreau observed nature in its wholeness instead of piecemeal, learned its rhyme and its rhythm.

There is an old nursery rhyme that begins with the loss of a horseshoe nail. This small cause eventually leads to the loss of a battle, and finally to the loss of a kingdom.

In the same fashion, every small happening in nature touches off other happenings. Spring thaw and rock slide, the birth of a fawn, the fall of an oak—such events set up a series of results within the living community. From a single cause flows a running stream of effects.

A poet once said that one could not pluck a flower

without troubling a star. This is another way of saying that the living and the nonliving are all linked together. Lives are altered by changing temperature, climate, and moisture, by the very shape of the land and the chemicals that are in it.

The courses of streams are shifted by dam-building beavers. Rock is turned into soil by the action of frost and plants, of water and small animals. The population of mosquitoes is reduced by the first cold snap. An entire forest may be set ablaze by a flash of lightning.

The naturalist Charles Darwin had a story that showed the endless chain of causes and effects. In Great Britain, he pointed out, roaming cats eat field mice at the edge of town. It seems that the number of wild bumblebees is controlled by the mice, which destroy their nests. If the mouse population is kept down by the cats, then there are more bees to pollinate the red clover plants. As a result of all this, the British fields are deep in clover.

Others playfully added to Darwin's story. British beef cattle grow fat on clover. And the British navy depends upon beef. Old maids become more plentiful as the navy takes more men for sea duty. And old maids like to keep cats. Put it all together and it would seem that old maids are responsible for Britain's mighty navy!

In dealing with nature, man is often puzzled by strange turns of events. Unseen causes may lead to hunger and illness, to crop failure and human tragedy.

The people of Ireland once depended upon the potato as their main source of food. The summer of 1845 proved to be a poor one for potato-growing. It was a good year for a tiny fungus that destroys potatoes.

In the tragic days that followed, famine struck the island nation. When it was all over, a million people had died. Two million more had to leave their homeland.

A chain of events may be touched off by man's own doings. It may begin with the crack of a rifle or the bite of an ax.

An upland forest is cleared of trees. The area is turned into a pasture which soon becomes overgrazed and bare. Now the rain water is no longer held in the ground by the deep roots of trees and shrubs. Instead, the water runs swiftly off the surface, forming gullies. On the hillside farms the good wells run dry. In the valleys below, the raging streams rush wildly together, flooding the countryside.

The explanation of such events that have long puzzled mankind seems tangled in a thousand threads. Today scientific study is beginning to clear up some of the old problems and many new ones as well. The science of cause and effect in the natural community is called ecology.

One of the newer branches of biology, ecology is concerned with the associations of living and nonliving things. It begins its study of life—as Thoreau did—in the wildlife communities, seeking answers to very important problems in the patterns of nature.

The work of the ecologist has sometimes been called "the science of everything." He studies the "why" of nature. Usually, the answer is contained in a thousand bits and fragments of fact. His clues may be as varied as the flyways of geese or the surge of an underground stream, the busy work of bacteria or the damming of a river.

The behavior of living things is often strange and complicated. But certain patterns of life do repeat themselves. An orderly design can be discovered. Developments can be predicted. Events can be understood.

The methods of the ecologist, like those of other scientists, begin with the careful study of the facts. Precise information is gathered, checked and rechecked endlessly. Out of a large body of facts emerges a small but growing set of scientific principles.

The name "ecology" was formed about a hundred years ago out of the Greek word *oikos*, which means "home." Ecology is the study of the home life of living things, how they relate to one another and to their nonliving environment.

The ecologist works in the laboratory. But he can probably be found most often in the field. He may be taking a census of earthworms. Or he may study how the population of the arctic fox varies with that of lemmings or how the number of red oaks in a forest depends on the number of acorn-burying squirrels.

In its quiet beginnings, the new science of ecology is becoming an important problem-solver. It is more than that. It is the growing edge of our understanding about the living fabric of nature.

The life of the seas and the uplands, of the prairies and the forests, is a web of species. In some places the fabric is time-tested and strong. In other places the weave is loose and can be unraveled by the tearing of a single thread. At times, the texture within a particular region is richly patterned. Or else it may be riddled and threadbare.

Woven throughout the fabric of life is man, the most powerful of the species. To the ecologist, man is increasingly important in the whole design of living things. Ecology deals with the web of life as it has been changed by human beings.

The ecologist may investigate the number of acres of prairie that will properly support a herd of sheep. His main interest may be the health of an olive grove or an oyster bed. His searches may take him to the gloomy sea depths, where natural communities tend to be stable and a few of them may have existed since the beginnings of life on earth. Or he may be at work on the problems of an entirely new kind of community—the life-support system aboard a spaceship.

A group of ecologists at a midwestern university have set up a tiny living community. This tightly sealed "hothouse" is a mock-up for some future spacecraft. This is the kind of community that may be used to support life on an expedition to the moon or a visit to a neighboring planet.

Small mammals and insects, assorted grasses and shrubs live inside, amid apparatus and instruments. The animal life is being carefully studied to determine its needs. The plants are chosen to keep the air clean, to reclaim waste materials, and to offer high yields of suitable foods in a limited growing area.

This is a "closed system," where plants and animals are all in balance. Each form of life supports the other, and each makes use of what the other produces.

The essentials for long-time support of life are the same everywhere—whether in an outpost flung into space or in some wild place in the forest. These communities are small worlds where plants and animals share life together.

—*S. Carl Hirsch*

THINKING IT OVER

1. Name all the inhabitants of the "Logtown community." Why did the author call this dead log a town?

2. In what four ways did the author define ecology? How does this science help us understand life around us?

3. What do you think was the author's purpose in writing this article?

THOUGHTS AT WORK

1. Find the descriptions of Henry David Thoreau and read them again. What was he? What wasn't he?

2. The author said that Thoreau "observed nature in a special way." Describe this special way. What tools did he use?

3. In your own words tell what the poet meant when he said that one could not pluck a flower without troubling a star.

4. According to the naturalist Charles Darwin, how did cats affect the clover in British fields?

5. What are some of the effects of clearing a forest of trees?

6. Describe what an ecologist does. Then list the four methods he uses in his work.

7. Find two examples in the article to support this statement: "Every life depends upon other living and nonliving things."

8. Give an example to show how man is affecting the ecology of the area in which you live.

The last frontier on Earth is the ocean where many scientists believe that life began. Now man returns to explore that ancient home of life on Earth. There is adventure and danger in such a return, as you will see in the next selection which takes place in the Pacific Ocean, some five hundred miles east of the Philippine Islands.

ADVENTURE ON THE LAST FRONTIER

For ages man has used the ocean to discover new lands. Now he is spending a great deal of time and money discovering the ocean. We already know a great deal about this last frontier, as it has been called. But we still need to learn much more about it. We know that the ocean is rich in minerals that the world needs. We know, too, that it contains enough food to provide protein for all the world's people. We know that if the salt could be taken from it, the ocean could turn the deserts into farm lands. We have begun removing salt from the ocean water, but the process is still too costly to be practical except in special situations.

Today's scientists explore the sea in ships outfitted for this purpose. One of these, the *Kane*, even has a large computer aboard to process the information which the scientists receive each day. Some scientists have descended into the sea's depths in specially built objects called bathyspheres. Sitting in their bathyspheres, the scientists are able to turn on very strong

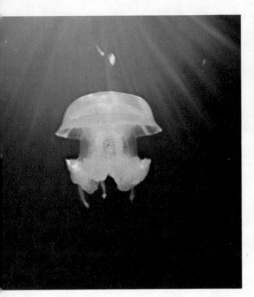  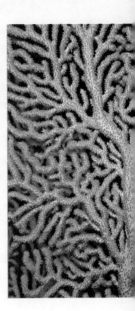

lights which shine through the ocean's darkness and show them the strange sea life inhabiting the depths of the sea.

There are also scientists who work by themselves, depending on the native inhabitants of certain ocean areas to help them. Such a one is Eugenie Clark. She founded and directed the Cape Haze Marine Laboratory in Florida for sixteen years and now teaches at the University of Maryland. In the following story, she tells of some exciting days in Pacific waters when a native diver called Siakong[1] was her helper.

Siakong was just over fifty when I knew him. He was the best spearfisherman in the Palaus.[2] I'm not saying this because he taught me spearfishing and

[1] Siakong (sē'ə kong)   [2] Palaus (pə lous')

266

one hundred other things about the underwater world. His great skill was an accepted fact among all the Palauans.

Siakong knew a native, Niraibui,[1] who owned an inboard motorboat that could hold up to six people. Sometimes, besides the three of us, we took with us some of the other scientists who had come to these islands in search of specimens.

Siakong knew the best places to get the kind of fish I was after and these seemed to be where there were the most beautiful coral reefs. These reefs were a long way out from the town of Koror, the most important community in this group of islands. We usually went there by way of a harbor where we could look deep down into the clear water and see sunken battleships from the war days.

[1] Niraibui (nī rā′ bē)

267

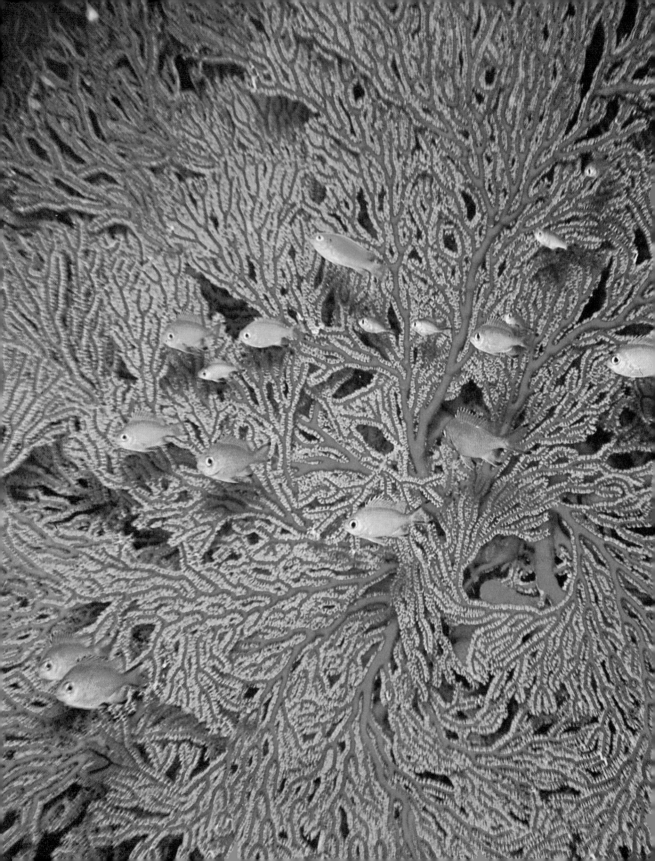

It was great fun to watch Siakong spear fish from above the water. He would stand on the bow of Nirai-bui's boat as we putt-putted to the outer reefs, a long spear in each hand. I would sometimes stand up searching the water too, but I could never spot a fish before Siakong did. A spear was flying through the air as I opened my mouth to call out, "There's a fish!" If the first spear missed, the second one was on its way in a flash and Siakong seemed to predict the direction in which the fish would dodge the first spear.

Underwater it was different. He never made a sound, but I could see him grinning broadly and his eyes sparkled through his water goggles. Here, there was no doubt about whether or not Siakong would get the fish he was after. It was only a question of how long it would take him and by what trick he would get it.

Siakong was powerfully built. He wore only a small red loincloth and homemade goggles when he went underwater. The rest of the time he wore an old pair of khaki shorts over his loincloth.

Once I pointed out a fish to him, it was as good as mine. He was a keen observer. His years of underwater experience made him an expert in the ways of hundreds of varieties of reef fishes. He didn't always go directly after a fish but would watch it a few seconds, determine its next move, and then head it off into a place where it could easily be caught.

One of Siakong's methods of spearing fish underwater was breathtaking, as well as remarkably simple. He would find a reef well inhabited by fish and then dive calmly to about ten or twenty feet, sometimes

weighting himself with a rock so he could sink without swimming. He'd get a firm grip on the reef with his legs or his free arm, hold his spear in readiness, and then *wait* for the fish to come to him!

The first time I watched him do this it alarmed me. He dived and lay motionless on the reef, like an animal about to spring on its prey. His brown body and red loincloth blended in with the varied colors of the surrounding reef. The fish began to regard him as part of the corals and came very close.

I was watching from above. Not used to Siakong's extraordinary lung capacity, I began to worry after a long time passed and he didn't move. So I swam down to him and tapped him on the head to make sure he was all right. He turned and looked up at me with his usual underwater grin as I reached for a piece of coral to hold myself down. I tried to make a gesture with my face to ask him what he was doing, but he was looking at my hand and the grin had dropped from his face. He reached for my arm as I felt the "coral" under my hand suddenly move.

I was holding onto the side of a giant "man-eating" clam. The clam had just snapped shut and my fingers were only a fraction of an inch from the opening between the two halves of the shell. These close with a grip so tight that it can hold a diver's arm or leg until he drowns.

As we swam up to the surface, Siakong pointed to the wall of coral along which I had carelessly descended. Partly hidden in the corals were dozens of these clams, all with their shells gaping open. The shells looked like gray dead corals. Inside, the soft flesh had the beautiful colors of surrounding living corals and the plants and animals that encrust them. Some were bright green, others blue, purple, and shades of brown mingled with irregular darker patches. They were well camouflaged, but from then on I learned to distinguish them from anything else.

Siakong taught me, however, that even the largest of these clams can be handled safely and that they are among the most delicious of raw sea foods. He would dive down to an open clam and wave his hand over it. Often this was enough to stimulate the light-sensitive flesh inside and the clam would close. If not, he tapped the side of the shell. Then he pried the clam

loose and brought it up with him. With a rock or his chisel he chipped open a part of the curved meeting edges of the shell—just enough to slip in the blade of his knife. Then a little cut in just the right place and the shell would fall right open and we could reach in and pull out all the "meat." Almost every part of the giant clam can be eaten raw. But the adductor muscle that connects the two halves of the shell is truly delicious. It became a regular part of our reef picnics along with raw fish, a tasty, pinkish seaweed that grew in spaghettilike strands, and tiny limpets.

Ordinarily rain didn't stop us from spearfishing. The reef water was so clear that it took more than average rain clouds to make vision bad. The first time we started spearfishing in the rain, however, I thought it would prove a waste of time. When I got into the water and looked around, it was full of wavy lines and everything was blurred as if I weren't wearing my face mask. But Siakong and Niraibui were diving without concern. Then I took a dive too and when my face reached about four feet below the surface, the water became its usual clear self. Then I realized that the blurring near the surface was the result of the fresh rain water mixing with salt water. I've never come across an English word for it, but German chemistry books call the phenomenon *Schlieren.*[1] So for spearfishing in the rain, one merely has to dive below the *Schlieren* layer and reach the sea water to see clearly.

It was on such a rainy day that we came across the largest giant clam I ever saw alive. Siakong and I were

[1] Schlieren (shlir′ən)

272

swimming across some open water toward the reef where the boat was anchored. Niraibui was sitting in it keeping his head dry under Siakong's straw hat. We swam along, diving now and then below the *Schlieren* layer for a look around.

Whenever I swim in deep open water, I keep glancing around through my face mask with a mingled feeling of fear and hope. I don't want to miss seeing it if a large shark should be cruising nearby. But on each of these dives I saw only empty water in all directions. Not the smallest fish was in sight. From above I could see Niraibui was still over one hundred yards away, and I looked forward to reaching him and seeing the comforting walls of reef and the mass of familiar fish that would be swimming there. It is a strange feeling to swim underwater away from any signs of rock, coral, the bottom, or sea life. It's like swimming in the middle of the ocean. It was nice to be able to find Siakong in the water nearby.

I was getting a little ahead of Siakong, as he was stopping for deeper dives, when I heard him call me back.

"Nechan,[1] come see here."

I swam over to him, dove under the *Schlieren*, and looked where he was pointing down below. I couldn't make out much until I was down a few more feet. Then I could see a sandy bottom and sitting in the sand was a clam. It looked like an average-size, giant clam. However, there was nothing around to compare it with and I couldn't estimate the depth.

[1] Nechan (nē'chən)

273

We swam to the surface and treaded water easily and forced a long series of deep breaths. We had been swimming for quite a while, and I wasn't prepared for a deep dive. When I felt a little rested and filled with fresh air, I nodded to Siakong. He started to dive toward the clam and I followed, swallowing to adjust my ears to the increasing pressure.

I've never measured how deep I can dive; but I know that at more than twenty feet under, my face mask cuts into my head and my ears and nose feel uncomfortable. Usually I don't go much deeper for I have always found enough activity in the top twenty-five feet to keep me occupied and satisfied. But this time I followed Siakong until I felt I was well below my usual limit and I knew my breath wouldn't last descending any deeper. Perhaps if I had dived with a weight and not spent so much energy swimming downward, I might have been able to stand another ten feet — but I still wouldn't have been anywhere near bottom. From the depth I did manage to reach, I could see Siakong far below me getting smaller and smaller until he reached the clam.

Then I saw it was truly a giant.

Siakong looked like a midget beside the clam which seemed nearly four feet across. I saw him give it a kick to close the huge jaws which could have held all of Siakong with ease. And then I had to shoot for the surface. I was still panting heavily when Siakong finally came up with no sign of strain.

We got Niraibui to come over with the boat. The anchor wouldn't reach bottom. It hung loose, far above the clam. We couldn't find anything long enough to

reach bottom and help us haul up the clam. The three of us dived toward the clam again, but I stopped at a comfortable depth and clung to the dangling anchor while Niraibui continued on with Siakong. I doubted that even the two of them together could lift it an inch.

The clam's jaws were open again. Siakong reached it and kicked it shut. Niraibui hovered about Siakong's head for a second and then headed back for the surface where we met, both well out of breath.

"O kina ne!"[1] (It's a big one, isn't it?) Niraibui exclaimed to me.

Siakong still had not come up. Niraibui and I dived under again. As we descended I made out a sight that sickened me with horror. *Siakong was caught in the clam.*

The jaws of the gigantic clam were shut tight and

[1] O kina ne (ō kē nə nā)

Siakong's arm was in it up to the elbow. Siakong wasn't moving. I expected Niraibui to dive all the way and at least attempt a rescue, but the fellow swam back to the surface. In the excitement my breath was shorter than ever. I came up gasping and started hollering at Niraibui in panic. My poor Japanese came out all mixed up and he looked at me surprised and then blankly. I felt helpless and desperate. Siakong was trapped and would be dead in a few seconds if we couldn't find some way to help him. How could Niraibui tread water there so calmly.

Short of breath and good for nothing, I nevertheless adjusted my mask to dive again. But just then Siakong popped up beside us—panting but grinning! He lifted his arm out of the water, the one I had seen in the jaws of the clam, and held up the biggest adductor muscle I had ever laid eyes on.

277

I was doing a mixture of laughing and crying as the three of us climbed back into the boat. Niraibui of course had understood all along that the clam—which must have weighed at least a quarter of a ton—was impossible to lift off the bottom and that Siakong had broken the lip of the huge shell enough to reach into the clam and cut loose the adductor muscle with his knife. The two men got a big kick out of my fright.

"She was ready to kill me because I didn't try to save you!" Niraibui told Siakong, who howled with delight. I started to feel a little silly, but when they continued to kid me I got angry. Finally they stopped and the rain which was still falling cooled me back to normal. Soon we all sat contentedly in the boat, munching on a delicious adductor muscle the size of a man's thigh. Niraibui and Siakong stuffed their mouths to keep from laughing any more.

I never saw Siakong spear a shark underwater, although several times he showed up with six- and seven-foot specimens neatly speared through the gills. He explained that the gills were the best place to spear a shark because the skin was too tough and if you missed getting the spear in, the shark might not give you the opportunity for a second try.

All of Siakong's spears were of the primitive hand type. He had none of the fancy arbaletes or CO_2 cartridged spearguns that shoot sixty feet through the water—the equipment of the hundreds of modern skin divers in the United States these days. When Siakong speared a fish, his powerful arms were the only propelling force behind the spear. And the fish, though

278

it be a shark, was then caught on one end of the spear while Siakong held on to the other.

One day Siakong and Niraibui put on an underwater turtle rodeo. They were in a clowning mood. Siakong caught hold of Niraibui's foot and tickled the bottom of it until Niraibui had to laugh out all his breath and almost drowned before Siakong let him go to the surface for air. They were having great fun. Then Niraibui

spotted a large sea turtle resting quietly on the bottom and he sat on its back. Siakong latched onto Niraibui's back and they began taking turns knocking each other off the turtle and riding the bewildered animal around underwater. They could steer it any way they liked by holding the shell just behind the poor turtle's neck, pulling back to make it swim upward, pressing down to make it dive, and leaning sideways to make it bank and turn. All the while the turtle flapped its finlike legs desperately and strained its long neck forward trying helplessly to get rid of the playful tormentors.

Finally they brought the turtle on the boat. Niraibui was pleased when I took his picture with it and I promised to give him a print.

As my weeks in the Palaus came to an end, Siakong asked when I would be back again. "Perhaps many years later," I said because I hated to tell him, "Probably never." "That's O.K., Nechan, I'll still be a good spearfisherman when I'm eighty." And he might have been too. But a few years later I learned that Siakong, when on a fishing trip, took a deep dive after a turtle and never came up again. The area was combed by other divers, but they couldn't find a sign of him nor a clue to his disappearance. Perhaps with his great skill in the water, Siakong found a way to stay alive underwater indefinitely. He may still be happily swimming around those reefs that he loved so much, playing with the turtles and fish. Who knows what the story of his mysterious disappearance will be when the Palauan children of today tell it to their grandchildren?

—*Eugenie Clark*

THINKING IT OVER

1. The author of "Town in the Forest" said that ecologists can "be found most often in the field." Is that statement true of Eugenie Clark? Why or why not?

2. In this selection the author told about several of her adventures. Find in the story where each begins and ends. Think of a good title for each adventure.

3. What qualities do you think a scientist must have to be successful on an expedition like the one described here?

THOUGHTS AT WORK

1. Skim the first paragraph of this selection to find three ways in which the ocean can benefit man.

2. Describe the ways Siakong helped Eugenie Clark in her study of fishes.

3. Compare Siakong's method of spearing a fish from a boat and from underwater. Which did you find most interesting? Why?

4. What dangers might a scientist face while studying sea life? How could he avoid these dangers?

5. Skim the opening paragraphs of this selection, then list three ways scientists can study sea life.

6. Explain in your own words the term *Schlieren*.

7. List at least ten facts you learned about clams in this selection.

Nature does not need an invitation to enter an abandoned place. A deserted carriage house is ideal shelter with its emptiness and its spaciousness. Dark and cavernous, and smelling pleasantly of old leather, it says to the creatures, "Come. Welcome. You are safe here. Horses won't tread on you. People won't sweep you out of corners."

Who comes? Follow the boy in this story and find out.

THE OLD CARRIAGE HOUSE

At the edge of the wood stands a long-abandoned carriage house. In places brown shingles hang loosely from its sides, paint peels from its door and window frames, and wadded burlap replaces more than one broken pane.

The boy considers the carriage house his own, a refuge from sudden showers, an observation post looking out on field and wood, a hostelry which he shares with a variety of wild creatures. Bats roost in its cracks and crevices, wasps hang paper homes from its board ceiling, mice find it a shelter in winter, swallows and phoebes build on its timbers and under its eaves.

A sliding door closes the wide entrance through which proud horses once pulled shiny carriages. It keeps out the snows of winter, but when spring bursts the maple buds and the first birds return from the south, the door is left hospitably ajar.

It is not long before the phoebes enter. On a beam over the door is a line of nests, the homes in which many generations of young birds have been raised. Some are bigger than others, for at times the phoebes have added new stories on old homes.

Tragedy marked the phoebes' nest-building one year. A few horsehairs still remain in the old box stall, favorite material for nest-building. One of the phoebes, weaving a long hair into the nest, became entangled in it. On his next visit the boy discovered the dead bird, hanging from its nest by a horsehair wrapped tightly around its neck. That year there was no family, but the following spring a pair arrived on schedule, probably the surviving bird with a new mate.

There are other flyers who return with the spring. Little brown bats, who have spent the winter hibernating in inland caves, return late when the insect supply is plentiful. All

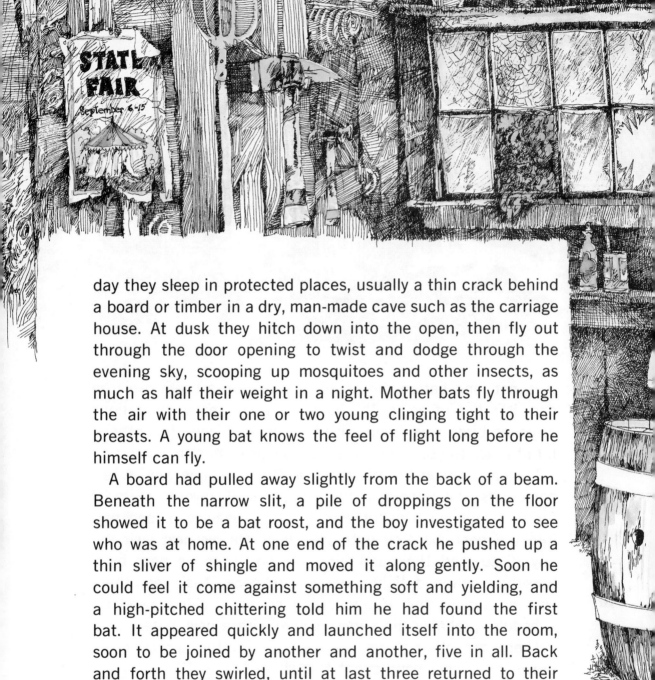

day they sleep in protected places, usually a thin crack behind a board or timber in a dry, man-made cave such as the carriage house. At dusk they hitch down into the open, then fly out through the door opening to twist and dodge through the evening sky, scooping up mosquitoes and other insects, as much as half their weight in a night. Mother bats fly through the air with their one or two young clinging tight to their breasts. A young bat knows the feel of flight long before he himself can fly.

A board had pulled away slightly from the back of a beam. Beneath the narrow slit, a pile of droppings on the floor showed it to be a bat roost, and the boy investigated to see who was at home. At one end of the crack he pushed up a thin sliver of shingle and moved it along gently. Soon he could feel it come against something soft and yielding, and a high-pitched chittering told him he had found the first bat. It appeared quickly and launched itself into the room, soon to be joined by another and another, five in all. Back and forth they swirled, until at last three returned to their quarters. The other two settled in a corner under a beam, and

284

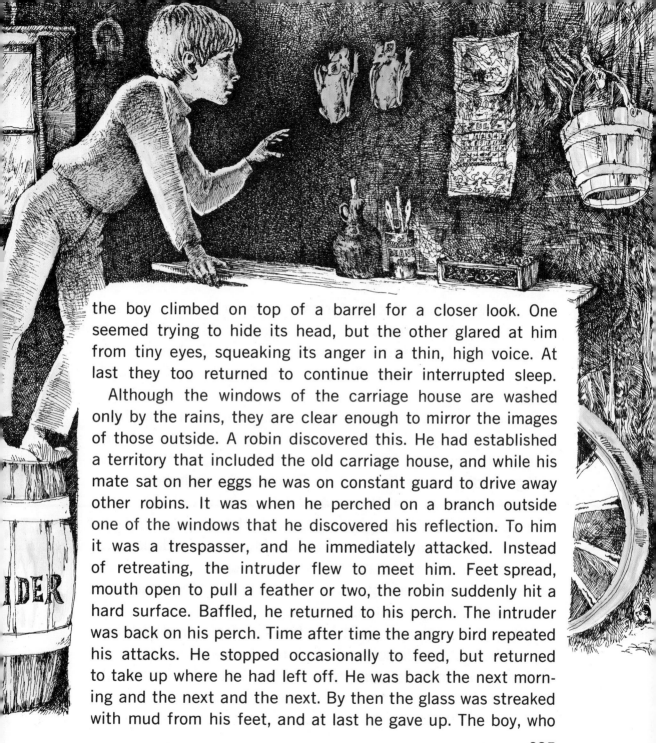

the boy climbed on top of a barrel for a closer look. One seemed trying to hide its head, but the other glared at him from tiny eyes, squeaking its anger in a thin, high voice. At last they too returned to continue their interrupted sleep.

Although the windows of the carriage house are washed only by the rains, they are clear enough to mirror the images of those outside. A robin discovered this. He had established a territory that included the old carriage house, and while his mate sat on her eggs he was on constant guard to drive away other robins. It was when he perched on a branch outside one of the windows that he discovered his reflection. To him it was a trespasser, and he immediately attacked. Instead of retreating, the intruder flew to meet him. Feet spread, mouth open to pull a feather or two, the robin suddenly hit a hard surface. Baffled, he returned to his perch. The intruder was back on his perch. Time after time the angry bird repeated his attacks. He stopped occasionally to feed, but returned to take up where he had left off. He was back the next morning and the next and the next. By then the glass was streaked with mud from his feet, and at last he gave up. The boy, who

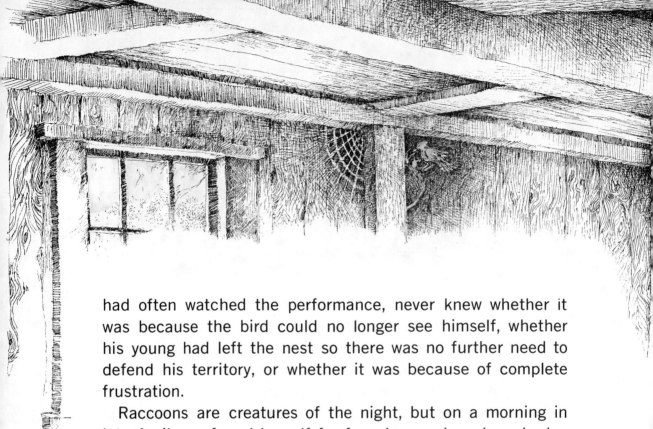

had often watched the performance, never knew whether it was because the bird could no longer see himself, whether his young had left the nest so there was no further need to defend his territory, or whether it was because of complete frustration.

Raccoons are creatures of the night, but on a morning in late April one found herself far from home when dawn broke. Outside the carriage house a fallen limb lay against the brown shingle siding under a window. The raccoon climbed to the sill and looked inside. It was a dark cavern, a welcome cave. She scratched at the glass, then backed to the ground and set out to find an entrance. The fieldstone foundation was solid, but at last she came to the open door. For a moment she stood in the opening, sniffing suspiciously, then squeezed inside and took up residence.

Although the boy stopped by often, it was more than three weeks before he discovered that the carriage house had a new tenant. On that morning he slipped quietly through the door opening, not wanting to disturb the phoebe if she was on the nest. Inside he paused to listen. Sometimes his silent

286

approach was rewarded with the squeak of a startled mouse, the scampering of unseen feet, or the swish of wings. This time he heard a slight scratching and shuffling overhead. He went to the foot of the narrow stairway and started up. His head had almost reached the level of the upper floor when suddenly another head appeared. Black eyes peered into his from a black mask, hardly more than a foot away. For a startled moment the boy and the raccoon stared at one another. Then, with surprising speed, the coon whirled and raced across the board floor. By the time the boy's eyes had become adjusted to the semidarkness of the loft, she had disappeared.

There are few hiding places in the loft. A closet, a wall cupboard, a few stacked boxes, and an old trunk are about all. There are spaces under the eaves, but the openings are so narrow that it hardly seemed possible for anything as large as a coon to squeeze through. Nevertheless, the boy peered into each one, his face pressed against the sloping roof boards. His flashlight revealed tangled spider webs, debris of old mouse and squirrel nests, piles of nut shells and seed

287

husks, and at last the shining eyes of the raccoon. Her brown, furry body seemed to fill the cramped space to overflowing, and she stared fearlessly at the boy. Then there was a movement under her chin, and another black mask appeared, a much smaller mask with two inquiring eyes peering from it. The boy gasped in amazement, and then a second round face pushed out from under its mother's thick fur. Where there had been one raccoon a few weeks before, now there was a family.

The boy was never certain how many baby coons he had seen. Little faces constantly appeared and disappeared, but he thought there must be four, possibly five. He had no opportunity to check his count, for that night the mother moved her children to other, and hopefully less cramped, quarters.

Another animal that strayed into the carriage house found it more difficult to leave. Probably the skunk had entered to hunt mice, not to seek shelter, but in any event it found itself trapped in an empty grain bin. A pile of boards outside made it easy to climb to the rim, and the open cover was an invitation to tumble in. Once inside, however, there was no way

288

out except to climb straight walls, and unlike the raccoon, the skunk was no climber.

The boy had not visited the old building for several days, so he had no way of knowing how long the skunk had been in its prison. However, from the aimless way it shuffled back and forth, back and forth, it seemed to have given up all hope of escape. It would need help. A board slid over the edge as a ladder would be too steep for it to climb. There seemed only one answer: the skunk would have to be lifted out.

The boy had never before caught a full-grown skunk, but he had seen his father do it. He had been told that the scent sacs at the base of the animal's tail were closed off by a bone when the tail was down, but when it was raised the sacs were open and ready to shoot a spray of penetrating musk to the rear. He hoped he had been told correctly

Slowly the rescuer leaned over the waist-high front of the bin and reached down. The captive stopped his pacing and started to raise his tail. The boy froze. When the skunk dropped his tail and again began pacing, the boy reached still lower. There were several such stops and starts. As long as that

289

tail was down, the boy knew he was safe. Slowly, very slowly, he reached out.

The skunk's head was in a far corner of the bin and he rocked from side to side on his front feet. The boy's hand reached for the black and white tail, nearer, nearer, nearer. Suddenly he lunged, grabbing the bushy tail and lifting at the same time. As the surprised animal's hind feet came off the floor, his tail and backbone were in a straight line. The musk sacs were closed. The boy stood up, holding his prize at arm's length. Four black feet clawed vainly at thin air. There was a slight sickening odor, but the snatch had been too quick for any real discharge. The boy carried his catch outside. Going around to the stone wall, he reached across and dropped the confused animal on the far side. There was no resentment at the rough handling, no angry departing spray. Instead, as the

290

boy peered cautiously over the wall, the newly freed skunk waddled off through the trees. He was in no great hurry. He seemed as certain of immunity to attack as his tribe has always been. Even his late unsettling experience did not seem to have shaken his self-confidence.

Few wild creatures live together in peace and harmony. The varied inhabitants of the old carriage house and the occasional visitors who wander in are not seeking company. They come for reasons of their own, and most of them either endure or ignore one another. It has attractions for so many, however, that it is a natural gathering place, the community center of the wood.

—*Henry B. Kane*

THINKING IT OVER

1. The author said "few wild creatures live together in peace and harmony." Why do you think the animals lived peacefully in the old carriage house?

2. This selection is made up of several short episodes. Describe how each one begins and ends.

3. Would the author of "Town in the Forest" have considered the old carriage house a town? Explain your answer.

THOUGHTS AT WORK

1. Choose three of the animals the boy met in the carriage house and list three or four facts you learned about each one.

2. Which of the animals described did you find most interesting? Why?

3. If you read between the lines, you learned some things about the boy. How would you describe him?

4. For what reasons do you think the carriage house had been abandoned?

5. Why do you think the raccoon sniffed suspiciously before she took up residence in the carriage house?

6. Which of the creatures described did not live *in* the carriage house? Why do you think the author included it in the article?

7. Tell about an experience you have had observing wildlife. Where were you and what did you see?

A BIRD CAME DOWN THE WALK

A bird came down the walk:
He did not know I saw;
He bit an angle-worm in halves
And ate the fellow, raw.

And then he drank a dew
From a convenient grass,
And then hopped sidewise to the wall
To let a beetle pass.

—*Emily Dickinson*

This story tells of perhaps one hour in the life of a family of golden eagles. It shows what man can do to the eagle, and how the eagle can respond to the challenge. As you read, notice how the author has described this magnificent bird, often going beyond scientific observation and fact to suggest possible reasons why the bird behaves as it does. Note, too, how this adds excitement and interest to the story.

THE GOLDEN EAGLE

From the rocky bank of the small, swift stream at the bottom of the canyon, the cliff rose up, straight as a wall for nearly seven hundred feet into the sky. About sixty feet below the rimrock at the top, there was a shelf that thrust out over the empty air for ten feet and ran along the face for twenty. Near one end of it there was a cave four feet wide and six deep. A man on his knees could just about move around in it. From this cave and the shelf there was a wide view of the canyon, across it over the lower ridge on the other side, and beyond to the Colorado plain, fading off into the haze to the east.

In the middle of the shelf there was a golden eagle's nest. It was made of crisscrossed sticks and brush and was covered on the outside with gray-green moss that blended into the gray rock of the cliff face.

There were two young eagles in the nest, one much

larger than the other. This was the female. She would always be a third larger than her brother, after the manner of birds of prey. They were both about ready to fly. The crown and hackle feathers on the male's head were dark and would grow paler as he matured. The female's were already dark gold and gleamed in the sun.

They had been quiet for a time, lying together in the nest. But presently the female, whom we shall call Kira, began to grow restless. She stood, bowed her bright head, and stretched the great seven-foot wings up over her back. After she folded them again, she looked at her brother and decided to bedevil him. She often did this, and he knew he would be roughly handled. He scrambled out of the nest and ran along the ledge to the mouth of the cave. Kira started for him, but after several steps she noticed the hindquarters

of a jackrabbit in her path. Her foot, longer than a man's hand and armed with great, curving, needle-sharp talons, shot out and clamped upon it. She dropped it; caught and dropped it again. She picked it up with her hooked beak, tossed it a foot away, and ran after it. This play foreshadowed battles of the future that would not be playful. Her foot came out again and took the hindquarters in its grip. She looked at the prey in

her foot, dropped it, flapped her wings, and screamed in triumph.

It was not a very impressive scream for a bird of her size. But golden eagles are rather silent creatures. Many hawks scream more frequently and with greater volume. It is not their screaming that makes eagles noble. It is their great power and courage and their regal dignity. Their race circles the world.

Kira had got her mind off her brother. She moved to the ledge's lip, and her dark, hooded eyes searched the canyon. Her sight was excellent, fashioned to find prey at immense distances. She saw, among the scrub oak and cottonwood along the stream, wand lily, creeping

297

holly grape, stonecrop, and bracted alum root blooming. Several tiny chipmunks ran in and out among the rocks. The old coyote who lived in the canyon had moved out of cover and lay drowsing in a sunny opening, muzzle on forepaws.

She raised her head, searched the sky, and fixed her gaze to the east. Far off, a tiny dot in the blue, the old female eagle was coming in high above the other ridge. She set her wings for the long glide to the ledge, and as she came nearer, Kira saw that there was prey in her foot and began to move about with anticipation. The young male had seen his mother too, and ran back from the end of the ledge. Over the canyon the old bird dropped a little, swooped up to slow her speed and as she landed on the ledge, opened her foot and

dropped a half-grown jack-rabbit. As it slid toward them, both young eagles started for it. Kira's foot flashed out and she caught it. She looked at her brother and he moved back a little, remembering just in time that he was over-matched and had better wait his turn.

He watched hungrily until Kira had eaten as much as she wanted and had climbed back into the nest, then he moved in to finish what was left. His mother, calm and unruffled, beautiful in repose in the clear light of the Front Range, watched him with her head tilted, her golden hackles bright in the sun.

The three men, carrying ropes, came out of the pines which ended a few yards back from the edge of the cliff. It was the male eagle (called the *tiercel* because he is a third smaller than his mate) who saw them first. He had swung back over the ridge when he came in from the prairie; he approached from behind the men, several hundred feet over the pines, with a five-foot rattler, which he had decapitated, in his foot. When he saw the men directly over the nest, he began his alarm cry: Kiah! Kiah! Kiah! The sound echoed among the great rocks and stony spires on each side of the cliff face. A lonely trout fisherman in the stream far below heard it and looked up but could see nothing for his roof of leaves.

The tiercel swung past the edge of the cliff and circled higher, still screaming his apprehension. The old eagle on the ledge heard him, cocked her head, and saw him mounting into the sky. She knew at once that there was trouble, and jumped off the ledge. Her great wings opened and took hold on the air; she slanted off across the canyon to a place where there was usually an updraft which would help her gain altitude. She found the warm and rising current of air and began to circle higher in it. The canyon dropped beneath her, and she saw the men.

She screamed at them too, but continued to rise. Her temper was shorter than the tiercel's and the young were more her concern. Had the creatures upon the top of the cliff been anything but men, she would have stooped at them in fury, roaring down on folded wings to drive them away. There were few animals in her world that she wouldn't meet in battle, but her ancestors had survived the schemes of Indian plume hunters for so many generations that it had become an instinct to avoid men.

They watched her as she mounted higher and drifted off to circle with the tiercel in the distance. Then they dropped a rope's end over the cliff and payed out the rope until it reached the shelf. Having thus measured the length they wanted, they took the other end into the pines, ran the rope around the nearest pine—which was to be used as a snubbing post—and made the rope fast to another tree further back. They came back to the cliff's edge again, pulled up the rope, and arranged it around the lightest man so that while he sat in a loop of it, he was also supported under the arms.

He walked around to assure himself that it was fast at all points, and comfortable. "I think it's all right," he said. "Suppose there are two of them?"

"Take one. We don't need them both."

The men put a big musette bag over his shoulder, and one of them walked back to the snubbing post. The other took hold of the rope. The one who was going over the cliff turned his back on it, and holding the rope backed over the cliff's edge. It was rounded there;

there was no sharp edge to fray the rope, and the man sitting in the loop, holding himself off with his feet, began his descent as the rope was slowly payed out. He looked very small against the cliff.

The young eagles on the ledge had been puzzled by the tiercel's screaming, for they had never heard the alarm call before. They watched their mother take off, and when her voice was added to the tiercel's, they began to grow uneasy. Their familiar routine had been disturbed, something was happening to which they had no key, and some of the old bird's apprehension came through to them. They both ran to the familiar nest, climbed into it, and crouched down. Then Kira's eye caught movement above as the man started down the cliff. She looked up, staring at him. The young tiercel followed her glance. Swaying a little on the end of his rope, the man seemed all sprawling arms and legs. He was a deadly enemy, and momentarily growing nearer.

As the man descended, the young eagles moved back in the nest until they were on the inside edge of it, pressed against the rock. Confusion held them there until the man was almost level with them. As he came closer he grew more menacing, with his pale face looking down and the scuff of his shoes on the rock. Suddenly Kira was freed of the paralysis of fear that had held her. She jumped from the nest and ran along the shelf to the cave, and her brother followed her. They scrambled into the cave; its roof and walls closed protectively around them and shut out the sight of the man.

The man kicked out from the cliff, and by pulling himself up a little as he swung back, landed on the shelf. He had a little slack now and signaled for more by giving two jerks on the rope. The men gave it to him. He could move about a little now, but he didn't like his position. He thought of being pulled up again to be dropped before the cave but decided against this. He crawled along the shelf, pressing against the rock, to the cave. When he appeared in the mouth of it, breathing quite audibly, his

outlandish crawling shape outlined against the sky, the young eagles jammed their backs against the rock. Their hackles rose and they stared with menace and fear.

The man grinned at them and crawled closer, spreading his arms to keep them together. It was his plan to move in a little more, crowding them still with his arms wide, and then make a quick, sweeping grab for the legs of one of them to immobilize its feet. He could ignore the strong, hooked beak. Eagles do not use their beaks for offense. But he had great respect for the damage the talons could do to him. Once they were locked in him somewhere, it would be impossible for him to get them loosened by himself. The power of an eagle's grip is unbelievable.

He crawled an inch closer, and suddenly Kira could stand it no longer. She had always been an aggressive bird, and now this trait sent her forward. Her advance was certainly more for escape than for attack, but some of both were in it. She ran toward the man, who was badly startled and fell back a little, jumped toward him, touched one of his extended arms, and pushed against it to launch herself through the mouth of the cave.

She had often exercised her wings on the shelf, rising and holding herself up two or three feet above it, but solid footing had always been under her and she had never dared the empty air. Now she was in it. Her feet dropped and for an instant she tried to walk upon the air, but it had no substance; she was falling through it. She had a moment of terror, but then

the memory of the supporting air under her wings as she exercised them, and her nerve reflexes took over. Her wings took hold on the air and her tail spread and buoyed her up. She was flying. It was a shaky and uncertain performance; she almost lost her flying speed and stalled several times. When rising from flat ground, eagles start slowly and heavily because of their weight. They have to exert themselves to get airborne. But Kira had the impetus of her drop and plenty of empty space under her and wasn't confronted with this condition. All she had to do was glide at such an angle that her flying speed was maintained. This preoccupied her so much that at first she didn't realize how fast the other side of the canyon was sliding toward her. When she did realize it, she fell into confusion, tried to turn, and came very close to stalling again. Her mother had seen

her jump from the nest and although her instinct told her to stay far from the men, she broke her circle, came roaring down, braked, and rose beneath Kira. Her presence and her solid back supported the young eagle and gave her confidence again. By skillful maneuvering beautiful to see, alternately rising beneath her and dropping away, she managed to help Kira land on a wide shelf on the other side of the canyon.

It wasn't a graceful landing, but at least Kira was on the ground again. She was somewhat ruffled, but now that she had dared the air and had got safely out of it for the first time, she shook her feathers into place, looked around, and bowed and talked excitedly to herself in congratulations. Her mother rose away and took up her distant, watchful circling. Kira watched her go and began to run about on the shelf, opening her wings and making several short, clumsy flights from one rock to another. The feeling of being airborne remained with her for a time, so thrilling that it dulled the memory of her fright. She remembered the feel of the air, the exhilarating freedom of it, and the speed of her flight, when she was borne up, weightless, high above the earth.

While she was preoccupied with these things, the man, with her brother hooded and crammed into the musette bag over his shoulder, emerged from the cave and was pulled up the cliff face, walking up the rock on the end of the rope. He reached the top and went over it. His companions untied the rope, coiled it up, and all of them vanished into the pines.

After they had gone, Kira's mother slid down the air from her high post, screaming in relief from the tension that had held her. This unusual sound in the canyon brought an old horned owl, who lived

305

in a pothole far below and had slept through the tiercel's alarms, blundering out to see what the screams were about. The eagle saw him. He was something to vent her rage and frustration upon, and although they had managed to live in peace together since early in the spring, she stooped and struck the owl a terrible blow. One of her rear talons opened him up like a cleaver. There was an explosion of feathers and the owl fell dead toward the stream. Before he vanished through the trees, the old eagle had swung up and landed beside Kira on the shelf.

The tiercel, knowing himself safe now, came out of the sky on a long, sloping stoop with his wings half backed. He still had the rattler in his foot, and when he landed Kira ran to him, snatched it, and began to break into it. She was hungry again from all the excitement. Her first experience with men was over and she had got well out of it. But there would be more experiences, more encounters brought about by man's ill will, before she lived out her life.

—*Robert Murphy*

THINKING IT OVER

1. The dictionary defines the eagle as a large strong bird with keen eyes and powerful wings. Find several facts in the story that prove this statement.

2. Think of another title that would fit the story well.

3. In this story what effect did man have on ecology?

THOUGHTS AT WORK

1. Reread the first paragraph, then draw a diagram showing the cliff, the ledge, and the surrounding area.

2. Give several reasons why the ledge made a good home for the eagles. Keep in mind what you have learned about golden eagles.

3. List the steps the men followed to capture the tiercel, from the moment they came out of the pines until they disappeared again into them. Why were three men necessary to capture one eagle?

4. The author does not say, but for what reason do you think the men wanted to capture the eagle?

5. Find the following phrases in the story, then explain in your own words what each one means.
   a. the prey in her foot (page 296)
   b. not a very impressive scream (page 297)
   c. calm and unruffled, beautiful in repose (page 299)
   d. a five-foot rattler which he had decapitated (page 299)
   e. was to be used as a snubbing post (page 300)
   f. opened him up like a cleaver (page 306)

6. The author included much information about eagles. What did you learn about their appearance, size, food, flight, enemies, and family life?

7. The last sentence hinted that Kira would experience more trouble with man. What kinds of trouble might she face?

In this selection Isaac Asimov, a noted scientist, has described a Moon colony of the future. As you, the earth-man, read about this colony, notice how moon-man will create an environment on the Moon, how he will make his own ecology. Notice, too, how his actions will determine man's future in space just as your actions now help to determine man's future on Earth.

THE MOON COLONY

Four hundred years ago people from Europe were taking part in a great adventure. Some of them were getting into sailing ships to go to the American continents and colonize them. Now there is another adventure. Men have reached the Moon and walked on it. In a few years men will be getting into rocket ships to colonize the Moon.

Crossing the ocean was very hard in the old days, as hard as crossing space now. It was even harder, in fact. The sailing ships took weeks to cross the stormy Atlantic, while the rocket ships take only days to reach the Moon. Besides, the sailing ships could not keep in touch with home by radio, but the astronauts can.

Life was not easy in the first colonies on the American continents. Many of the English colonists who settled in Jamestown, Virginia, in 1607, and in Plymouth, Massachusetts, in 1620, nearly died of disease and starvation. The colonists didn't know how to deal with the new land. They didn't know how to farm the wilderness or get along with the Indians.

308

Gradually, those who stayed alive learned to fit themselves into the surroundings. Some things they learned from the Indians. Other things they discovered for themselves. They learned about new crops like tobacco. They learned how to live in the woods and fight Indian-fashion. They matched their way of living to their surroundings. They made themselves part of the ecology.

The Moon colonists will have an even harder time in some ways. At least America had air, water, and food. The Moon doesn't. The Moon has a two-week day and a two-week night. It has a low gravity. Men will encounter many more difficulties on the Moon than the early settlers found in the New World.

On the other hand, men know much more about the Moon today than they knew about the American continent long ago. Men are much more advanced in science nowadays and can plan the Moon colony carefully. We hope that when the Moon is colonized, the settlers won't go through the terrible times of disease, hunger, and fear that made life difficult for the first colonists of Jamestown and Plymouth.

The picture on the next two pages is an artist's notion of how the Moon colony might look once it is a large, comfortable place to live. Notice that it is underground, inside a hill, so that it is protected from the dangerous rays of the Sun. The cover of soil and rock protects it from the great heat of the day and the great cold of the night, and also shields it from small meteors. After you have studied the picture, read about a Moon colony of the future.

Nuclear power station. (1) This will supply the energy the colony will need. Almost everything that goes on in the colony will use up energy. Without it, everything would come to a halt. The power station will be set away from the colony. If an accident should occur there, it might destroy the colony if the station were inside the dome. Outside, it will be safe and the colonists will have time to repair whatever has gone wrong.

Ore and rock mines. (2) The colonists will get necessary raw materials from the crust of the Moon. It will not be wise to bring everything from Earth because transportation will be too hard and too costly. If the Moon colony is to do well, the colonists must use as much of the Moon itself as possible. From the rock, they will get metals such as iron and aluminum, also uranium for the power station. They can make cement, fertilizer, and all sorts of chemicals out of the rock.

Rock processing. (3) Near the mines will be the factories where the rocks are treated and turned into metals, chemicals, and other materials. These useful products will be shipped to the dome, while the leftover materials will be dumped far from the colony.

Even water will come from the rocks. There is no water running free on the Moon in the form of rivers, lakes, or oceans. Scientists think, however, there was once water on the Moon many millions of years ago. Most of it has vanished into space, but some has probably remained, having soaked into the soil and rocks. If the Moon rocks are crushed and baked, steam will form. If the steam is cooled, water will be produced. It can be collected and sent to the colony.

312

Some of the water will be treated with electric currents to break it up into hydrogen and oxygen. These gases will be collected separately and cooled into frigid liquids. Nitrogen gas will be obtained from nitrogen-containing minerals in the Moon's crust and turned into liquid too. The nitrogen and oxygen will be used to make an atmosphere for the colonists to breathe inside the dome. Naturally, the dome will be airtight so that the atmosphere doesn't escape.

The hydrogen will be used for other purposes. Some of the hydrogen, a special kind called "heavy hydrogen," will be used in very advanced nuclear power stations. Heavy hydrogen will be made to yield vast quantities of energy.

Underground lights. (14) The colony will be supplied with light and electricity from the energy furnished by the nuclear power station. Large lights in the ceiling will make the dome bright as day. When it is time to sleep, the lights can be dimmed. In this way the colonists will have normal day and night, as on Earth.

Farm domes. (11) The colony will need food and it will be grown in the dome. The Moon's crust is similar to the Earth's and can be broken up to form a soil in which plants will grow when fertilizers and water are added. Plants that grow need energy. On Earth green plants get the energy from sunlight. In the Moon colony where the large dome will shut out the dangerous rays of the Sun, plants will be bathed in special fluorescent lights to provide the necessary energy.

The growing plants will keep the atmosphere fresh and useful. You see, when men breathe, they gradually

313

use up oxygen and replace it with another gas called carbon dioxide. The plants will use up the carbon dioxide as they grow and produce oxygen. Therefore the men and the plants together will keep the oxygen and carbon dioxide steady in the atmosphere.

Men will let some of the plants continue to grow, but they will eat the rest. The wastes men produce from the food they eat will be treated to kill germs. Fresh, clean water will be baked out of the wastes, and the left over material will be used as fertilizer. Everything moves in a cycle: the water, the oxygen, the carbon dioxide, the wastes. The only thing that will be used up will be energy from the power station.

Of course, the cycle will not be perfect. Some water and oxygen may leak away. An accident may cause some of the air to be lost. Small additional amounts of water, oxygen, and nitrogen will then be brought in from the rock-processing plants.

Eventually, when the farm domes are going well, small animals will be brought in. Perhaps the colonists may even raise chickens or rabbits. Then they will have meat to eat.

Transportation. (5, 6, 16) Naturally, some things will have to come from Earth; seeds for new kinds of plants, for instance, or animals that can start breeding on the Moon. The colonists will also need gadgets they can't make for themselves. And no doubt they will want a supply of books and films. Besides, people will want to travel back and forth on visits to Earth for fun or business.

Therefore, a lunar port outside the colony will be

necessary (5). Perhaps it will be reached by a moving sidewalk (6), for energy may be cheaper on the Moon than on Earth. The cost can be cut down because in addition to the nuclear power station, energy will be obtained from the strong sunlight on the Moon during each two-week day.

There will also be special cars (16) for use by people who must explore the Moon, or who perhaps just want to go sightseeing. The cars will have special wheels that can travel over the uneven ground, and they will be sealed to keep in the atmosphere.

Moon-orbiting space station. (4) Rocket ships rising from the Moon will break their trip at one of several space stations that will circle the Moon. There will be space stations circling Earth. They will supply fuel, food, and other things needed to make the flight much more comfortable and pleasant.

Housing. (7) Inside the colony, there will be apartment houses which may be very much like those on Earth. They will feel quite homelike.

Education. (8, 9, 10, 15) People must be educated on the Moon just as on Earth, perhaps even more so, since the Moon colonists will have to operate complicated machinery in order to keep the colony going. There will be schools, even a university (8). There will also be places where new scientific knowledge can be gained. For instance, at a research center (10) people will study ways of using the Moon's high and low temperatures and the airlessness (vacuum) on the Moon's surface.

There will be an astronomical observatory (15) so

that men can study the sky. Such study will be much easier on the Moon because there is no air, so there are no clouds, fog, or mist to blot out the sky. There will be a large radio telescope outside the dome (9) to study radio waves from the sky. Scientists on the Moon will learn a great deal that Earth scientists can't find out now.

Fun. (7, 12, 13) Naturally, the Moon colonist will want to play and have a good time too. Behind the apartment houses there will be ball parks, bowling alleys, and playgrounds (7). There will be museums and art galleries (13) for people to enjoy. One thing the Moon can supply that the Earth can't is low gravity. Because of low gravity, it will be possible for the colonists to fit themselves with strong wings of light plastic and glide or actually fly. When the colony has become large enough, there will be special places (12) where grownups and youngsters can have flying games. However, the Moon colonists will have to get used to walking and moving under low gravity. They may need to keep themselves fit in special gymnasiums in case they have to return to Earth and live under high gravity again.

In the end, the colonists will have set up surroundings in which they can live. They will be adjusted to the conditions on the Moon. They will be part of a new ecology.

It won't be easy, though, and at first, there will be much danger. Just two or three men will be sent to the Moon at any one time, to begin with, and they will not stay more than a few days. Perhaps a special ship

316

will be buried in the Moon's crust to serve as the home of the first colony. It will hold only two or three men. But little by little, the space under the surface crust will be enlarged and the underground settlement will begin to grow into a large, comfortable place for many people to live.

In the beginning, all materials will have to come from Earth, even food, air, and water. Slowly, parts of the nuclear power station will be brought in and put together, as well as parts of complicated machinery for processing rock. Traffic between Earth and Moon will be active for a while. Then as the years pass, less and less will have to be sent from Earth. The Moon colonists will do more and more for themselves.

Even after the Moon colonists have a large and comfortable colony, there will still be dangers. What if a meteor breaks through the dome? What if a piece of essential machinery breaks down?

What if there are some dangers about the Moon we don't know yet? For instance, what about the Moon's low gravity? It is only one-sixth the Earth's gravity. Can human beings spend long times under such low gravity without harm to the body? If they do, will they become so used to low gravity that they will never be able to come back to Earth? Maybe colonists will have to stay on the Moon all their lives.

Even so, it will be well worth the effort, for the Moon colonists can learn much that will be useful to Earth people as well as to themselves. They can study the Moon's crust, for instance. It was formed at the same time as the Earth's crust, but the Earth's crust has been disturbed by air, water, and living things. The Moon's crust has not. It can tell us a great deal about the early history of our own world.

The Moon's crust may have chemicals in it that will help us to understand how certain chemicals formed on Earth very early in its history and then developed into living things. It may even be that the Moon's crust contains very simple germ-like creatures of its own. They will give us another kind of life to study.

Because of the Moon's airlessness, scientists can study the outer universe much better on the Moon than on Earth. The Moon's low gravity makes it much easier to launch rockets from the Moon than from Earth. The Moon may therefore be the base for new explorations. What's more, Moon colonists will be so used to living under low gravity inside a dome that they may be more at home in a rocket ship than humans would be. After all, it only takes days to reach the Moon, but it will take many months, or even years, to reach the other planets. Can humans stay cooped up in a rocket ship for months and years when they are used to a great wide-open world? Maybe Moon colonists will be needed to command the ships.

Most of all, though, if the Moon colony works, it will show us how to run an ecology properly, how to make every bit of air and water and energy do its work, and how to keep from spoiling and ruining the environment. Earthmen will have to learn that lesson before it is too late.

— *Isaac Asimov*

318

THINKING IT OVER

1. How will colonizing the Moon be easier than colonizing America was four hundred years ago? How will colonizing the Moon be more difficult?

2. Write the subtitles in this selection. Beneath each one write in a sentence or two the main idea of that section.

3. List four ways in which the Moon is physically different from Earth. Tell how the colonists will deal with each of these differences.

THOUGHTS AT WORK

1. Turn to the picture of the Moon colony. Name the places these phrases describe.
   a. place to bowl and play ball
   b. a place to land space ships
   c. a means of controlling night and day
   d. a place for learning
   e. a place to do research
   f. a supplier of energy
   g. a source of metals and chemicals
   h. a place to study the sky
   i. a means of producing water and chemical elements

2. Explain how men and plants will help each other on the Moon colony.

3. Skim the last section of the article to find at least three advantages to colonizing the Moon.

4. Study the picture of the Moon colony carefully. What things would you add to make living safer and more comfortable? Tell where you would place these things and why.

5. Pretend you are living on the Moon colony and describe one day in your life. Include as many of the objects in the picture as possible.

6. Then as a Moon tourist, plan a sightseeing trip around the Moon colony.

FUELED

Fueled
by a million
man-made
wings of fire —
the rocket tore a tunnel
through the sky —
and everybody cheered.
Fueled
only by a thought from God —
the seedling
urged its way
through the thicknesses of black —
and as it pierced
the heavy ceiling of the soil —
and launched itself
up into outer space —
no
one
even
clapped.

— *Marcie Hans*

320

BIBLIOGRAPHY

A Tree Called Moses, by Laura Nelson Baker.
> The life story of a giant Redwood that has lived in the Sierra Nevada Mountains for more than twenty-five hundred years.

The Tale of Whitefoot, by Carl T. Brandhorst.
> A little mouse lives out her life and dies. The author shows how animals, insects, and plants affect one another.

Men in the Sea, by Peter Briggs.
> Stories about the oceanographic pioneers who explore the secrets of the ocean depths.

A Place in the Sun: Ecology and the Living World, by Lois and Louis Darling.
> This book shows how all life is closely interwoven and how man fits into the world of nature.

Swamps, by Delia Goetz.
> The author describes the animals, plants, and people who live in these soft, wet lands.

The Crab That Crawled Out of the Past, by Lorus and Margery Milne.
> The life story of a horseshoe crab, one of the strangest creatures in nature's world.

The Pyramid of Living Things, by Edith Raskin.
> The author explains how plants and animals depend upon one another to survive in the web of life.

The Snake Tree, by Glen Rounds.
> From an old deserted farmhouse the author observes the busy animals and insects, their many quirks and oddities.

Birth of a Forest, by Millicent Selsam.
> A thousand years in the life of a forest is described as it develops from a pond.

Calendar Moon, by Natalie Belting.
> A book of poetry about the Moon in folk beliefs and legends from all around the world—the friendly-moon of Japan, the grumbling-moon of the Maoris, the mosquito-moon of Siberia.

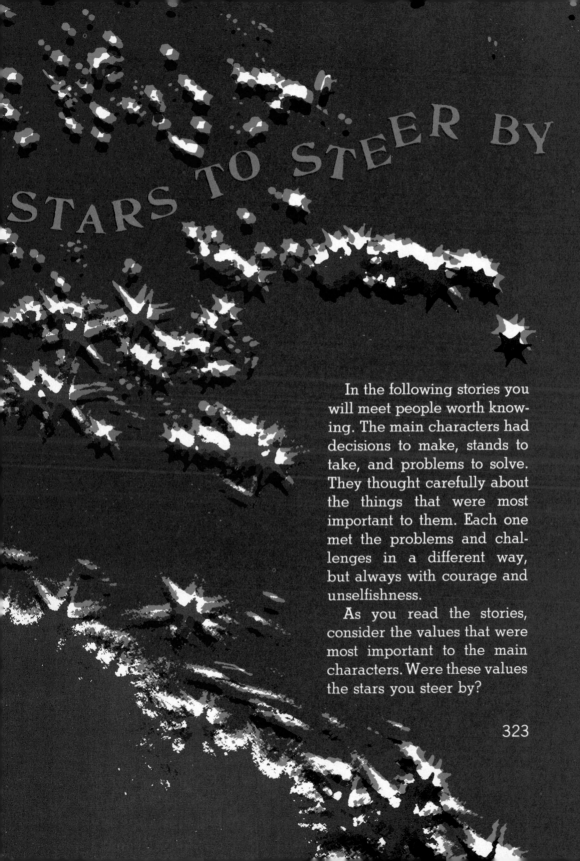

STARS TO STEER BY

In the following stories you will meet people worth knowing. The main characters had decisions to make, stands to take, and problems to solve. They thought carefully about the things that were most important to them. Each one met the problems and challenges in a different way, but always with courage and unselfishness.

As you read the stories, consider the values that were most important to the main characters. Were these values the stars you steer by?

323

This story is about a period of time nearly seventy years ago, in the early part of this century. The setting is California, and the main characters are based on real people—the author and her sister. Read the story to see how "The Last Day" tested their courage and unselfishness.

THE LAST DAY

Julie and Elizabeth had finished breakfast and now were in their upstairs bedroom getting ready for the last day of school. Next to Christmas, the Last Day was the best day of the year since it marked the beginning of summer vacation. In honor of the Last Day, they would wear their best dresses and their brand-new, patent leather, Mary Jane slippers.

Elizabeth stuck one foot out and wiggled it as she admired the sheen of the black leather. Suddenly she put her foot down.

"Will Ethel Tucker have shoes today?" she asked Julie.

Though most of the boys had been going barefoot for the past couple of months, none of the girls, except Ethel Tucker, ever did.

From down the hall came Father's voice, singing with fierce energy as he shaved. Though perfectly tuneless, his songs were always well-worth listening to, for while the first line and rhythms were always the same, the words varied to fit the occasion. Now, as the two girls wondered about Ethel Tucker, they heard,

"And then he told
    those children
And those children
    they did say,
That no more they'd
    leave their father,
For today was the
    Last Day."

The phrases of the song came jerkily between razor strokes.

"Will Ethel Tucker have on shoes today?" Elizabeth asked again.

Julie turned from studying the ash maple outside their window. "Maybe she'll just stay home."

Ethel had started coming to school only two weeks ago. While there was little to distinguish her from several other girls in Miss White's room, she was distinctly in a class by herself. Though she was the only girl who came to school barefooted, this in itself would not have been enough to set her apart. Ethel's claim to distinction at Orchard School lay in the fact that she was poor. She was poor among a group of children none of whom was rich. It was suspected that she didn't always have enough to eat. To cap it all, Ethel Tucker had no mother. She was poor indeed.

The Tucker family had established itself in the little shack next to the blacksmith shop a block up the street from the school. This was handy for Mr. Tucker, who worked at the blacksmith shop with Mr. Rogers, the owner.

Though at first the Tuckers had caused a stir of interest at Orchard School, it wasn't long before everyone was taking them in stride. Ethel's poverty and bare feet came to be accepted, just as Herman Dilling's unquenchable badness had come to be accepted. Every school had at least one bad boy in it; so inevitably, every school had to have some poor children in it. Ethel Tucker, the poor girl, became at last simply poor Ethel Tucker.

"How will she get her report card if she doesn't come on the Last Day?" persisted Elizabeth.

"Someone could take it up to the blacksmith shop," answered Julie. "Miss White would."

Elizabeth nodded, feeling reassured. You could count on Miss White.

Down in the kitchen they stopped for their mother's inspection.

This morning the inspection was rather prolonged because, of course, this was the Last Day.

"You look very nice," she said at last. "I shall be proud of you this afternoon." Mother was referring to the parts they were to take in the program.

She gave Elizabeth's hair ribbon a parting twitch and

said to Julie, "Remember, dear, it's not 'thus on its sounding anvil-shape,' but 'thus on its sounding anvil— *shape* each burning deed and thought.' Pause after 'anvil.'"

Julie, who loved horses, had chosen "The Village Blacksmith" for the Last Day. Now she nodded, moving the highlights on her smooth dark bangs.

"Yes, I'll remember," she promised.

Elizabeth had chosen "Abou Ben Adhem"[1] because it reminded her of *The Arabian Nights*, a book she loved. She knew the poem perfectly and understood most of it.

They kissed their mother good-by, picked up their lunch boxes, and left the house to begin the long walk to school.

Julie and Elizabeth, though a year apart, shared the same classroom. But Julie, a fifth-grader, sat next to the windows. Elizabeth was with the fourth-graders on the other

[1] Abou Ben Adhem (ä bü′ ben ä′dem)

side of the room. Ethel Tucker, though the oldest child in the room, sat across the aisle from Elizabeth. Evidently, Ethel had missed a good deal of school during the eleven years of her life.

The moment Elizabeth entered the classroom, she saw with dismay that Ethel had not stayed home after all. There she sat behind her desk, her face unusually animated as she watched the children coming in. Had Ethel, too, caught the excitement of the Last Day? For once her hair was combed. It was neatly parted in the middle and hung in two tight braids fastened each with a rubber band. It wasn't until Elizabeth had taken her seat that she was able to check on Ethel's feet. Today, as on all other days, they were bare. Carefully Elizabeth looked at the other children. As near as she could tell, they all had on shoes. Even Herman Dilling was wearing shoes today. She

tried to catch Julie's eye across the room to signal the dreadful news that Ethel Tucker was the only child without shoes on the Last Day. But Julie, deep in a book, wouldn't look up.

A second row of windows ran along the back of the room, and in the corner where the two rows of windows met, Miss White had her desk.

Miss White had red hair and usually wore a green dress. You could count on Miss White's wearing green. You could count on her for other things too.

"I think we will take time this morning to go over the recitations once more," said Miss White. "Alberta, we start with you."

Alberta rose and minced to the front of the room. She was a rather stout little girl with a wide blank face, wide vacant gray eyes, and a small demure mouth which she kept folded up like a buttonhole. She began her recitation.

328

It concerned a heroine named Grace Darling who had rowed across a storm-tossed sea to some ship-wrecked people and rescued them. When she had finished, she curtsied and sat down to rather derisive applause, for no one really liked Alberta.

"Lester, you're next," said Miss White.

Lester had chosen a short poem about circles. It was just about the shortest poem he could find anywhere. But Miss White liked it so much she said he might learn it if he looked up all the words. The only words Lester hadn't known were *heretic* and *flout*. He had explained them to the class. So now he spoke easily and with conviction.

"He drew a circle that shut
  me out—
Heretic, rebel, a thing
  to flout.
But love and I had the wit
  to win.
We drew a circle that took
  him in."

Few of the children bothered to listen to him; they had heard it before. But this morning, for the first time, the poem spoke to Elizabeth. She listened with excitement as the words began to have real meaning for her. A very special meaning. "We drew a circle that took him in."

She glanced across the aisle to where Ethel Tucker sat, one bare foot resting upon the instep of the other.

Quickly Elizabeth reached down a hand and unbuttoned the strap of one Mary Jane slipper. Next, she unbuttoned the other. Now for the stockings. While Miss White commented on Lester's recital, Elizabeth dug frantically to free them. She had one off before Miss White said, "Now we'll hear from the fourth-graders. Elizabeth, will you favor us, please?"

Elizabeth, her face rosy from her struggles, slid off the second stocking and rose. She cast a beseeching eye

330

toward Julie and padded to the front of the room in a perfect stillness. Her eyes were lowered to her white naked feet, so she missed Julie's shocked eyes, the boys' delighted grins, and Alberta's buttonhole mouth, now a round O of surprise.

At last it was over and she was back in her seat, her face scarlet and her heart pounding. What would Miss White say?

"I think, Elizabeth," came the teacher's calm voice from behind the desk in the corner, "I think it would be better if you spoke more slowly this afternoon. You will have a larger audience, remember, and each word must be heard and understood to the very back of the assembly room."

You could count on Miss White!

Two other children were called on and then it was Julie's turn. Elizabeth hadn't raised her head since she had finished her recitation.

331

But now she lifted it to look at her sister. And her heart nearly leaped out of her chest. *Julie was barefooted too!*

Again Miss White refused to take note of anything unusual. She even praised Julie for remembering to pause after *anvil*.

With Julie's performance, the recitations came to an end. All the other children in the room were to be bunched with the soloists for the singing of "The Star-Spangled Banner." Miss White's room would perform last and thus the program would conclude on a suitably patriotic note.

So now all the children rose and arranged themselves at the front of the room in the places they would have on the stage. Miss White had put the soloists in the back row, thus equalizing honors for the audience of parents. This placed Ethel Tucker smack in the middle of the front row.

The whole school was seething with excitement when the pupils trooped back to their rooms following the noon recess. The performance would begin at two. But much before that time, the parents would start arriving. And as each automobile or horse-drawn vehicle pulled up in front of the schoolhouse, every head in the classrooms on that side of the building would twist to see who it was.

Miss White had not appeared after the noon recess. And no one felt any concern, for this was the Last Day. Even Miss White's daily routines might be affected by it. In her absence, an eighth-grade girl was "keeping order," and Herman Dilling was having the time of his life.

With genuine relief, Elizabeth noted that Ethel Tucker, too, had not returned from lunch. Evidently she had wisely decided to stay home. Now the drastic plan which she and Julie had determined upon would not be necessary. It was nothing less than to leave off their shoes and stockings when their turn came to recite. It was a daring plan and one which they well knew might have serious repercussions. Never in all their lives had they gone barefooted, and to appear so in public might stretch their mother's love and understanding to the breaking point. They felt somewhat less worried about Father. He could nearly always be counted on to see their side of things. But this was different. They had never risked public disgrace before. Still, Ethel mustn't be the only child in school without shoes on the Last Day.

Two o'clock came and still Miss White had not returned.

Occasionally there was the sound of applause from the assembly room upstairs where the upper classes had begun performing. Tension began to mount. Where was Miss White? At last, at half past two, the door opened and

there she stood. She looked flushed and a bit harried as she beckoned the children to her. Their time had come! Quietly they slipped out of their seats and toward the door. On tiptoe, she led them across the big hall and up the wide stairs and down another hall past the assembly room to the door which led to the backstage area. And there in the gloom the first person Elizabeth spied was Ethel Tucker! She hadn't stayed home after all. She was standing in an almost dark corner and there were several other children between her and Elizabeth. But it was Ethel, all right.

The sisters exchanged glances and in the feeble light each read the despair in the other's eyes. They must go through with their plan, and as one, they bent to take off their shoes.

They watched with hopeless eyes Alberta's and Lester's shadowy outlines as each in turn mounted the short flight of steps to the stage, parted the curtains, and stepped before the audience. In terribly short time they were back with hearty applause ringing behind them. Then it was Elizabeth's turn.

Blindly she pattered toward the steps, unaware of Miss White's desperate attempt to reach her. She stumbled painfully once, but kept resolutely on. Nothing was going to stop her now. Ethel Tucker was not going to be the only child without shoes on the Last Day. Fumbling, she parted the curtains and faced a blur of faces in the bright light from the windows ranging along one side of the assembly room. If she heard the faint gasp which greeted her appearance, she paid it no heed.

Faintly she began, "Abou Ben Adhem, may his tribe increase." . . . And with those words, the audience swam into focus and Elizabeth recognized two faces gradually

emerging from among those in the back row. Father and Mother! Father looked bewildered and Mother shocked. But Elizabeth kept staunchly on until the merciful moment when the poem ended and she could disappear between the stage curtains.

Coming through the curtains, she bumped into Julie, who stood barefooted and ready to pounce upon the stage the moment Elizabeth left it.

"It's not your turn," Elizabeth whispered. But Julie gave her a shove and stepped into the light.

Elizabeth, wondering, pattered down the stairs to join the others in the gloom of backstage. There, "Under the spreading chestnut tree," came to them in ringing tones.

The waiting children remained utterly still while Julie's voice went confidently on. She even remembered the "anvil — shape" business and spoke the line correctly. You

336

would almost have thought she was wearing shoes!

When at last she had finished and returned to Elizabeth's side, she was tensely quiet. Without a whisper between them, the sisters waited while the last two performers spoke their pieces. Just once Elizabeth asked softly why Julie had gone ahead of turn, but Julie only shook her head and placed a finger on her lips.

Now it was time for the grand finale. All the children started up the stairs to the stage, the ones in the first row going ahead of all the others. Among these was Ethel Tucker. Elizabeth fastened her eyes on the little figure for whom she and Julie had dared so much, and her heart almost turned over. *Ethel Tucker was wearing shoes!*

She turned to Julie. Her eyes had a shocked, puzzled, and questioning look.

"Miss White got them for her this noon," whispered Julie. "She told me while you were reciting. That's why I went right after you."

"But you were barefooted too," said Elizabeth.

Julie nodded as they took their stations in the back row and waited for the curtain to be drawn open. "Miss White tried to stop you, and I was afraid she would try to stop me, so I stayed up by the curtain. I knew she wouldn't make a fuss there. I didn't want you to be the only one."

"Will the whispering in the back row please stop?" said Miss White.

Now the curtain was drawn wide. Sudden crashing chords shook the scarred old upright piano below the stage as Miss Harvey, working from the shoulders down, sounded the first notes of "The Star-Spangled Banner."

With one upsurging movement, the audience came to its feet. "Oh, say can you see . . ." rang out gloriously

337

from the stage, across the assembled parents, through the windows, and beyond the school grounds. For now the whole audience was singing. Elizabeth thought the song had never sounded so grand.

"Whatever put the idea in your heads?" asked Father.

They were all in the big red car, whizzing down the road at a good thirty miles an hour.

Miss White had explained everything and Mother had promised to call a meeting of the Grange ladies at once to take up with them the matter of the Tucker family.

For a moment silence followed his question, and then Elizabeth spoke.

"It was a poem," she confessed shyly. "Lester's poem about the circles. I wanted to make a circle that took her in."

Nobody said anything more until they were past the elderberry bush and their tall white house had come into sight. Then Father burst into tuneless song:

"And then he told those children
That those children can't be beat,
And he's proud to be their father,
Though there's nothing on their feet."

—*Doris Gates*

THINKING IT OVER

1. At the end of the story Elizabeth said, "I wanted to make a circle that took her in." How did these words explain the decision made by Julie and Elizabeth?

2. Several times in the story it was said that "You could count on Miss White." What were these times? What did they tell you about Miss White's character?

3. Would you say that Elizabeth and Julie showed courage? Why?

THOUGHTS AT WORK

1. Lester's poem had a very special meaning for Elizabeth. In what other situations in or out of school do you think it would apply?

2. At what point in the story did you first get a clue that Elizabeth and Julie might be in for a surprise?

3. What alerted Miss White to Ethel Tucker's problem? What did she do about it?

4. How do you know that Ethel Tucker had certain standards of her own?

5. What words were used to describe Alberta? How do you think the author wanted you to feel about her?

6. Who do you suppose the Grange ladies were? What do you think they might do?

7. Read between the lines and tell what Father was really saying each time he burst into song.

Old Two-Toes, the old raccoon who had escaped traps for many years, was one of the fine, free creatures of the wilderness. And Punk, living in the mountains of Tennessee many years ago, knew it. Do you think he'd ever tell where that raccoon was hiding? Do you think he'd ever help a trapper? As you read this story, look for clues to the character of Punk, the boy who finally had to take a stand.

PUNK TAKES A STAND

The Hood boys were always laying for Punk, though he never knew exactly why. It was really Toad Hood who was the bully. His younger brother, Spider, was an eerie little fellow without the power of speech. He had to do all his talking by signals. But he was mean as poison and whenever Toad waded into Punk, Spider did his share, kicking and biting. Mostly Punk avoided that part of the woods where the Hood cabin stood just off the country road. But there were times when Toad waylaid him and then Punk either had to stand or run. Usually he ran because Toad was bigger, and then there was always Spider around the edge of the fracas.

340

The situation finally reached a point where Punk knew he would have to take Toad on and lick him if he could. Toad, strong with the knowledge of Punk's fear of him, was beginning to go after the younger boy. It was becoming harder for Punk to avoid running into him. There would have to be a showdown.

The day Punk was to give the Hood boys their come-uppance was a day like any other August day on the Ridge. The sun came up bright and hot, shining all day, and then setting in the west in a red ball of fire.

"Reckon I'll leg it over to Horseshoe Lake for a swim," he announced when his last chore was done.

"Be back before dark, Punk," his stepgranny said, adding gently, "Dusk time is lonesome time in a cabin when its menfolks are away."

Punk flashed a swift smile at her. Then he was out of the cabin and his feet were fair skimming the earth as he took to his heels. Light of foot and light of heart, he raced down the hill into the shade of the woods.

Slowing down, he took a deep breath. No matter how often he came to the woods, he was always taken with the mystery and the quiet. Reckon someday after he'd had his schooling, he might get it all down in writing for other folks to read.

It was no time at all until he was in sight of Coon Rock and Horseshoe Lake. He paused on the crest of the sloping hill to take a long look at the place. There was the huge boulder that was Coon Rock, reaching up into the meadow and wild hayfield. There was the waterfall spreading over the rock, filling the lake with foam.

He began pulling off his shirt and then his pants, being careful to roll them up and hide them in the crotch of the oak tree by him. Being prepared was mighty important in the woods. One never knew what might slip up on him. His grown-up friend Hummy had pointed out more than once that in pioneer days the way they had survived was by keeping a keen lookout at all times.

"No matter how peaceful a place be, a smart fellow always gives it a scance; that is, if he wants to be all in one piece. How else do you reckon did Daniel Boone make it through these forests? He looked afore he stepped, let me tell you." Those had been Hummy's very words.

Punk grinned to himself as he recalled them. Well, he'd look afore *he* stepped too. So he gave a long look to his surroundings, taking in the countryside. Then he brought his eyes to the waterfall. Reckon the heavy fall of rain had made it so dark. In dry spells the water trickled pale and sickish. But now it glowed in shades of mint green, flowing and spilling down the slope in darker shades.

He couldn't wait any longer to feel the cool water on himself. He was right ready to jump forward when, suddenly, he was aware there was someone else in the woods besides himself. The crackling of under-brush and snapping twigs grew into more definite sounds of pounding feet.

Punk sat very still and listened. He could tell that

whoever it was, was heading for Horseshoe Lake. Then the sounds ceased for a second only to be revived in a few seconds by a loud shout.

"We had him, Spider! We had that ole son-of-a-gun! We sure did!"

It was Toad Hood's voice that rose in the timber, as ugly a sound to Punk as the caws of a thieving crow robbing a bird's nest.

"Look a-hyar, Spider! Old Two-Toes done had the trap sprung on him. Brung the blood, b'golly! Wh-o-o-op-ee!"

The sweat on Punk's body seemed to freeze so that a chill settled in on him. He clenched his teeth and wished desperately he had someone to turn to, man-size and real like Hummy.

"Hyeaah! Thinks hisself smart, huh, gittin' away. Well, he done run smack into his doom. Looky at them bloody tracks. We got that rip-tailed scooter, sure as sows drop litters! Hyar! Hyar's the trail and it's leadin' us right whar that old bandit done holed up!"

Such fury rose in Punk as to leave him sour-stomached. Old Two-Toes, King of Clearfork and the Big Honey Creek, the smartest raccoon on the Ridge, tricked by the meanness of the Hood boys.

"Old Two-Toes is the spirit of the wilderness," Hummy had said. "He's all the fine, careless, free things . . . he's Nature pitted against man and his gun and his hunting dog."

Punk's mind raced. Could the fine, free things survive in the world without help? Hummy had said most men hankered for life to be fine, though it wasn't an easy thing to come by; and sooner or later, a fellow must

make a stand. Did he, Punk, have to pit his measly strength against Toad Hood who went bear hunting with a switch? Say now, was this the time for the comeuppance that Hummy was talking about?

Punk groaned, recollecting the last beating he'd had from Toad. If only he had someone with him. But it was as Hummy had said. A time came in a fellow's life when he had to stand on his own feet, alone, defending what he thought was right. Guess it was time.

Punk Bunn stood up. He pushed aside the shielding oak leaves, making his presence known, not with a blast of trumpets, nor a great handclapping, but with a manly dignity he was unaware of.

"Hey!" It was a single word. It had no distinction to it, but in all likelihood it was one of the bravest words Punk Bunn was ever to speak.

Toad and Spider were startled into a dead stop. They had been carefully tracing the tracks of the crippled coon along the sandy ledge of the lake to the side of Coon Rock.

Punk walked down the slope toward the Hood boys, each step bringing him closer to the mean-featured Toad and the dumb boy, Spider.

Toad was the first to speak.

"B'jig, jig, jiggered! Hyar's my meat for supper!"

Spider's feet played a swift, happy shuffle on the ground.

"Bunny rabbit meat, ain't nuthin' tastier, is thar now, Spider?" Toad said with a leer.

Punk kept right on walking toward Toad, easy-like, considering what tactics to use. Bluff was his only weapon, he knew right well. He could never hope to win in a physical combat, but maybe there'd be a chance at using the brain God had given him. The thing was to act quick and put Toad on the defensive.

"Setting traps out of season again, Toad Hood!" he began. "Reckon if the hunting men at the Ridge store heard about this, there'd be a considerable amount of hard feelings, riled up feelings."

Toad stood stock still and thought, his eyes peering craftily out over red rims.

"Take Hummy Humphreys for instance, and the Snow brothers, and Gum Muller too," Punk was talking calmly. "Fair play's mighty important to them. I'd sure want to sidestep a-past any of them if I'd been caught trapping out of season."

"A tattletale, b'jig!" Toad spat tobacco juice right at Punk's feet. "Wal, the way we handle them kind ain't fitten for them fair-play men to watch."

"Toad," Punk was steady as a rock, "I don't aim on tattling. Seems as if you and me could strike a bargain. Let Old Two-Toes go; let him hole up where he will and we'll call it quits."

"Quits? Huh! You and me? We ain't never quits till I tear your innards out with my bare hands!"

"It seems to me, Toad, you livin' in the woods and all, you'd understand about Old Two-Toes. He's a part of the Ridge same as Horseshoe Lake, the creek banks, the big timbers — why, same as you and me."

"Wal, now ain't that purty! Did you hear that, Spider? As purty a spiel as I done ever heard!" Toad's lips were peeled off his gums. "Teacher talk goin' round,

346

you maybe gonna be a writin' guy someday. So's I figger hyar and now, it be up to Toad Hood to give you somethin' to put down in yore book."

Toad's big hand reached out and clamped itself about Punk's neck.

"Don't be twistin' round, bunny rabbit. Ain't no way fer you to get out of this'un."

The smell that rankled Punk was as unpleasant as that of a wet dog. He was toe to toe, shoulder to shoulder with Toad Hood, a hulking brute of a half-grown man, who never had *right* on his side, but who, forever and a day, seemed to need only his *might*. What chance did a scrawny boy like Punk Bunn have, a boy who had been brought up by a stepgranny who preached "Do unto others as you would have others do unto you."

"Hyeah, Spider! You watchin'? This hyar gonna be plumb comical! I aims to put a considerable dent in ole bunny rabbit's head! You watchin'?"

There were no answering foot taps. Punk felt Toad's hand loosen around his throat as he turned to look.

At the same instant, they both saw Spider, who had left the bank and was crawling up the narrow path on Coon Rock.

"Hyeah! Spider! What you up to?" yelled Toad.

Spider turned, waving jubilantly back to his brother. With his left hand, he pointed back behind him to the coon tracks and then in front of himself. He was perched precariously close to the waterfall.

"Consarn it!" Toad ran down a piece. "Git off'n that slick rock! You want to drown yourself?"

347

The dumb boy grinned and hunched himself flat against the wall of the rock, inching himself along. It was plain he was trailing the crippled coon straight to his hideout.

Punk stood rooted to the spot. Was his secret of Coon Rock to be discovered? Were they about to find his secret cave? The cave he shared with Old Two-Toes? He was bogged down with dread as the thought came to him that Old Two-Toes had taken himself to the secret cave under the waterfall. It was bound to be. Crippled from the trap, he'd known he'd have to find refuge close by. By all the signs of the bloody tracks, he'd made it to the cave, his last stronghold. Maybe he wasn't so badly done in but time and rest would heal him; that is, if he could keep hidden for a

spell. And now, there was Spider not far from the hanging moss and spilling water that screened the small opening in the rock.

"Come on, Spider." Toad's voice was a whine of fear. "Come on down hyar!"

It came to Punk right out of the blue that Toad was not only deadly afraid of the water, but he was half out of his mind at what could happen to his brother. He cared! Toad Hood cared about something besides himself! It was almost beyond believing. Cracky, here was one of those lessons that Hummy could have told him: even the meanest human beings had feelings.

"Spider, whatcha want to do that fer? Git down, I say!"

It happened then. Spider's foot hit against a slimy

piece of moss and he started slipping there before their eyes, his hands wildly snatching at rock and moss. Toad and Punk stood rooted to the place for a second.

Toad plain went crazy. He let out a howl and began running up and down the bank. Punk knew, as did everyone on the Ridge, of the Hoods' fear of water.

His heart leaped right up in his throat and nearly choked him. He'd seen a drowning boy once when the Big Honey Creek had overflowed. It had been a sight to haunt him in many a nightmare: the wildly clutching hands, the frantic churning of the water, and then the terrible stillness.

He was lonely and frightened as he realized there would be no help coming for Spider unless he himself was the rescuer. And being a rescuer didn't mean he could save Spider or himself, either. B'dogged, if he owed the Hood boys anything! Why should he risk himself for this miserable dumb clod who had plagued and tormented him as long as he could remember?

Spider's head bobbed up out of the water; not a sound coming from his open mouth, his white hands despairingly churning the emptiness. Another wild howl came from Toad, who was now ankle-deep in water, as if he'd throw himself into the lake. His terror was past bearing.

Punk dove into the water, cutting the surface cleanly and surely. He surfaced and sent his body hurtling through the water. Didn't seem as if he'd had any other choice, being raised as he had been by a "do good" stepgranny.

350

He reached the spot where Spider had last gone down, and tread water, being careful to keep a distance. He knew he'd be no match for the dumb boy's frightened strength should he get within arm's reach.

Again Spider's head bobbed up, his eyes as wild and terrified as any trapped animal in the woods. He saw Punk there almost within reach and a look of hope flashed into his eyes.

Punk waited tensely for the boy to come up again, measuring the exact time he could swim in safely. As Spider came up the third time, Punk came in from the back, putting an arm lock around Spider's neck, lifting the dumb boy's face out of the water. There was no fight left in Spider. Punk was able to pull him in to the bank where Toad was quick to haul him up to dry land.

All in the world Punk wanted to do then was to lie down on the bank, catch his breath, and think about things. But the ruckus Toad was making with his blubbering and calling out to Spider made it clear to Punk he wasn't through. He was plumb frazzled out, but that didn't mean he was going to get any rest. He pushed Toad out of the way as he bent over Spider and went to work, pumping out the water in the boy's lungs by the methods Hummy had taught him.

"Dead! Dead! Dead!" howled Toad.

"Oh, pipe down!" Punk was real cross. As far as he was concerned, it'd been better if Nature had made Toad dumb too. "He's only waterlogged!"

He rolled Spider back over just as his eyes opened. Punk found himself looking directly into Spider's

352

eyes, eyes that met his in a long, knowing look. Punk marveled at the expression. Cracky, that dumb Spider was sharp as a needle. He watched as Spider's eyes looked up at Toad, then out at Horseshoe Lake, up to Coon Rock, and back to Punk. It was plain his mind was sorting out each fact and putting everything together.

Toad flopped down on his knees and grabbed Spider up in a bear hug.

"I'm gonna bash yore head in, Spider, you do sumthin' like that again, you hyar?" The two boys looked at one another a moment, then Toad said, "Aw, Spider, I thought you was dead!" And he rocked him back and forth in his arms, comforting himself.

Punk wondered if he'd ever understand anything. Because the Hoods were bullies and ornery, he'd never thought about them having feelings. He grinned suddenly to himself. He was learning, he reckoned. Guess it'd take all of a lifetime to learn the things he wanted to know.

Spider was suddenly at his side, looking directly into his eyes. He had something to say. Punk watched as Spider first tapped himself on the chest, then he reached out and touched Punk's shoulder. His touch was light as a moth settling on a stalk. Wasn't anything scary or upsetting about it, the way Punk had always figured it'd be. But then his figuring didn't seem to be adding up. Like now, would he ever have thought that Spider Hood, the dumb boy of the Ridge, would be talking to him? Or that they would understand one another?

Wasn't any chance of *not* understanding the smile that was on Spider's face as he clasped each of his hands together in a handshake. It was a bid for friendship. Punk nodded his head. Seemed as if Spider was all stewed up with longing to show his gratitude. Abruptly, the boy whirled about and bent down, picking up the steel trap that had been sprung by Old Two-Toes. He lifted it and dangled it there for Punk to see, then in a wide, arched movement he swung the trap far out into Horseshoe Lake.

Toad let out a howl.

"Whatcha doin', Spider? You lost yore mind? You gone crazy, huh?" And the hand that only a few minutes before had been gently patting his brother, flayed out and gave him a cuff on the side of the head.

Spider reached down for a rock and advanced.

"Now, Spider, now. . . ." Toad began backing away.

Spider gestured to his brother and then to Punk. With a sweeping motion of his arm, he took in all of Horseshoe Lake and Coon Rock at the same time, shaking his head at Toad.

"No sirreee!" bristled Toad. "I ain't gonna promise that! I ain't gonna say we don't set traps along hyar no more. Reckon we 'uns got as much right to this hyar spot as that ole bunny rabbit thar. . . ."

Spider let go with a well-aimed rock, at the same instant bending and picking up another one.

"Aw, come on, Spider," Toad whined, "don't be astartin' that. If'n that's the way you want it, all right. But jes' wait till Ma hears about you throwin' away a good trap. Jes you wait. . . ."

354

Spider gave Punk a quick, knowing look, again clasped his hands together and then turned in the direction of home.

"I'm much obliged to you, Spider," called out Punk, glorying in the reformation of the Hood boys. Guess his feelings were like Brother Trapp's when he led his flock in the paths of righteousness . . . guess. *Wham!* Toad, passing by, delivered a hard kick to Punk's shin, then he was gone on a dead run. For a second, Punk was so clabbered up with hard feelings that all his lofty thoughts flickered out.

He rubbed his shin, feeling kind of foolish. Well, a leopard didn't change its spots after all. Things had been happening too fast and he'd been kind of muddled, but now he was back on familiar ground.

It began to seem funny. He laughed at himself, at all the cuckoo things in the world. His laughter stirred the woods back of him. A whippoorwill called out its evening plaint, a saddened cry for all mankind. An owl let out a harsh hoot, a hoot of derision as if men were too absurd to be taken seriously. And Punk laughed again.

He was all fired up with being a growing boy with all the time in the world ahead. He raced along the bank and jackknifed into the water. He held his breath and dove to the bottom of the lake. He came up and filled his lungs with air. Turning over on his back, he floated free and easy as a leaf, ending up at Coon Rock. Face up, under the trickling water, his eyes blurred until the green of moss and fern, of light and shadow, blended into streamers of color.

He turned and swam to shore. He shook the water drops off himself and slowly started up the narrow path of Coon Rock. He'd have to look in on Old Two-Toes now, that is if he were hiding in the cave.

Pausing at the spilling waterfall, he looked about. All was easeful. Quickly, he ducked under the water, sliding through the narrow opening in the rock.

The darkness of the cave blinded him. He waited for his eyes to adjust to the murkiness.

A rustling, a stirring close by set his pulse to throbbing. It was plain spooky. What if it weren't Old Two-Toes; what if it were something else? A wildcat?

Careful-like, Punk began to move back to the ledge where he kept his candle stubs and matches. His fingers fumbled for endless seconds before they hit upon the deerskin-wrapped parcel.

Remembering to take his time, easy-like he lighted the candle. Didn't know when light had been more welcome. He held it cautiously out and up and had himself a look around. There! He caught his breath. There, not more than two feet from him, was Old Two-Toes, all hunched into a large ball.

Punk spoke softly, "Hi, Old-timer."

Boy and coon looked at one another. The coon's eyes caught the glint of light and seemed to throw off sparks. Punk knew a big boar coon that was cornered could be mighty mean.

"Are you all right, feller?" he questioned, keeping his voice low. And then he scolded, "How come you walk right into a trap, as old as you are and as smart as you are? How come?"

356

As if reassured by Punk's voice, Old Two-Toes accepted his presence in the cave and began to lick his paw. The boy saw it was the right one and that it was bloody. He sighed. Guess they were lucky at that. A coon'd know how to take care of an injured foot and licking it was the best medicine in the world.

"What business you got getting so careless? Tell me that! You ought to have your head examined!" Punk's voice rose.

Old Two-Toes paused and looked over at the boy as if his words had registered.

He kind of ducked his head as if in agreement and

358

then his mouth pulled back for all the world like a grin. Punk felt good all over. Old Two-Toes was going to be all right.

Blowing out his candle, he placed it back in its wrappings and laid it onto the ledge. Then he slipped out of the cave.

The trickle of water eased off his shoulders, down his back, as he sidestepped out from under onto the edge. He looked down into the swirling water of the lake, watching the foam float lazily on the surface. Punk felt good as he dove deep into the clear, cool water.

—*Cena Draper*

THINKING IT OVER

1. What clues did the author give you to Punk's character? What situations revealed the kind of boys Toad and Spider were?

2. At what point in the story did the author create suspense that kept you guessing until the very end?

3. Do you think "Punk Takes a Stand" was a good title for the story? Why or why not?

THOUGHTS AT WORK

1. The author gave you several clues to the setting of this story in time and place. What were they?

2. Punk was surprised to learn something about Toad. What was it and why was it important?

3. What did Spider do to show his gratitude after Punk saved his life? What was the reaction of Toad? of Punk?

4. Each person has his own scale of values, ideas about things that are important. What do you think Punk held most important? What proof could you give for your answer?

5. On page 343 find what Hummy said about Old Two-Toes and about taking a stand. Would you like to have him for a friend? Explain your answer.

6. Skim the story to find places where the boys' speech seemed strange to you. How would you say the same thing in your own words?

7. Some of the ideas included in "The Web of Life" might have helped Punk in his plea to save the life of Old Two-Toes. What were some of those ideas?

DAYS

Some days my thoughts are just cocoons—all cold
   and dull and blind,
They hang from dripping branches in the grey woods
   of my mind;
And other days they drift and shine—such free
   and flying things!
I find the gold-dust in my hair, left by
   their brushing wings.

—Karle Wilson Baker

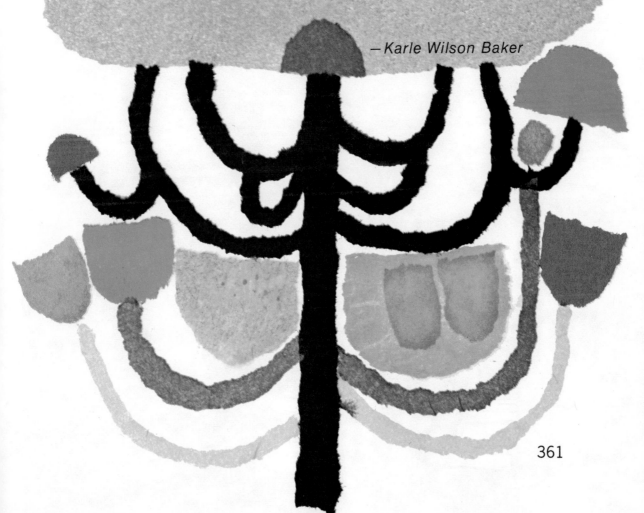

361

James Forten, a real person, was nine years old when the War for Independence began in 1776. Because of this war he was faced with several difficult decisions which boys usually do not make alone. He had to think deeply about the things that were most important to him. As you read this story, notice the decisions he made and think what you might have done in his place.

FORTEN SAILS WITH DANGER

War had come at last between the newly-declared United States of America and Great Britain.

To nine-year-old James Forten, first listening to that Declaration on the streets of Philadelphia in 1776, it meant little. He could hardly know, as he hurried along delivering an order of groceries, that in only a few years his life would be greatly changed by it.

James Forten was the son of free Negroes in the city of Philadelphia. He was a bright and willing lad, and had gone to school to a famous Quaker teacher, but schooling had ended with his father's accidental death. James had to go to work to support his mother and sister. But he never stopped reading everything he could get his hands on. And he never stopped improving his skill at marbles. This was well, for a marble game was to play a large part in the boy's future.

A year following the Declaration, the government of the United States encouraged owners of private vessels to put these in the service of the new government. They were fitted out with cannon and supplies and given orders to hunt down British merchant ships. These armed sailing vessels were called privateers.

When an American privateer captured an enemy ship, both the ship and its cargo were taken into an American port and sold. The money from this sale, called prize money, was shared by every member of the crew. The captain drew the largest share, and the lowest-ranking member of the crew drew the smallest.

Philadelphia, the leading city and capital of the new nation, was one of the chief ports to which the captured ships and their cargo—the prizes of war—were brought for sale. Hundreds of people gathered to watch these sales, among them James Forten.

Like most youths, his imagination was easily stirred. His brown eyes shone bright as he listened to the tales of adventure brought back by the privateersmen. The sailors' stories of little fortunes made quickly especially attracted him, for with each passing month the Fortens' situation became more desperate. The war had caused prices to rise to such a pitch that James' wages as a grocer's clerk could hardly suffice to keep the little Forten family in food and clothing.

One day James, now fourteen, approached his mother. "Ma," he said, "please let me sign on a privateer. I hear the *Royal Louis*[1] is looking for men."

After much pleading, Mrs. Forten allowed her son to become a member of the privateer's crew.

On July 23, 1781, the sun glistened brightly on the new privateer as it weighed anchor and sailed out of Philadelphia on its first mission. Below deck, James Forten, combination powder boy and ship's boy, was barely able to stow his two cherished possessions, his Bible and a bag of marbles, before he was summoned to the ship's ammunition store to learn his duties.

The wind was fair in Delaware Bay. Soon the *Royal*

[1] Louis (lü′ē)

364

Louis was standing out to open sea. At noon James, carrying a tray of food to the officers' quarters, heard the man upon the mast cry, "Sail ho!"

"Where away?" shouted the officer of the watch.

"Dead ahead, sir."

"What's her rig?"

"Looks like a brig of war, sir."

Captain Decatur[1] stared at the vessel through his long spyglass. "English colors," he called. "Set sail. Pipe all hands to the battle stations."

James, his heart quickening, heard the shrill pipe of the boatswain. In a moment the *Royal Louis* was a scene of disciplined activity. Men with muskets climbed up into the rigging. Others threw sand on the decks to keep them from becoming slippery with blood. Quickly the cannon were made ready on the gun deck and the whole vessel fitted for combat.

A sailor standing by a cannon yelled to James, "Over here." Young Forten, as he had been instructed, ran over and stood a little behind one of the gun crews, ready to pass along the powder and ball to the gunners.

In the distance he could see a British brig dipping and swaying over the swirling gray water. Soon it was within musket shot of the *Royal Louis*, near enough so that James could recognize it as the *Active* and distinguish the officers from the men. He particularly noticed the captain, a big, broad man with a large gold-laced cocked hat on his head and a speaking trumpet in his hand.

"What ship is that?" bawled the English captain.

[1] Decatur (di kāt'ər)

Captain Decatur did not answer the *Active's* captain. Instead he gave a sharp order to his own men. "Give her a broadside."

Instantly, a tremendous roar and flash of cannon shook the *Royal Louis*. The great guns jumped back, straining against the ropes that held them. James coughed as smoke and fumes blew in from the gunports and spread through the gun deck.

As the guns were being readied for a second broadside, James ran to the powder storeroom for more ammunition. Shielding the powder from flying sparks with his jacket, he dashed back to his cannon.

As he ran, the *Active's* big guns spat out their deadly fire. A charge of grapeshot sprayed into one of the privateer's portholes, wounding two men.

For an hour the two vessels poured broadside after broadside into each other. The smoke around both ships was so thick that only the flames coming from the enemy's gun showed the gunners where to aim.

After a time the guns ceased as both vessels drifted close together, close enough for boarding. Over the deck rails went the fighting men of the *Royal Louis* to attack with their cutlasses the fighting men of the *Active*. A furious hand to hand battle followed. Suddenly in the midst of the din, a feeble cheer went up from the weary men of the *Royal Louis*. The British ship had struck her colors.

Captain Decatur immediately placed a prize master and crew aboard the captured vessel and ordered it to Philadelphia. The *Royal Louis*, her mast and sails repaired, continued out to sea. James shared in the general good feeling. Success won so soon by a brand-new privateer was a good omen, the sailors said. Surely the *Royal Louis* was a lucky ship.

Toward late afternoon of the next day, the privateer fell in with a brigantine of fourteen guns called the *Phoenix.*[1] The *Phoenix* crowded on all sail and proceeded to run away from the privateer.

The *Royal Louis* also crowded on all sail and was gaining on the other vessel when the black clouds of an approaching thunderstorm brought on an early darkness. The *Phoenix* disappeared into the sheltering night.

"She's hereabouts, all right," Decatur said grimly. "Keep watch."

Suddenly, by the flashes of lightning, the crew discovered the brigantine standing in a different direction from the one they had expected. The *Royal Louis* shifted course and pressed on all sail in pursuit. At last they came up to the *Phoenix.*

"What ship is that and where from?" roared the captain of the *Royal Louis.*

"The brigantine *Phoenix* from Charleston, bound to London," was the reply. A flash of lightning showed English colors at the brigantine's mast.

The American crew was ready for action. Each member of the crew stood at his battle station, alert and waiting for orders.

"Give her a broadside," shouted Decatur.

A ball smashed into the rigging of the *Phoenix*, but the brigantine's guns remained silent.

[1] Phoenix (fē′niks)

"Haul down your colors or we'll blow you out of the water," Decatur yelled through his speaking trumpet.

The *Royal Louis* must have looked very powerful, or else the *Phoenix* did not wish to fight, for a moment later, a lightning flash revealed the English flag fluttering down in surrender.

The victory had been quick and easy and again the Americans cheered. A boat with a prize master and crew immediately put out from the *Royal Louis* for the captured vessel. They rejoiced to find that the *Phoenix* carried a rich cargo. With the English crew imprisoned on the *Royal Louis*, both ships set sail for Philadelphia. At noon the next day they dropped anchor in the harbor amid the cheers of the crowds on the wharves.

James hurried home to tell his mother the good news. Soon he was saying, "I'll get a nice little share for my part in these captures, Ma. The *Louis* is a lucky ship. Maybe next time we'll take a prize with an even better cargo, even gold."

But his mother could not share his enthusiasm. "Lucky ship?" she said. "Who knows, James? The next time *you* may be the cargo."

In October the *Royal Louis* again prepared to sail. James packed his Bible and his bag of marbles, took farewell of his family, and his ship sailed away.

Early the next morning the lookout sighted a sail. Captain Decatur fixed his glass on the distant vessel. "A full-rigged ship," he called.

About noon a hail from the other ship came across the water. "This is His British Majesty's ship *Amphyon*."[1]

[1] Amphyon (am'fē ən)

A British warship!

Minutes later, the lookout shouted again. He had spotted two more ships and these, too, were men-of-war. The *Royal Louis* could not fight three warships all at once and Captain Decatur gave the command to make a run for it.

For six hours the chase continued, but gradually the three warships overtook the American vessel. She was hit by a broadside which tore holes in her rigging.

"Strike those colors," the British captain shouted, "or we'll blow you out of the water."

Captain Decatur had no choice but to surrender. "Strike," he ordered, and the American colors floated down in defeat.

Fear prickled along James Forten's spine. What would happen to him and to the nineteen other Negro seamen aboard the captured privateer? Negro prisoners, he knew, were seldom exchanged for the British captives held by the Americans. Instead they were sent in chains to the West Indies to be sold into slavery. They were sold like cargo. Like cargo! James recalled his mother's words.

Now he ran to get his Bible, some clothing, and his bag of marbles before the boarding party of the *Amphyon* could reach *Royal Louis*. Soon the enemy was aboard and the next thing James knew, he was being pushed over the side of the *Royal Louis* and into one of the enemy boats waiting below. In a short time, he

370

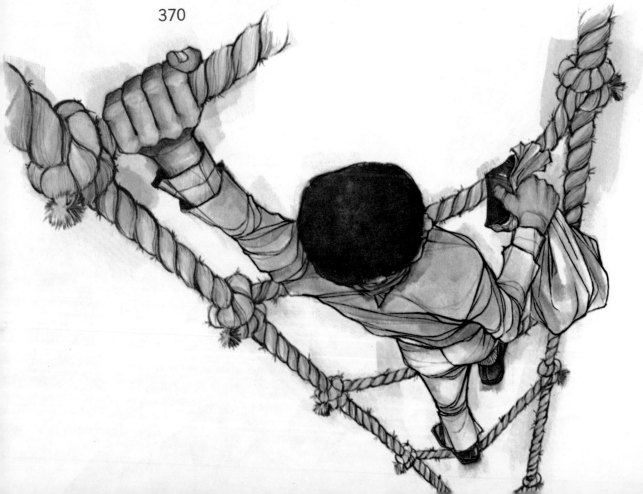

was being hurried up a rope ladder to the deck of the *Amphyon*.

The British captain was Sir John Beasly. As the captured seamen were lined up before him, he gave James a particularly searching glance. "How old are you?"

"Fifteen, sir."

Sir John's sharp eyes fell to the small cloth bag James clutched in his hand.

"What've you got there?"

"Just marbles, sir."

"I had an idea that's what the bag held. Well, you're a likely looking lad. Perhaps a game of marbles will be just the thing to cheer up my Willie."

Later that day, as James sat under guard on the deck with his captured shipmates, a sandy-haired boy about his own age approached him.

"I'm William Beasly. My father said you've brought marbles aboard. I'd like a game."

This was the first of many games the two boys played upon the deck of the *Amphyon*. The English boy's face, once so depressed, looked more cheerful. One day he asked his father if they could take James back to England with them and there educate him.

Sir John was himself impressed with young Forten. "An open and honest face. Strong, and of excellent intelligence," was the comment he made about James to the *Amphyon's* lieutenant.

The fact that James was so plainly a superior person bothered the British captain. It was true, as James had heard, the Negroes captured while fighting with the American forces were sold into West Indian slavery. Sir John disliked to think of such a fate for James. On the other hand, if James shared the lot of the other prisoners from the *Royal Louis*, he probably would be no better off. Sir John knew that they were all to be taken to the most dreaded of prison ships, the *Jersey*, which lay with its rotting human cargo off the lonely shore of Long Island.

But at last Sir John decided to give in to his son's plea. He sent for James to come to his cabin. When the youth heard what the captain had to say, he truly didn't know what to answer. Here he was being offered a chance to live in a fine house with his friend, Willie Beasly, and to receive a good education, something he and his mother had dreamed of. Surely he would never have such a chance again. And yet he didn't know. He returned Captain Beasly's gaze uneasily.

"Come, come, boy." Sir John was impatient and surprised that James would hesitate for even an instant. "Surely you wouldn't be fool enough to turn aside such a stroke of good fortune."

"I'm afraid I must, sir," James is reported as saying. "I am here as a prisoner for the liberties of my country. I cannot prove a traitor to her interests."

So now James would be transferred along with the other American prisoners to the prison ship *Jersey*.

The day before James was taken off the *Amphyon*, Willie Beasly ran to him and hugged him tight. He handed James a note. "This is for you, James," he said with tears in his eyes. "It is from my father. It will help you."

The note was to the commander of the prison ship informing him that James Forten was "an excellent youth and should not be forgotten on the list of prisoners exchanged."

James carefully placed the note in a safe place. "Thus," he remarked often in later years, "did a game of marbles save me from a life of West Indian slavery."

It was dark when the American prisoners were finally aboard the *Jersey*. Lanterns lighted the deck. Although he handed Sir John's note to the officials, James seemed of no particular interest to them. In a few minutes he was ordered down to the main prisoner quarters.

For the rest of the dreadful night James lay huddled between the restless, moaning men, anxiously waiting for daylight. When dawn came he found himself amid a collection of the most wretched and disgusting-looking objects he had ever seen in human form. Their faces were pale with disease and thin from hunger and worry. Their hair was matted and filthy. James stared at them in horror, wondering how long it would be before he would look as they did.

At sunrise the prisoners were allowed to go to the upper deck where they gratefully gulped the fresh air. James, scrambling up the ladder with the rest, searched through the horde of ragged, dirty, half-starved men for a familiar figure. After a while he found one—a wiry, freckled-faced boy from Philadelphia named Daniel Brewton, who had also been a ship's boy on the *Royal Louis*.

Daniel was only fourteen, a year younger than James.

373

When he saw the sturdy, brown-skinned Forten, he flung his arms around him and tried to keep back the tears.

Everything aboard the *Jersey* was horrible. The drinking water was slimy and foul. The food was rotted and smelled. The prisoners were all filthy, though they tried to keep clean by washing their clothes and bodies in sea water.

James hated the idleness about this horror-ship, and offered to do whatever work he could. Often he was ordered to bring up the bodies of the unlucky men who had died during the night.

But his cheerful face and helpful nature won him many friends among the prisoners. One of these was an officer in the American navy who told James that he was to be exchanged for a British officer. He asked if James would help carry his sea chest to the boat which was to come for him in the morning.

James's glance went to the sea chest, and his dark eyes brightened. The chest was a large one—large enough for James to hide in. His heart began to beat fast. Would the officer allow him to crawl into the chest during the dark night and be secretly carried off with it in the morning? The officer was willing.

Joy flooded through the youth. Soon he would be off the hated ship. After four months of horror and suffering, he would again be where water was clean and food was not spoiled.

He was sitting on the officer's sea chest making final plans for his escape when his friend Daniel Brewton came up to him. Daniel looked dreadful. His

374

face was as white as a sail. His eyelids were red from lack of good food. He was covered with sores. Too weak to stand alone, he flung himself down at James's feet.

Young Forten stared at him. He knew that if Daniel did not get away from the *Jersey* soon, he would die. James did not want Daniel to die. He was only fourteen years old and, like James, he had a mother and a sister waiting for him at home in Philadelphia.

In an instant, James made up his mind. "Quick, Daniel," he said, "you get into the sea chest. I'll see that you get safely off the ship."

The next morning James and the officer carried down "a chest of old clothes" to the boat which had come to carry the exchanged prisoners back to freedom.

As the boat disappeared toward the shore, James tried to shake off a feeling of gloom. Would he ever get off the *Jersey*? How much longer could he endure the horrors of this ship?

James Forten remained a prisoner of the *Jersey* for three more months, seven months in all. Then, with the war almost over, he was released in a general exchange of prisoners. Without shoes and clothed in rags, he walked the whole distance to Philadelphia. After he had rested a few days, he looked up his friend Daniel Brewton and was overjoyed to find him safe and restored to health.

Daniel Brewton never forgot what James Forten had done for him. Fifty-six years later Brewton told his

376

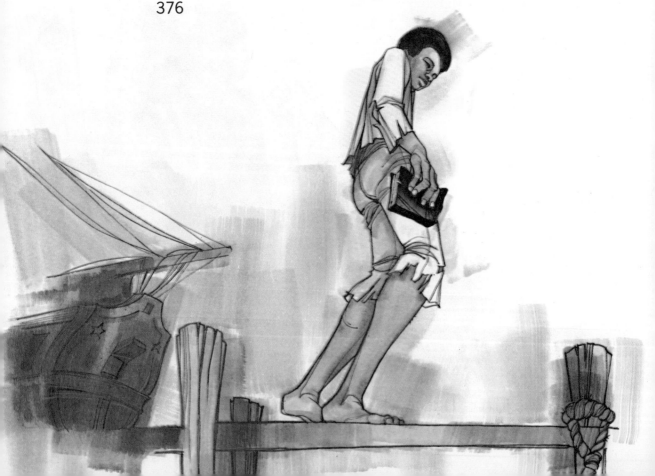

story to William Nell, an early Negro historian. "With tears raining down his face," Nell wrote, "the old man (Brewton) told how James Forten had saved his life when they were both captives on the prison ship *Jersey*."

As for James Forten, his courage and compassion were splendidly rewarded. After making a trip to England as a seaman on an American vessel, James returned to his own country where he became a worker in the shop of a famous Philadelphia sailmaker. He continued to read everything he could get his hands on, and he tried to be the best worker in the shop. After a while, he became head man in the sailmaking shop. After a few more years, he was able to buy the business for himself. The money for this purchase was loaned to him by a rich merchant who had known James all his life and had faith in him.

James Forten lived to an old age, a rich and highly respected citizen.

—Esther Douty

THINKING IT OVER

1. What qualities in Forten did you like and admire? Where in the story did you find proof of those qualities?

2. At the beginning of the story what two predictions did the author make about Forten's future? How did each come true?

3. At what points in the story were you worried about Forten and his future?

THOUGHTS AT WORK

1. List the decisions Forten made and give his reasons for each one.

2. What do you think Forten's life would have been like if he had been sent to the West Indies to live?

3. Why do you think the *Phoenix* surrendered without a fight?

4. Why do you think Forten chose to be a sailmaker? What qualities do you think helped him succeed in his work?

5. What did the following sea-going terms mean in the story?

rigging	dead ahead	privateer
sail ho	below deck	weighed anchor
brigantine	ship's boy	fair wind
broadside	all hands	strike colors

6. How did Forten's courage differ from the courage of Punk? What stars did each boy steer by?

7. Did any part of this story make you glad that you live in today's modern world? Why did you have this feeling?

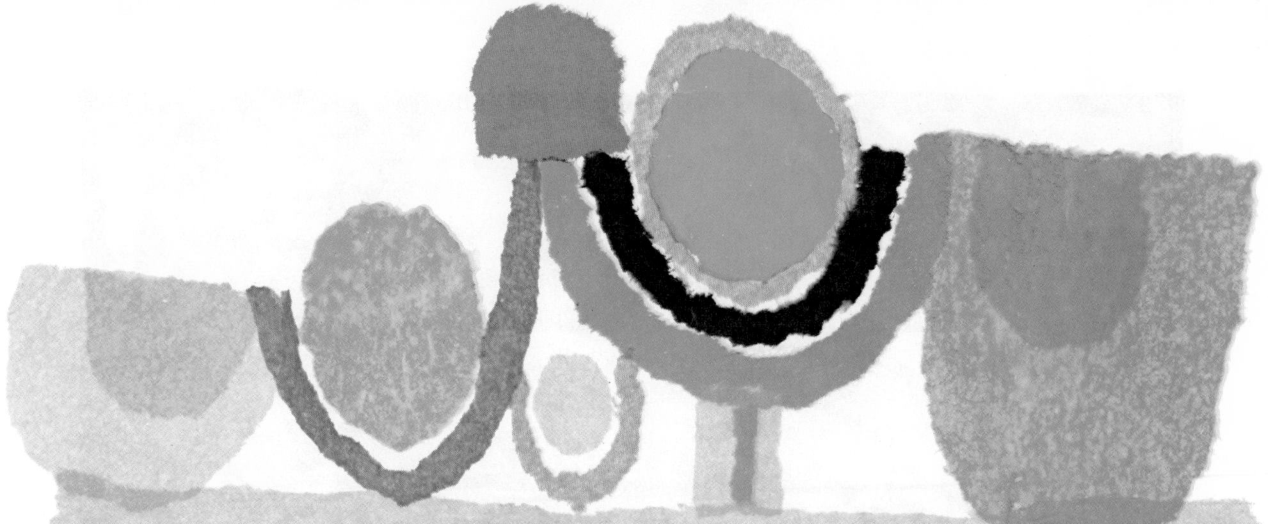

WHERE THE RAINBOW ENDS

Where the rainbow ends
There's going to be a place, brother,
Where the world can sing all sorts of songs,
And we're going to sing together, brother,
You and I, though you're white and I'm not.
It's going to be a sad song, brother,
Because we don't know the tune,
And it's a difficult tune to learn.
But we can learn, brother, you and I.
There's no such tune as a black tune.
There's no such tune as a white tune.
There's only music, brother,
And it's music we're going to sing
Where the rainbow ends.

—Richard Rive

379

Fear and courage are found everywhere in the world. A person can show both, almost at the same time as you will see when you read this story about Mafatu, a chief's son, who lived many years ago on an island in the South Seas. How he met this challenge leads to a series of exciting and often frightening events which you will share with him.

380

CALL IT COURAGE

Mafatu[1] was afraid of the sea. It had taken his mother when he was a baby, and it seemed to him that the sea gods sought vengeance at having been cheated of Mafatu. So, though he was son of the Great Chief of Hikueru,[2] a race of Polynesians[3] who worshiped courage, and he was named Stout Heart, he feared and avoided the sea. Everyone branded him a coward.

When he could no longer bear their taunts and jibes, he determined to conquer that fear or be conquered—so he went off in his canoe, alone except for his little dog Uri[4] and his pet albatross.

A storm gave him his first challenge, smashing his canoe and flinging him at last out to a deserted island where his own resourcefulness helped him to survive. Exploring the island one day, he came upon a great stone statue. Before it lay a heap of bones—human bones. Thus Mafatu learned that he had landed on the holy ground of a tribe of cannibals. Would they return and find him there? He began to hurry the work on the new dugout canoe he was making, hoping to escape the island before the savages should return to find him.

At last the day came which was to be Mafatu's final day on the island. For the last time he had set his fish traps and

---

[1] Mafatu (mä'fä tü)   [2] Hikueru (hī'kü rü)   [3] Polynesians (pol ə nē'zhənz)   [4] Uri (yur'ē)

now he was paddling through the lagoon in the new canoe. He dipped his paddle with a swinging rhythm, the rhythm of his thoughts swung in unison. "Tomorrow I shall start home! Tomorrow, tomorrow!"

He dragged the canoe up on the beach, placed the logs under the curving stem so that he might launch it easily on the morrow. He would never need to climb the high plateau to the lookout again. Let the eaters-of-men come!

As Mafatu waited for his supper to cook, he set about preparing for his homeward journey; he would start at daybreak with the ebbing tide. He would be ready. He filled bamboo containers with fresh water. He prepared a poi of bananas and sealed it into containers. Then he picked a score of green drinking nuts and flung them into the canoe. As he trotted back and forth across the beach and his supper steamed on the fire, one thought alone, like an insistent drum beat, echoed in the boy's heart: "Tomorrow I shall start home! Tomorrow, tomorrow!"

Never again need he hang his head before his people. He

had fought the sea for life and won. He had sustained himself by his own wits and skill. He had faced loneliness and danger and death, if not without flinching, at least with courage. He had been, sometimes, deeply afraid, but he had faced fear and faced it down. Surely that could be called courage.

When he lay down to sleep that night there was a profound thankfulness in his heart. "Tavana Nui,"[1] he whispered, "my father—I want you to be proud of me."

He fell into a heavy, dreamless sleep.

Before dawn he was awakened by a sound of measured booming, like the beating of a supernatural drum. Thump-thump, THUMP! Thump-thump, THUMP! It rose above the thunder of the reef, solemn and majestic.

Instantly awake, listening with every sense, Mafatu sat upright on the mats. Far out on the reef the seas burst and shot upward like sheeted ghosts in the moonlight. There it came again: Thump-thump, THUMP! Thump-thump, THUMP! Steady as a pulse, beating in the heart of darkness. . . .

[1] Tavana Nui (täv än'ä nü)

And then Mafatu knew. The eaters-of-men had come. Mafatu raced to his lookout and saw six war canoes drawn up on the beach. Mighty canoes they were. But what held the boy's eyes in awful trance were the figures, springing and leaping about the flames: firelight glistened on their oiled bodies, on flashing spears and bristling decorations.

Mafatu saw that the savages were armed with iron-wood war clubs. Zigzags of paint streaked their bodies. And towering above all, the great stone idol looked down with sightless eyes.

Lying there on his high ledge, Mafatu felt doom itself breathing chill upon his neck. He drew back from the edge of the cliff. He must flee! In that very instant he heard a crushing in the undergrowth, not twenty yards away. A gutteral shout ripped the darkness. The boy flung a desperate glance over his shoulder. Four figures were tearing toward him through the jungle.

He turned and ran blindly down the trail whence he had come. Slipping, sliding, stumbling, his breath all but choking in his throat. He felt as he had sometimes felt in dreams, fleeing on legs that were weighted. Only one thought gave him courage as he ran: his canoe, ready and waiting. His canoe. If only he could reach it, shove it into the water before the savages overtook him. Then he would be safe. . . .

He knew this trail as he knew the back of his hand. On he dashed, fleet as an animal. Through the trees he caught a glimpse of white beach and his heart surged. Then he was speeding across the sand, Uri at his heels.

The canoe was at the lagoon's edge. The boy shoved the craft into the water. The logs under the stem rolled easily. In that second, the eaters-of-men, yelling wildly, broke from the jungle and dashed across the beach. Mafatu was not a minute

384

too soon. He leaped aboard and ran up the sail, the sail he had woven from *pandanus* leaves. The savages rushed after him into the shallows. A gust of wind filled the sail. It drew smartly. Now the men were swimming. One of them, in the lead, reached to lay hold of the outrigger. His hand clutched it. The canoe slacked. Mafatu could see the gleam of bared teeth. The boy lifted the paddle and cracked it down. . . . With a groan the man dropped back into the water. The canoe, freed, skimmed out toward the barrier-reef.

The savages stopped, turned back toward shore. Then they were running back to the trail that led across the island, shouting to their fellows as they ran. Mafatu knew that it was only a question of minutes until the whole pack would be aroused and in pursuit. But he had the advantage of a head start and a light craft, while their canoes would have to beat around the southern point of the island before they could catch up with him. If only the breeze held. . . . Mafatu remembered then that the canoes he had seen drawn up on the beach had not been sailing canoes. There were strong arms to propel those black canoes, to overtake him if they could.

Mafatu's canoe, so slim and light, sped like a zephyr across the lagoon. The tide was on the ebb, churning in its race through the passage into the outer ocean. The boy gripped the steering paddle and offered up a prayer. Then he was caught in the rip-tide. The outrigger dashed through the passage, a chip on the torrent. The wind of the open sea rushed to greet it. The sail filled; the outrigger heeled over. Mafatu scrambled to windward to lend his weight for ballast. He was off! Homeward, homeward. . . .

Soon, rising above the reef thunder, the boy could hear a measured sound of savage chanting. They were after him!

Looking back over his shoulder, he could see the dark shapes in the canoes rounding the southern headland. Moonlight shone on half a hundred wet paddles as they dipped and rose to the rhythm of the chant. It was too dark to see the eaters-of-men themselves, but their wild song grew ever more savage as they advanced.

The wind dropped. Soon the black canoes were so close that the boy could see the shine of bodies, the glint of teeth, and flash of ornament. If the wind died, he was lost. . . . Closer,

387

closer the canoes advanced. There were six of them, filled each
with ten warriors. Some of them leaped to their feet, brandished
their clubs, shouted at the boy across the water. They were
a sight to quake the stoutest heart. With every second they
were cutting down the distance which separated their canoes
from Mafatu's.

Then the wind freshened. Just a puff, but enough. Under its
impetus the little canoe skimmed ahead while the boy's heart
gave an upward surge of thanks.

Day broke over the wide Pacific.

The six black canoes came on, now gaining, now losing. The
boy was employing every art and wile of sailing that he knew.
As long as the wind held he was safe. He managed his little
craft to perfection, drawing from it every grace of speed in
flight.

He knew that with coming night the wind might drop and then . . . . He forced the thought from his mind. If the wind failed, it meant that his gods had deserted him.

But with the falling night the wind still held. Darkness rose up from the sea. The stars came out clear and bright. The boy searched among them for some familiar constellation to steer by. And then he saw, and knew: there, blazing bravely, were the three stars of the Fishhook of Maui.[1] Maui, god of fishermen. Maui—his sign. Those were his stars to steer by. They would lead him home. In that moment he was aware that the chanting of his pursuers had become fainter, steadily diminishing. At first he could not believe it. He listened intently. Yes— there was no doubt about it: as the breeze freshened, the sound grew fainter.

[1] Maui (mou'ē)

By daybreak the chanting had ceased altogether. There was no sign of the canoes upon the broad expanse of the sea. The sunburst marched across the swinging waters. Far off, an albatross caught the light of gold on its wings. Was it his pet, Kivi?[1] Mafatu could not tell. The wind held fresh and fair.

But now the great ocean current that had carried Mafatu so willingly away from his home island, Hikueru, was set dead against him.

He put his little craft first on one tack, then on another. As the long hours passed, it seemed as if he were making no headway at all, even though the canoe still cut smartly through the water. There was a drift and pull that appeared to make a forward gain impossible.

"Perhaps," the boy thought wearily, "Maui is not yet ready for me to return. Is there still a shadow of fear in my heart? Is that it?" He was tired now in every nerve and sinew, tired in the marrow of his bones, tired of struggle.

The long hours passed slowly while the sun climbed. Mafatu lashed the steering paddle and slept fitfully. Uri lay in the shadow of the sail. The sun sank. Night came and fled. Dawn

[1] Kivi (kē'vē)

rose in a burst of flame, and still Mafatu's canoe skimmed across the sea currents, now on this tack, now on that.

He was to learn in the hours to come that all day, all time would be like that: hours of blasting heat, of shattering sunlight; nights of fitful respite and uneasy sleep. Only the sea and the sky, the sea and the sky. A bird now and then, a fish leaping from the sea, a boy in a frail canoe. That was all.

As one day dragged into another, Mafatu scanned the heavens for some hint of rain. Storm, anything would have been a welcome relief to this blasting monotony, to this limitless circle of sea. His store of *poi* vanished. The coconuts likewise. His water was being guarded, drop by drop. But there would come a moment when the last drop must be taken, and then. . . .

The season of storm was long past. The days, as they came, were cloudless and untroubled. Each day broke like a clap of thunder and night fell softly as a footfall. The Fishhook of Maui twinkled down like friendly eyes, luring Mafatu on. Then gradually as the canoe entered some other current of the sea, the wind slackened, this wind that had blown for him so long. Now the sail began to slat and bang in the dead air.

The boy paddled through the long hours, paddled, until the muscles of his arms and shoulders ached in agony and every sinew cried in protest. And at night, when darkness brought blessed release from the sun, there was always the Fishhook of Maui leading him on. But now when the boy looked up at the ancient constellation, doubt lay heavy on his heart. Hikueru—where was it? The sea gave back no answer.

"Maui," the boy whispered, "have you deserted me? Have you looked into my heart and found me wanting?"

And suddenly he was overwhelmed with despair. Maui *had* deserted him. It was Moana, the Sea God's turn. He looked over the side. Deep down in those cool depths it seemed to him that he could see faces . . . his mother's perhaps. . . . He dashed his hand across his eyes. Had the sun stricken him daft? Had he been touched by moon-madness? Then a wave of

overpowering anger brought him to his knees: anger at this dark element, this sea, which would destroy him if it could.

"Moana, you Sea God!" he shouted violently. "*You*! You destroyed my mother. Always you have tried to destroy me. Fear of you has haunted my sleep. Fear of you turned my people against me. But now"—he choked; his hands gripped his throat to stop its hot burning—"now I no longer fear you, Sea!" His voice rose to a wild note. He sprang to his feet, flung back his head, spread wide his arms in defiance. "Do you hear me, Moana? I am not afraid of you! Destroy me—but I laugh at you. Do you hear? *I laugh*!"

His voice, cracked but triumphant, shattered the dead air. He sank back on his haunches, shaking with spasms of ragged laughter. It left him spent and gasping on the floor of the canoe. Uri, whimpering softly, crept to his master's side.

393

Off to the northeast a haze of light glowed up from the sea. Sometimes the lagoon of an atoll throws up just such a glow. It is the reflection of the lagoon upon the lower sky. Lifting his head, the boy watched it with dulled eyes, uncomprehending at first.

"*Te mori*,"[1] he whispered at last, his voice a thread of awe. "The lagoon-fire."

There came a whir and fury in the sky above, a beat of mighty wings: an albatross, edged with light, circled above the canoe. It swooped low, its gentle, questing eyes turned upon the boy and his dog. Then the bird lifted in its effortless flight, flew straight ahead and vanished into the lagoon-fire. And then Mafatu knew. Hikueru, his homeland, lay ahead. Kivi. . . .

A strangled cry broke from the boy. He shut his eyes tight and there was a taste of salt, wet upon his lips.

The crowd assembled upon the beach watched the small canoe slip through the reef-passage. It was a fine canoe, artfully built. The people thought at first that it was empty. Silence gripped them, and a chill of awe touched them. Then they saw a head lift above the gunwale, a thin body struggled to sit upright.

[1] Te mori (tā môr'i)

"Aue to aue!" The cry went up from the people in a vast sigh. So they might speak if the sea should give up its dead.

But the boy who dropped overside into the shallows and staggered up the beach was flesh and blood, although wasted and thin. The brave young figure halted, drew itself upright.

"My father," Mafatu cried thickly, "I have come home."

The Great Chief's face was transformed with joy. This brave figure, so thin and straight, with courage blazing from his eyes—his son! The man could only stand and stare and stare, as if he could not believe his senses. And then a small yellow dog pulled himself over the gunwale of the canoe, fell at his master's feet. Uri. . . . Far overhead an albatross caught a light of gold on its wings. Then Tavana Nui turned to his people and cried: "Here is my son come home from the sea. Mafatu, Stout Heart. A brave name for a brave boy!"

Mafatu swayed where he stood. "My father, I . . . ."

Tavana Nui caught his son as he fell.

It happened many years ago, before the traders and missionaries first came into the South Seas, while the Polynesians were still great in numbers and fierce of heart. But even today the people of Hikueru sing this story in their chants and tell it over the evening fires.

—*Armstrong Sperry*

THINKING IT OVER

1. Mafatu showed both fear and courage. What dangers did he face during his adventure?

2. What was Mafatu's great problem? At what point in the story did he overcome it?

3. What, to you, was the climax or the most thrilling moment in the story? Why?

THOUGHTS AT WORK

1. What was the Fishhook of Maui? Why was it important to Mafatu?

2. On page 394 what mood, or feeling, did the author create as he described the great albatross circling over the canoe?

3. Skim through the story to find places where Mafatu's pets were mentioned. What part did each play in Mafatu's adventure?

4. List several preparations Mafatu made for his journey. How did each prove important?

5. Was Mafatu's father important to the story? Why or why not?

6. How did you explain the light on the sea? What was its message to Mafatu?

7. Think of something you were once afraid of. How did you overcome your fear?

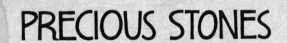

PRECIOUS STONES

An emerald is as green as grass;
  A ruby red as blood;
A sapphire shines as blue as heaven;
  A flint lies in the mud.

A diamond is a brilliant stone,
  To catch the world's desire;
An opal holds a fiery spark;
  But a flint holds fire.

— Christina Rossetti

397

BIBLIOGRAPHY

Aunt America, by Marie Halun Bloch.
> Lesya's aunt from America helps her to understand why her father was forced to desert her.

Skinny, by Robert Burch.
> After his father's death, Skinny finds a job in Miss Bessie's hotel.

Jed: the Story of a Yankee Soldier and a Southern Boy, by Peter Burchard.
> The setting for this story is the South in the 1860's.

Across Five Aprils, by Irene Hunt.
> The years during the War Between the States are hard, sad years for this family on a farm in Illinois.

A White Heron, by Sarah Orne Jewett.
> Sylvy knows that she can never betray the secret hiding places of the wild creatures in the Maine woods.

The Black Pearl, by Scott O'Dell.
> Diving for pearls off the coast of southern California, Ramón Salazar struggles with two enemies for the magnificent dusky pearl.

The Lone Hunt, by William O. Steele.
> Yance finds buffalo tracks near his home in Tennessee and follows them to the end of the trail.

Steam on the Line, by Philip Turner.
> David risks his life to prevent a wreck on the new train's first passenger run.

Ride a Northbound Horse, by Richard Wormser.
> Cav rides with the herd in this exciting cattle story set in the 1870's.

THE SECRET JOURNEY OF THE SILVER REINDEER

BY

LEE KINGMAN

It was in the far north country of Lapland, where the winter days are brightened only by starlight and glistening snow and the summer nights are dimmed only by heavy clouds crossing the sun, that young Aslak undertook a secret journey to save his family and his herd of silver reindeer.

It happened in the days when the Lapps, or Samer as they call themselves, could still migrate with their herds through Lapland far above the Arctic Circle; and this story began with Jouni Magga. He was a small but sturdy man, whose fight with a giant brown bear, whose luck with nuggets of gold, whose pride in his silver reindeer made him a legend. For who had sat by the hearth of his tent and talked of great hunters and herdsmen and not talked of Jouni Magga?

"He was the greatest of herdsmen," some said, for his deer shone like a silver river in moonlight and ran as fast as the silver streak of the lightning.

"He was a giant among hunters," some said, for only a man of great courage could have killed the biggest bear in all Lapland.

"He was a wizard!" some said, for only a wizard skilled with a magic drum could have found such gold.

400

Now Jouni Magga fathered three sons. The oldest, also named Jouni, was thrown from a sledge when a lad and half-smothered in snow. So he grew strong in body, but dim in mind. Gentle and kind, he did as he was told. Everyone called him Small Jouni.

The second son, Piera, was wild and reckless, fond of racing deer and making wagers, of fighting and scheming. After he lost two herds of his own through betting and a part of Great Jouni's herd through folly, his father reluctantly said, "You must leave my household and make your own way in the world, for I will give you no more. You may claim nothing from me as long as I live, even though I love you with all my heart and send you away in sorrow."

The third son, Tuure, was a faithful herdsman and skilled trail finder, who took joy and pride in the hard life of a nomad. As long as Great Jouni lived Tuure obeyed his father's orders.

When Great Jouni died, Tuure became head of the family. He cared for his mother, his brother Small Jouni, his wife, and his five children, of whom Aslak was the oldest. He was proud of the famous herd of silver reindeer which then numbered three thousand animals.

But though Tuure was a man of skill and courage, he had none of the luck of Great Jouni. A winter of the worst ice and sleet in a century cut down his herd by half, and the spring which followed threw brooks into treacherous torrents which drowned hundreds of the winter-weakened deer—and his wife. On the late autumn trek, a miserable journey of cold mists and sudden blizzards, Tuure fell ill of a mysterious disease. Neither the skill nor the herbs of Old Grandmother could save him. In the midst of their difficulties, fifty of the best beasts strayed or were stolen. While other Lapps came to the winter village looking forward to friends and the fun of the fair, the widow and grandchildren of the Great Jouni Magga arrived in sorrow and in fear.

"Someone has cast an evil spell over us and our herd," mourned Grandmother. "And who is left nowadays who has skill with the drum to tell me how the spell can be broken—and who has cast it?"

"Who believes in the drum?" asked Aslak, even though he had heard much of his grandfather's skill with it. "The church has told us there was never magic in the drum anyway."

So Aslak went to the mayor of the village, to report that fifty of his beasts were missing and he felt they were stolen.

The boy's tale upset the mayor. "Aside from murder, the theft of deer is the most serious charge you could bring. We have had no deer thieves in Lapland for years! You know each herd owner has his mark cut in the ears of his deer and that mark is respected." But as he saw the worry in Aslak's deep black eyes, he could not scold him further. "No, think on it, boy. Your journey was plagued by mists and storms. Your father was raving with illness, tied in his sledge. Your uncle Small Jouni knows summer from winter and a deer from a dog, but that is all. And strong as you are, you are not practiced in herding your deer through a hazardous journey. The deer were lost—not stolen. But the most serious matter, now that your father is dead, is what will become of you and your brothers and sisters?"

"That is no problem," declared Aslak. "I shall take care of my brothers and sisters and Old Grandmother and Small Jouni. It is no one's concern but my own."

The mayor smiled, but he shook his head. "You are only fourteen. And how old are the others?"

"By the time of the spring journey I shall be fifteen," Aslak said grandly. "My sister Merja is thirteen. My brother Pirkka is twelve. My sister Terhi is ten. And my little brother Petri is three. And don't forget Old Grandmother is always full of advice. Among us we know how to lasso and break deer, how to slaughter and skin them, how to make sledges and clothes, how to milk deer and make cheese. We know all we need to know to keep our herd together and let it increase."

Again the mayor smiled and shook his head. "Five children, a weak old woman and a dim-witted man could never survive the yearly journey of the deer. I have talked with the pastor and the teacher, and I have gone over the laws. The pastor and I believe the herd can be sold so that Old Grandmother may be taken care of and you children may stay at school together. We will have no trouble finding buyers for your deer."

"I do not wish to sell. Nor does my grandmother."

"Then I shall speak to her."

"No—I will talk with her," Aslak decided. "It is my duty to take care of her. But she would not be happy without us and the deer. So I must do what is best."

"You must do as your elders tell you, young Aslak," said the mayor severely, "whether you feel it is best or not."

But to that Aslak could not agree, and he parted from the man in silence, now bearing a burden of disapproval as well as anxiety.

Because he had promised, on his return Aslak asked Old Grandmother, "Are you too weary to make the journey with us this year? Would it ease you to stay at the village and rest while we see to the herd?"

And Old Grandmother had looked at him as if he were a little and ignorant child. "How could I rest, knowing you needed me?"

"It is true," said Aslak soberly. "And it is much to ask. But I do need you."

"Not more than I need you and I need the only way of life I know," she told him. "But you must be my strength."

"I will," promised Aslak. And bravely he told the mayor, "We will not sell our deer."

"We shall see," the wise man replied. "By the time of the spring journey, you may change your mind."

It was a winter to break a man's heart as well as a boy's. Again ice sheeted the snow, and the deer struggled to reach the moss far beneath. With their heads deep in the drifts, they were helpless victims of stealthy lynx and wily wolverine. Watch must be kept day and night, so Aslak and Merja took turns with Small Jouni and sharp-eyed Pirkka.

And throughout the long, dark, cruel winter the mayor's doubt gnawed at Aslak. Was he really man enough to keep his family and his herd together? Did the mayor and the elders have no reason for faith in him? Or was their real concern not the survival of five children, a simple man, and an old woman—but the fate of the silver-coated reindeer? Was someone scheming to take the herd away from him?

Grandmother grew weaker and wondered aloud if she would live to see the sun shine once more. One night she woke Aslak.

"I have had a dream," Grandmother said, "and you must take me on a journey at once. I must go to the camp of Kuisma, the witch-wizard, for I dreamed that he will help you keep your herd when I am gone. I know someone is scheming against you and plans to take your herd away."

Aslak was frightened to hear her confirming his own worries. Was it the mayor—making good his threat to talk good sense into Old Grandmother about selling the herd? Or was it the pastor, exhorting one of his fellow parishioners vigorously about the sternness of God and urging her to stay within reach of the church? Or was it the teacher, convincing her that her grandchildren should be safe and educated in school?

So Aslak was curious about Grandmother's dream. While he didn't really believe in wizards and drums, he could not spurn any way of keeping the herd and his family together.

He wrapped Grandmother in furs and tucked her into a sledge, tying it behind Fleet One, a buck broken to sledge-pulling but swift enough for racing. He put on his skis, and they raced through the forest, surprising deer and beasts of prey alike until they came to a frozen lake.

406

The old woman told him which stars to sight and on what far shore of the great lake he would find the tent of the wizard. The bitter wind froze silver tears on his cheeks, but Aslak did not falter. Nor did Fleet One. In three rushing hours, silent except for the howl of distant wolves, they reached the *kåta* of the wizard, and Grandmother called out her need of him.

Up through the smoke-hole of the *kåta* flew a snowy owl who stared in silence at the night visitors. The deerskin door flap parted to allow a pure white dog to come outside and glare at them. Then the owl hooted once and the dog barked twice and from inside came the words, "Enter, you who seek the wisdom of the wizard."

Aslak took Grandmother in his arms and carried her in. But he waited until the wizard pointed to a place on the reindeer skins by the hearth before he set her down. Then the wizard threw a handful of twigs to brighten the fire while he seemed to study their faces. Aslak saw the oldest man with the youngest eyes. His hair was white, as silver as ice, but his smile was as kind as summer.

"You are troubled, old friend," he said to the woman. "Tell me what knowledge you seek."

"Sorrow and woe and misfortune have been the lot of my son and now my grandson. It is beyond bad luck and bad weather, for others have not suffered in these years as have we. Tell me, O Wizard, what evil spell has been cast over the family of the Great Jouni Magga? Who has cast it? And how can the spell be broken?"

The wizard took up his magic drum, and Aslak watched in fascination. When the church had warned against the drums, many were burned and destroyed. But here one was, with symbols for reindeer and mountains and rivers and bears and gods and storms and floods and fire and herbs and health and evil and death etched on its taut old skin. As the wizard tossed the toe bone of a deer on the drum and began tapping, he closed his eyes.

With a start Aslak recognized the wizard. Of course! He was really blind Kuisma, who wandered to the winter fairs and about the summer camps, singing old verses or making up a *joik*—fresh words about new events sung to a familiar tune. He was a minstrel who brought news and knew everything.

Or was he a scoundrel, pretending to be blind and letting people feed him and care for him? Could he see his way under downcast lids? Is that how he could roam unerringly from camp to camp? Once out of sight he probably strode wide-eyed and farseeing! Had Aslak just made a three-hour journey to see a wizard who was no more than a pretender?

408

Then Kuisma opened his eyes and seemed to look right through Aslak. "I see before me a boy who does not believe in the magic of the drum because he does not believe in me. He thinks because he sees me wide-eyed by my hearth I am not blind. But let him learn that the brightest eye can be unseeing, for it is the spirit that sees all."

He closed his eyes again and tapped the drum, while the toe bone danced across the symbols. Aslak watched in wonder as the bone stopped by the reindeer and then skipped to the mountains and circled the symbol for evil, while the wizard, without looking down once at the dance of the bone on the drum chanted, "Reindeer you seek were parted from you on the journey and led to a different winter ground, and beware, O beware, the man who returns them to you."

Aslak felt a strange chill of fear, for although he had faith in his own knowledge and strength, who does not fear the unknown? Could he succeed in saving his family and his deer against forces beyond his control? Was he unwise to try?

While Aslak made himself stop trembling, the wizard ceased his chant, but swayed in rhythm to his tapping. The owl silently dropped to his shoulder and the dog suddenly appeared at his side. The only sounds were the whip of the wind around the *kåta*, the snap of the twigs on the fire, and the "Tip-tip-tap, tuppy-tup, tap, tip, tup" of the drum. Aslak felt the wizard was not there inside himself at all! And he saw that Grandmother, too, was nodding and swaying, her eyes dark and unseeing.

For a long time it was thus, while Aslak found he could not reason out his fears or his beliefs. It was as if he tried to keep his mind shut against some power that pried and pulled to reach inside him. Then the wizard's fingers suddenly whirred across the drum. The owl hooted. The dog barked. The wizard moved and stirred the fire, and Grandmother held out her hands to its warmth.

Kuisma turned his bright-blind eyes to Aslak. "Listen well, for when you reach your home tonight there will be only you alive to tell the tale."

A terrible tremor of fright shook Aslak, but Kuisma kept on, as if haste were now important. "There is a man who wishes harm to you because you have the goods and wealth of the Great Jouni Magga. It is his second son, your Uncle Piera, who hearing from afar of his father's death, returns to claim an inheritance. He has upon him some sign he says will prove Great Jouni left all to him. So it falls upon you, Aslak—son of Tuure, grandson of Great Jouni—to disprove him. You must find the true sign for yourself, so you may keep your grandfather's gold of the river Karasjoki, and the silver-coated reindeer. And with them, care for your younger brothers and sisters. You must stand firm but run fast. You must visit old places but seek new trails. You must reach the Cave of the Great Hunters in the Mountain of the Eagle's Head before your enemy. And now already time is rushing past you like the wind. You must return and rescue your brothers and sisters before it is too late."

"Grandmother, stay here with the wizard," Aslak

411

begged, unwilling to take her to her death. "Let me send a band of strong men to bring you back tomorrow."

"I care not about tomorrow," said Grandmother. "Only that you, who are the image of Great Jouni himself, shall break the spell put upon you by my deluded son Piera. You have courage. You must use it."

By the dimming firelight, the owl and the dog and the wizard slept, and on the magic drum the toe bone of the deer rested on the symbol of the mountains. Aslak carried his grandmother to the sledge, and they fled across the frozen lake and into the forest.

When he reached his *kåta,* Aslak picked up his grandmother and, carrying her in, quickly unwrapped the furs about her. To his joy she was still alive. The wizard was wrong!

Then Aslak saw that by the hearth sat the mayor and beside him a man he did not know.

Grandmother stared piercingly at the stranger. Then she said, "I could not go until I knew for certain that my heart no longer yearned for a lost son, and I tell you now that I believe the man who has returned is no true son to me. Aslak, remember this night and all you have heard. Now let me depart."

She lay back, and very soon she died, as surely as if she had been wrapped in skins and pushed away in a sledge to die alone in the snow, which once was done with the old in this cold land.

Merja and Terhi, huddled on the women's side of the hearth, began to weep quietly. "Oh, how sad that

Grandmother could not really see well enough to know her son after all these years. Aslak, the man by the hearth is Uncle Piera, and he has brought back the fifty reindeer lost upon the trail this autumn."

Piera Magga smiled at Aslak. "When I heard all the sad things that befell my father's family, I hurried to help and on my way it happened that I found fifty silver reindeer with the Magga mark. So I brought them to join the herd. I mourn that my mother's mind was too worn to know me, as were her eyes. But now that I am here, I will be head of the family and responsible for you all."

"Uncle Piera has brought us handsome knives!" exclaimed Pirkka. "One for you and one for me."

"And beautiful needle cases to hang on our belts!" exclaimed Merja. "One for Terhi and one for me."

But in Aslak the strange forecasts and the cold terrors of the night formed into resolve, and he found strength even in the death of his grandmother.

"Give back the knives and the needle cases," he ordered, "for we cannot take gifts from him. I am the head of the family. Did you not hear my grandmother reject this man just now? Besides I have been told Great Jouni sent him away saying he could claim no more."

"Ah—" said Uncle Piera, "let me point out that my father did not mean to disinherit me on his death. No! He said only that I could claim nothing from him while he lived. Nor have I! I have suffered many misfortunes since I was sent away without asking for one reindeer. Is that not true? Have I ever claimed so much as a discarded antler from my father's deer? Have I not now returned fifty straying reindeer to the herd?"

Aslak acknowledged that his uncle had made no claim.

"But I have spoken with the mayor and wise elders of the parish council, and they tell me you are too young to bear responsibility for a herd and a household. So the responsibility is mine as your uncle. And something more. You know of the famous nugget — the Luck of the Karasjoki?"

"Indeed," said Aslak, for he had heard many times the tale of how his grandfather's good fortune began.

"Everyone knows Great Jouni Magga's good fortune began the day he found that large nugget on a bank of the Karasjoki. Or rather, what he found were *two halves which fitted together so perfectly not a reindeer hair could slip between*. He showed this to us often when we were boys, and he always said that whoever possessed the Luck of the Karasjoki should possess the herd — because then he would have the luck and the skill to take care of it. And now — look —"

Uncle Piera reached into the pocket of his embroidered *atsaslieppa*, the dickey which filled the neck of his tunic. Unrolling a cloth, he held out a rough object which gleamed dully in the firelight. "Here it is—half of the Karasjoki nugget, sent as a sign for me to return and become the head of the family."

But Aslak stared at it, keeping his face as blank as the snow. "How did you come by this? Can you prove that this is half of the true Karasjoki nugget that belonged to my grandfather? Do you know where the other half is which matches it?"

"Two years ago at the winter fair at Kautokeino I met Kuisma, the blind peddler. When he heard I was Piera Magga, he cried out, 'Like the wind I have been searching the length and breadth of the north country for you. Your father is dying and he entreated me to find you and give you this talisman saying tell my son here is half of my luck—a sign that he must return and make the luck of the Magga whole again.' As to where the matching half is, surely that would be among Great Jouni's possessions—the box of secret belongings which every man of wealth collects during this lifetime, and which must have been kept by my mother after his death. By rights it is here in this *kåta* and I demand that you give it to me."

Aslak sat still, feeling again the trembling chill that shook him in the wizard's tent. But he knew he must be strong and test his uncle to find the truth.

While Merja and Terhi watched, their faces drawn with dismay, Aslak took off his four-peaked cap. Loosening the drawstring inside, he poked into one of the tips and held out what looked like a dirty rock. "Let us see if between us we have the whole then of my grandfather's nugget, for it is I who have the other half."

He heard his sisters stir with excitement, and Pirkka moved restlessly toward him.

Aslak explained. "When my father, Tuure Magga, could no longer speak, he pressed this into my hand. Until I looked, I thought perhaps he had followed the old way of choosing a rock or a stick with a face to be his good-luck god. Since so much ill fortune followed us, I was tempted to throw it away. But when I looked, I found it half a nugget of gold. Now—hold out your half and see if yours is the mate of mine. For if it is, then my grandfather must have decided to divide the luck and the herd between you and my father—that is, if your message be his true words. If it is not, then I believe you have come to deceive us."

The boy and the man reached toward each other in the flickering light of the fire. The mayor edged closer to observe most carefully. Merja sucked in her breath and Terhi wiggled impatiently. Aslak knew that his sisters, often resentful of his ordering them about, were intrigued by the sudden appearance of a handsome uncle, and too young to care deeply who was head of the family. Pirkka, too, was excited by the adventure and mystery of an uncle he scarcely remembered.

Aslak was exhausted from his trip and saddened by Old Grandmother's death. He longed for a moment to be only a boy and to be comforted. How easy it would be to let his uncle take on all the cares and burdens

416

of the family. For a swift second, he thought if the nuggets matched, he would not dispute his uncle's claim.

But twist and turn the halves as they might, there was no match—even when Uncle Piera impatiently tried to snatch the half from Aslak's hand. Had he managed to get hold of it, Aslak was sure his uncle would substitute the other half of the nugget he had brought—that it was up his sleeve waiting for a split-second sleight-of-hand switch.

Aslak pulled back. "This does not leave my grasp, for I do not trust you to return the right half to me," he said. "It is clear that we each have half a nugget, but one of them is false. I believe my grandfather never intended to split the herd and leave part to you. But who does have the true half? And where is the other?"

"Tsk, tsk!" muttered the mayor in bewilderment. "The parish laws—"

"—can have nothing to say about nuggets!" declared Aslak. "This is between my uncle and me. But I tell you in all truth that the box of secret belongings of my grandfather, Jouni Magga, is not in this *kåta*. He asked that it be left with him at his burial, but where that place is only my father knew."

A sullen look swept over Piera's face, as he turned to the mayor. "I doubt he tells the truth."

But the mayor had known Aslak ever since he was a small child. "No—Aslak does not lie."

"My grandfather died on the summer journey," Aslak explained. "My father took his body to the secret resting place of our ancestors, for he had been told how to find it. The knowledge passes from father to son, but when the time came, my father was too ill to tell me. I swear I do not know where it is."

Or had the wizard told him when he said to find the Cave of the Great Hunters in the Mountain of the Eagle's Head?

Then Aslak was silent for a moment. Was Kuisma really a wizard whose trance brought his knowledge? Or was he just a blind peddler, full of intrigue, who had plotted with Piera against Aslak? For according to Piera it was Kuisma who had brought him the half nugget and his father's message.

But if Kuisma and his warning were to be believed, if Piera had only used Kuisma's name in a lie, then Aslak must be bold and cautious at the same time! So he said, "Since my uncle and I both have half a nugget, let us each mark our own half now and each give his marked half to the mayor, who will keep them both. Then whoever finds the box of secret belongings will take it to the mayor, who will open it and see whose half the nugget in it matches."

When Piera agreed so readily, Aslak wondered if some sleight-of-hand had already taken place. Then he remembered the words of Kuisma, the wizard—and even though he half-doubted and half-believed what he had heard and seen, he knew his only hope was to discover the Cave of the Great Hunters before his Uncle Piera did.

But first they must mourn Old Grandmother and take her body out the rear of the *kåta*, through the opening only used in time of death. For small though

418

a *kåta* was, each place in it had its purpose—the food and utensils and goods always in the same area; the man of the house in one spot by the hearth; the woman by another; children and old people here; friends and strangers there. For no one might enter a Lapp tent without being bidden, nor disturb an empty tent if a log lay across the entrance, showing the owner's absence. Respect for custom was great among his people, and impatient as Aslak was to move his *kåta* and be off on a secret journey, he first took care of his grandmother's rites.

The village was now in a turmoil over the death of Great Jouni's widow, the return of the second son, Piera Magga, and the fate of five orphaned children and the silver reindeer. Aslak could not make open preparations to leave, nor could he whisper his plans to the children, for fear they would innocently give them away.

Anxiously he watched the weather. Moss under the snow was scarce and hard for the deer to find. Each day the forest rang with ax blows as men chopped down pines entangled with the black beard moss of Lapland—so the deer at least could eat that. But still the snow was too deep to take the deer from the forest. Nor did Aslak wish to travel alone on his skis to the mountains, for he distrusted his uncle too much to leave his herd and family behind. They must all go together.

In the meantime, Uncle Piera, saying his return was a shock to his nephew, moved into the teacher's turf-and-timber *kåta*. Every night he sat drinking coffee and telling of his travels to anyone who might come and listen and many did. Even Pirkka, to Aslak's dismay.

On the day when the sun, for the first time since autumn, rose above the horizon, people rushed from their *kåtor* and scattered through the forest to the shores of the lake, where they could clearly admire the sun. They laughed and sang. Dogs barked and raced. Boys and girls who attended the teacher's lessons became impatient for school to end. The pastor knew his church would soon be poorly attended and rang his bell for service all the harder.

Aslak felt the sun's brief warmth for four days and on the fifth, after the evening meal, he lingered at the hearth.

"I am going to the teacher's," said Pirkka, "to listen to the tales men tell."

"Go," said Aslak. "But if Terhi comes and stands at the door, step quietly outside at once and obey her message."

When Pirkka had gone, Aslak said to his sisters, "I know you are brave and will do what I say. Tonight

420

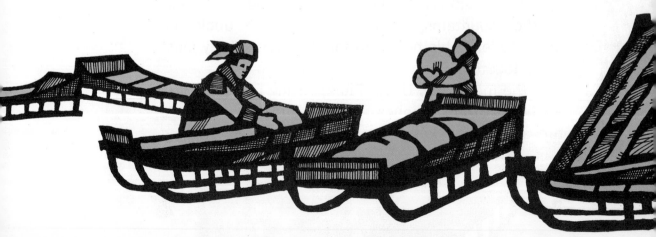

we leave for the spring camp, for we must reach the far mountains quickly this year. We will prepare everything now and force the deer off if we must. But I shall leave twenty deer to Uncle Piera, as he is too greedy not to accept them and they will keep him longer on the trail than if he traveled alone. Now I will put six sledges here by the *kåta*. Pack four quietly. In the first Terhi will ride with Petri. The last will carry the tent poles. Pirkka and Small Jouni will drive the herd tonight. Merja and I will lead the string of sledges. When all is ready here, we will fetch Pirkka and depart.''

Quickly the girls packed the sledges, or *akjor*, with boxes and cooking pans, food and furs. Aslak quietly rounded up the *härkar*, deer broken to bear burdens and pull sledges. He tied cloth around the clappers of their bells, in order to keep them silent. Now he was glad their *kåta* was farthest away from the church and the log school and the teacher's hut. When one of the dogs yipped, he shushed it.

But the sound that worried him most was that of the deer—the grunts they would make, like thousands of complaining, bronchial old men, and the click, click,

click of their hoofs as they ran. As it was not the touch of hoof to ice that made the noise, but the vibrating of a tendon over a bone inside the hoof, there was no way of disguising it. It was one of the deer's ways, along with a musky odor and a flash light white tail, of finding each other in storm and mist.

In quick time the household was packed and as Aslak and Merja pulled down the cloth of the *kåta* and loaded the poles on the last *akja*, he sent Terhi to bring Pirkka. That boy loved the bustle of the winter village and the schoolmaster's books. He would be lonely on the trail and lonelier than ever when he heard Aslak's plan. But he came, and seeing the preparations, he followed Aslak's orders.

"Quietly we shall lead this string through the forest and wait on the lake. Find Big Horn, the herd leader, and tie his bell so it will not ring and then Shaggy One, the herd follower. Drive Big Horn toward the lake with your lasso and make sure Shaggy One follows. Then the rest will go, and Small Jouni will keep them together."

"The dogs will help."

"Not this time!" Aslak showed Pirkka four unhappy dogs, all muzzled. "We cannot risk their barking. Someone might try to stop us from leaving the village, and we must have a full day's start on Piera Magga."

"Aslak, why do you fear him? Don't you think he means what he says? That if he is head of the family, he will provide for us all?"

"I not only distrust him, I am warned against him. You must believe me, Pirkka, and do as I say. And

422

before you and Small Jouni begin to drive the main herd, count off twenty and leave them in the corral for strays beyond the church. Here is a message to hang around the neck of one, saying they are a gift of Aslak Magga, head of the family, to Piera Magga. Then let us hope no one finds them before morning."

Fortunately a wind rose and wailed through the trees, bearing the sounds of the deer away from the teacher's hut, where men now sat, chanting a *joik* about the sun's return.

The touch of sun in the daytime had softened the snow crystals so the cold dark of night brought a crust. With cloven hoofs the deer could run once more across the crusty snow—and the sledges could swing along to their gallop. Aslak and Merja on their skis guided the string of sledges, or *rajd*, while Pirkka and Small Jouni skied close to the herd.

Above the stars gave little light, for they no longer burned with the stirring glitter of the Christmas skies. But the frozen snow cast a glow of its own as they rushed over lakes and bogs, through stands of stunted pines snowed into the shapes of trolls, past bare-branched willows flogged by winter gales, and on and on and on.

At last the far white hilltops caught the sun's first fire. Aslak stopped to unmuzzle the dogs and untie the herd leaders' bells. Then, leaving the string of sledges to Merja, he raced ahead to guide the herd away from the open plain to the shelter of a stunted forest. The day's warmth melted the crust and the deer could no longer quickly cross the snow. They rested and grazed.

423

But there was no rest for the four big children and Small Jouni. The sledge *härkar* were turned loose to forage; the *kåta* poles were put up and its canvas wrapped around; the fire was made and the cook-kettle hung on its chain. They took turns eating and sleeping and watching the deer.

When Aslak was with the herd, he spent as much time searching the horizon to see if they were followed as he did looking for strays or attacking lynxes and wolverines. And with the night they packed again and harnessed again and traveled again, northward and westward. They went this time with dogs racing and barking and all the bells ringing, for in the vast loneliness of the Arctic night sounds were brave and comforting things.

To Aslak's joy it snowed for three days, not hard enough to keep them from traveling, but enough to cover their tracks. With each day's journey farther from the winter village, Aslak felt more confident. The exhilaration of the air and the continual movement about him kept him full of excitement and energy.

But soon he was faced with a problem. While Terhi and Small Jouni watched the herd, he sat by the hearth talking to Merja and Pirkka. Beside him, Petri played with a puppy.

"In two days we should come to Great Jouni's camp by the lake. Always before we have stayed there in spring to prepare for the summer trek to the mountains and again in autumn to make the winter preparations."

"It will be good not to travel every day," said Merja.

"But Great Jouni's camp is well-known, and anyone looking for us will go there first," said Aslak. "I don't think we should stay there."

"Who will be looking for us? Just why did we leave in the dark, and why have you rushed us over the *fjells* as if Stalo-the-monster were chasing us? So early in spring there are only stray hunters and trappers about. Why should they bother us?" Pirkka asked.

"It is Uncle Piera who will hunt us down. He did not believe me when I told him I don't know where Great Jouni is buried. So he will follow me, expecting me to lead him to the burial place," Aslak reasoned. "Then if I find it, I don't know what will happen, Merja. He is an evil man. Perhaps he will trick me out of the nugget, should it be there. Perhaps he will simply kill me and take it away."

Merja was suddenly terrified to think of her mysterious uncle as a man who could be so ruthless. "Then why did you make us leave the village, where the mayor and the elders could protect us? Why have you brought us here, for if he kills you, he will probably kill us, too."

"So I can pit whatever strength and cunning I have against him. Out here it is just between him and me. The mayor and the elders at the village were too taken in by his promises. Besides, he could have prevailed on the elders to send you to school."

"I would like that," said Pirkka.

Aslak's eyes dimmed in despair. "Maybe I've done the wrong thing, dragging you with me. But I thought you felt as I do—that this is our life and no man can

425

take it away from us without a struggle. I swore it to our father at his death—so I must try to keep the Magga family and the deer together. Help me, Pirkka. Help me, Merja. And I swear to you that it will be a better life than watching the world go by from a village window all your years."

But he could see they were doubtful. The hardships of the journey brought them no reward—no mother's comfort, nor father's praise, nor worldly goods.

Then Merja said, "There's no sense in going back. So we can only keep on and see what happens. But let us go to the spring camp, Aslak. We must—the meat we need for our journey is stored for us there."

"With a thousand deer anyone can find us anywhere in Lapland!" Pirkka pointed out. "Uncle Piera showed me his telescope once, and how you see the feathers one by one on an eagle far overhead. He can find you no matter where you hide! So does it matter where we camp?"

"That is probably true," Aslak sighed. The children's doubts and the enormity of his undertaking began to weigh on him.

"And remember," said Merja, "the does will soon have their calves, so we cannot travel every day. We should stay at the camp and rest. The herd has a rhythm of its own and that we cannot change. If you tried and lost the new calves, then the elders would say you were too foolish to be the head of the household."

So they decided to stay the usual time at the camp.

It was by a lake on the south slope of a rolling hill

426

where patches of pale, spongy moss were already free of the snow. The bucks were separated now from the does, and all the deer rested and gathered strength. The dogs sniffed for old bones. The children, too, looked forward to a feast, hoping no animals had stolen the supply of reindeer meat slaughtered and frozen in the fall and stored in wooden shelters built atop high posts.

But when Merja saw the three storehouses, she cried, "Look! Broken into! The doors are ripped off and half the meat is gone!"

"How high the snow must have been for the wolverines to reach it!" said Terhi.

Aslak said little, but when he had time he brought a ladder and looked closely at the doors. "There are no claw marks on the wood. I do not think it was four-legged animals who took the meat."

Merja, too, as she swept out the *kåta*, made of turf-and-timber, felt someone had used it after they had left in the autumn. It was a dread feeling, making even the familiar dwelling seem strange and uncomfortable. She threw out every old twig, sending Terhi and Petri to the dwarf willows and birches by the lake to gather fresh ones. When Petri brought her a funny stone with a face he had found on the shore, Merja set it defiantly in the same place where Old Grandmother had kept her good luck gods.

"Please take away the feeling of the unknown which is in this house," Merja suggested politely.

"Perhaps it was only someone who took refuge in a storm!" said Pirkka, for that was permitted.

"I hope no one comes while we are here now!" Merja said, picking up Petri and hugging him close.

"I will protect you," said Pirkka. "Anyway, we are safe in this *kåta*." He pointed to the high log doorstep and low log lintel. Anyone entering had to bend his head at the same time he stepped up and over, so a stranger could be clubbed senseless before he had both feet in the door.

But the children felt safe enough so they could fall asleep after a good meal of reindeer meat stewed long and drawn steaming from the cook-kettle.

Each day the sun's goodness pushed back the snows as well as the hours of darkness. Soon the does, the *vajor*, began to drop their young, and the children counted the stick-legged calves struggling up from the snow. While one child slept, the others watched — to make sure that bears, awakened hungry from their winter sleep, did not eat the calves. Even Petri was put on the back of a *härke*, where he could be safe but see over the herd, and told to cry out if he saw any animal but a deer or a dog.

Aslak, looking out over the *fjells* and the lakes and the bogs, remembered that it was days since he had seen a tall tree, and he was conscious of time, for he wanted to hurry the herd on to the mountains. He wondered in what fold of the *fjells* his Uncle Piera lurked and whether he had in his greed kept the twenty reindeer with him.

Yet so far in all the empty earth about him he could see no other life. There was nothing but the sky; and in starlight or sunlight, peacefully moonlit or tumultuous with clouds, it was a tremendous arc above and beyond the limits of the eye at the farthest horizon.

But there was other work to do besides keeping watch. Small Jouni tarred the six sledges again to make them waterproof, and then stored them away. Halters and reins and packsaddles needed repair. Aslak and Pirkka both needed new lassos, cut and braided from good deerskins.

This was the time of the year when their mother and grandmother had made new boots and mittens, woven bootlaces and belts, and twisted root fibers into the patterned mesh of cheese molds. Merja cried when she thought of Old Grandmother sitting by the hearth, pulling out dried deer sinews and twisting and rolling them against her cheek to make thread. For now it was all she could do to mend their boots and mittens, and cook their food and count the calves and milk the does and make cheese for their next journey.

Because the sun barely dipped into enough dusk for them to rest, she worked long hours and her only pleasure was to sit late in the evening by the lake and listen to the thrush and bluethroat sing.

Ice melted, and fish in the nearby streams and the lake made a tempting change from their year-round diet of reindeer meat, which they ate braised and stewed with herbs in the cookpot; or smoked and dried and chewed down cold many a time on their journeys.

One evening Pirkka lay motionless on a rock by the lake and saw a large pike in the shallows. He knew he should run to find a net. Then he felt the sudden chill of a shadow and heard a body brush against the rock.

"The fish is there," he whispered, expecting to see Aslak's hand cast out a net. Instead a large brown paw thrust out before him and a huge fur shoulder passed close enough to warm his face as a bear plunged upon the fish.

Pirkka shook to think the great beast must have stood behind him as he dreamed. Breathlessly he slid from the rock and stepped silently as a lynx. Outside the *kåta* Petri played with a pile of stones and Pirkka picked him up and plopped him inside.

430

Merja looked up from braiding a belt, startled.

"What is the matter?"

"A big bear is fishing in the lake. He nearly fished me. Where is the gun?"

Pirkka had shot wolves and wolverines, and he knew it was dangerous for a boy barely five feet tall to shoot a bear almost nine feet tall. The first shot must be the last. He must walk out with the courage of a man.

Pirkka did. He even felt it unfair that the bear should be so busy fishing that he could take him unaware. Then as he approached Pirkka's foot slid on a loose stone, making a sudden *chink* of sound. The bear swung about and saw Pirkka just as the boy took aim. WHAM! Pirkka's shot was true and hit the heart. The bear fell.

Pirkka started toward it, when Aslak, running at the sound of the shot, called out, "Wait! Bears are treacherous. Let me see first if he is really dead."

Aslak fetched a ski from the edge of the snow field and prodded the bear. Then he called in Small Jouni, and together they skinned it, while Merja roasted some meat. Aslak told Pirkka they would cure the skin and he could keep it or sell it at the winter fair. "With such a brave brother to help me, how can the mayor say we should give up our herd and go to school!" Aslak praised him.

Pirkka was so full of joy in his accomplishment that he sat on the rock in the evening sunlight, making up a *joik* about wonderful Pirkka, the bear hunter.

"You are boasting!" laughed Terhi, who sat with him, holding a sleepy Petri. "Many men shoot bears."

"But this is my first," insisted Pirkka, "and it is big enough for a song."

As the days lengthened, ice and snow sank into the earth and the streams roared and boiled in their stony beds. Suddenly spring buds appeared, and Aslak, watching this time with a man's eyes instead of a child's, understood why his people believed so long in magic. For spring became summer in a single day, as if an incantation changed bud to full leaf while he watched. In hours the wand-bare birches became fully clothed in green, and the willow's leaf burst out as bright as sunlight. The cuckoo called out, "Summer is here."

But with all the glory of the new life shooting up through the *fjells* came the pests—the midges and

432

horseflies, mosquitoes and gadflies—pests of the people and enemies of the deer, for the sting of the gadfly injected eggs under the reindeer's skin that hatched to torment and sometimes kill the deer. And the mosquitoes hummed in swarms, hovering around deer and humans like a horrid outer garment. Awake or asleep, it was impossible to escape them.

The insects were the sign Aslak awaited to tell him it was time to move to the farthest mountains.

"Ahead lies a difficult journey," he told his brothers and sisters. "And we must seek new trails and find a summer camp by ourselves."

"Oh, Aslak! Why can't we stay near our friends as we always do!" Merja begged.

"I know there is a boy from Kaaresuvanto you long to see again," Aslak teased gently. "And if I can find what I seek in time, we will join the others before the summer roundup. But we must go alone and stay alone while I search for the Mountain of the Eagle's Head."

"I have never heard of that," said Merja.

"Nor had I," said Aslak.

"Aslak Magga!" called a voice just outside the *kåta*. "Let me come in."

The children's hearts jumped with fright. But Aslak rose quietly, his hand on the sharp-pointed *puuko* sheathed at his belt. Who stood outside? Who heard him speak of the Mountain of the Eagle's Head? He hoped it was not his uncle.

Even so his heart missed a beat when he saw blind Kuisma with the owl on his shoulder and the dog at

433

his side. But Aslak invited him in. Petri cried at the sight of the owl, and the puppies snarled at the intrusion of the strange dog. The *kåta* was a small dark place to hold such noise and confusion, but at last all settled down. Terhi gave Kuisma a bowl of stew.

Merja, who knew Kuisma only as the blind peddler, cried, "Tell us who you have seen and where you have been! Do you know if our friends from Enontekio and Kaaresuvanto are coming this way?" And both girls begged to see the gay ribbons he brought for sale in his pack.

Aslak let them ask their girlish questions, but when they were through, he told Kuisma to follow him to the lake, and began abruptly, "Since you know all, tell me where is my Uncle Piera and what is he doing?"

"Ah, my boy!" the old man's face was as wrinkled as the lake in the wind. "How can I tell you that? For I am only a blind peddler, carrying my pack from camp to camp. And your uncle has no camp that I have seen."

"You mean he is free of a herd? He can travel swiftly and alone?"

"I am told he kept six of your *härkar* for a sledge string and four bucks for racing and gambling. He sold the rest to buy food and supplies for his search. He left the winter village not long after you, telling the mayor he would meet him at the summer roundup — bringing Great Jouni's box of secret belongings and the other half of the Karasjoki nugget, which he expects to find wherever your grandfather is buried."

"Then without a full herd and does and young calves

434

to watch over, he can have searched the whole of Lapland before I can even see the mountains on the horizon!" Aslak hit the rock by which they stood in anger. "And how do I know, since you acted as go-between with my grandfather's message and handed him that half-nugget of gold that you have not also told him of the Cave of the Great Hunters in the Mountain of the Eagle's Head! How do I know that you have told me a true thing?"

"What message? What half-nugget of gold? When was I a go-between for your grandfather? Aslak, you are sorely tried and worried, or you would not speak so," said the old man sadly. "Did *I* ever tell you that I gave Piera Magga a nugget and a message?"

"No! I did hear it from his lips, not yours! Forgive me, but I have not known whom to believe. Then you have not told my uncle about the Cave of the Great Hunters or the Mountain of the Eagle's Head?"

"I have told him nothing. Nor would he listen to a blind peddler. He has used me in his lies because he is fool enough to think his word worth more than mine. But I know all about him. I know he has hidden around the countryside these seven years, living in the camps of others, stealing reindeer for food. I know much and my drum told me more."

"Then will you use your drum again? If I could only know which pass in the mountains leads to the cave."

"When I crossed the lake to the village to mourn the death of my old friend your grandmother, my drum was stolen. Perhaps by Piera, who has no respect for sacred things and hopes to sell it for gold. Without it I am only poor blind Kuisma, the peddler. You must find my drum for me, Aslak, so I may be Kuisma the wizard once more.''

Aslak sighed. How much more would fall upon his shoulders? How much could he accomplish with the burdens he bore of children and a herd of deer and treacherous rivers and mountains to cross? A loon sat upon the lake and shrieked with such laughter that Aslak shivered.

Kuisma spoke. "I tell you to start upon your summer trek at once. You will know the Mountain of the Eagle's Head when you see it. But be careful lest you take an easy way which will prove disastrous. I will wait for you at the summer roundup.''

Then the owl took flight, the dog padded ahead, and the peddler followed them over the *fjells*.

ow that the snow had melted from the *fjells*, more *härkar* were harnessed and burdened, for sledges could no longer be pulled and everything must be borne by the deer. Aslak and Pirkka tied things on carefully, so nothing would slip as they climbed the mountain passes, or be torn off as they swam the savage streams.

Now, with the sun never falling from sight, they could travel at any hour, stopping at any time to pitch their tent, eat and sleep. Small Jouni and the dogs stayed close to the herd, while Aslak often climbed higher places by himself to study the range of mountains on the horizon.

"I wish I had a telescope like Uncle Piera," he sighed. "I wish I had listened more to father when he talked about his journeys. Once we cross the next stream, I must find a new way through the mountains so we will be above and beyond the summer camp grounds."

"But why couldn't we go to camp with our friends? The deer would be safe there, and you could leave us while you searched by yourself?" Merja pleaded. "It would be quicker and easier."

"Quicker and easier, yes," Aslak answered, remembering Kuisma's warning. "But it would not be safe." He did not say it aloud, but if he were by himself his uncle could push him over a cliff or drown him in a torrent and no one would ever know it was not another sad accident to Great Jouni Magga's unfortunate family.

Except for the click of the reindeer's hoofs and the clack of their bells or the shriek of a buzzard whose silent world was startled by the caravan, it was a quiet journey until they came to a mountain brook, or *jokk*. Terhi shivered to hear its threatening shout long before she saw it, for this was where their mother had drowned. In late summer the stream would have barely enough water to wash its stones. But now, swollen with melted snow fields and cruelly cold, savage with the rush of raging rapids, the water screamed defiance as it hurtled past.

Aslak and Pirkka added to their weight by putting stones inside the spacious pocket made by the top of their belted tunics. Then they helped Small Jouni start the herd across. Even strong Big Horn, the herd leader, had to be shoved and Shaggy One, the herd follower, coaxed to start the procession, for the *jokk* was furious in its force. The weakest calves were swept and tumbled down the stream. When three were crushed and drowned before he could save them, Small Jouni cried.

438

Back and forth through the icy, waist-deep water went Aslak, shouting and encouraging until all the herd spread out on the other side to graze. Then he and Pirkka tightened the *härkars'* packsaddles once more and with a slap on the rump urged them into the swirling stream.

Terhi was frightened, and Merja tried to calm her. They pulled their skirts as high as they could and squealed as the icy water filled their boots. When they were waist deep, they stopped squealing, for the cold clutched away their breath.

Pirkka splashed and scrambled next, and then Aslak, making sure nothing was left behind, swung Petri onto his shoulders, holding him tight by the legs.

"Be careful! You've pushed my hat over my eyes!" he scolded. Petri pulled it back. Step by slippery, shivery step, Aslak crossed the stream and dropped his little brother thankfully on dry ground. Another year, another crossing!

In the warm sun they dried out their soaking tunics and leather pants. They spread out the sedge-grass with which they filled their boots instead of wearing stockings. They put up the dripping *kåta*, splashed by the churning water, cooked a hot meal and slept— all but Aslak, who kept himself awake worrying about crossing the mountains ahead, and Small Jouni, who counted and recounted the herd.

When they set out again, Aslak bravely turned them northward instead of westward. "Once I remember our grandfather telling of a journey made in a spring of such floods that he had to cross all the streams much higher in the mountains and he found a series of passes in mountains which from afar seemed to have no passes at all—just great jagged heights. Beyond was a plateau with a small lake, and he spent most of the summer there before journeying south to the roundup. So we will go north until I see a mountain chain that looks impassable." Again he remembered Kuisma's warning not to take the easy way.

Merja was afraid and shook her head. But she did not argue now with her brother. On the trail there were hard decisions to make, and she saw that Aslak suffered over them even more than they all suffered from the insistent biting of mosquitoes and the long hours of tiresome walking.

On the rolling trackless *fjells*, Aslak could relax and say, "We will follow the deer." He could study the herd, and sometimes carry a weak calf for a way.

But at the edge of swift streams, he must tie a lasso around his waist and, giving Small Jouni the other end with which to pull him in like a wounded fish if necessary, he must test the currents and sudden deep drops until he was sure the children and burdened deer could cross.

For a few days they followed a stream that wandered toward the northwest. One evening Aslak walked ahead, trying to decide where to turn away from its roaring bed. Pebbles and stones were rough beneath his feet, and as he stood there staring down he saw a nugget of gold. He picked it up and a plan suddenly filled his mind. He smashed the nugget in two and placed the pieces in his hat.

In the next days, they turned west and soon were climbing up, until peaks that had been a distant blue rose overhead, black rocks. Usually Aslak loved the mountains, for in them he felt far above the world and free of it. Enchanted by space, he could forget the heavy weight of winter crushing them under its darkened sky. But on this trek he worried lest a rocky ledge stop at the edge of nothing, or stones loosened by wind and weather fall and frighten the deer into a stampede. The winds were high and mournful, and the loneliness was unending.

Yet each time Aslak said, "I cannot see where this day's journey will end," a pass opened out.

But one day he looked ahead in dismay. "There is a glacier!" he told the others. "A small one. But dangerous. Yet we must cross it. And beyond—that is a snow field full of crevasses. We must camp here and take only a few deer at a time."

Untying the skis from one of the *härkar*, Aslak began

441

the treacherous task of guiding the deer and the children. Each time the passing of the deer made that trail unsafe, he sought a new track before bringing the next deer across. Back and forth he went, until at last they were all safe on the far side. During this, he did not sleep for almost a two-day span. When it was over, he lay down on the first patch of safe ground and slept unmoving in the full blaze of summer night.

Finally they climbed the back of the mountain chain and started down the other side. Below Aslak saw a moorland protected on all sides by mountains. In the middle of the plateau was a lake.

"There!" Aslak exulted. "We have found our camp."

He looked at his weary brothers and sisters. Even Small Jouni was thin and tired, and the deer were more like shadows than beasts. "You are brave! Braver than I had any right to ask. But only one hazard remains—this last steep mountain side."

The deer, free to make their own pace, could breast through the softening snow as through waves. But they could not be allowed to rush on top of each other in panic, for the calves could be trampled and smothered. The *härkar*, too, had to be held back— lest the weight of their packs push them too fast and they lose their footing and roll down the slopes. Going down with sledges would have been even more dangerous, and ropes would have been tied on the runners for brakes. But Aslak had left the sledges behind, for he had not realized his route would take them through so much snow.

Yet it was the snow fields on the lower slopes which saved the deer from the tortures of insects. Some Lapps nearer the sea always took their herds to islands even though the deer had to swim across deep *fjords* to reach them. But Aslak's people used the mountain snow fields instead, for the deer could climb away from the insects in the day's warmth. These were the snows that never melted even on the warmest, longest summer days—the eternal snows. Aslak, whose life was made up of ceaseless change, found the fact this snow was always there, oddly comforting.

Terhi and Petri delighted in their private camp ground, and in the tiny flowers and berries they found all around. But Merja was sad. She looked forward each summer to seeing friends among the Lapps who journeyed from other regions to the same great plateau, now miles away from her.

Pirkka, too, missed the visiting from tent to tent, the summer lessons with the schoolmaster, and the competition to see who could lasso calves the quickest. He hoped they would arrive in time for the great roundup, where all the herds were sorted out in an uproar of excitement—dogs barking, deer grunting, dust rising, men yelling, lassos swishing, and girls cheering!

But Small Jouni was content. He would spend his summer hours sleeping and fishing and carving knife handles and spoons and needle cases from reindeer bone and horn.

They ate salmon and trout from brooks and sour-sweet seedy cloudberries from bogs, and lay back in

443

carpets of heather and mountain forget-me-nots. Pirkka and Terhi brought out the wooden *tablo* board and played a game of "catch the wolf" with reindeer toe bones as the playing pieces.

But Aslak walked to the snow fields, put on his skis, and climbed to a high peak, where he sat staring out over the mountains which seemed to ring the world. There was a crag as sharp as a buzzard's beak, and there a range as solid as a bear's back. But where stood a mountain with the shape of an eagle's head?

As he became more familiar with the mountains, he decided there were three that might be the right shape, but they were all in different directions. He felt an urgency to start out at once, but he realized it might be a long search, and there were things to take care of first with the herd.

Then one day he saw a light flash up from a mountain nearby again and again. He wondered if it was the sun striking the lens of a telescope and if his uncle had discovered them. That night Petri's puppy in the *kåta* barked until he set the herd dogs barking.

"Is someone lurking around the camp?" Terhi asked.

Merja sighed. "I wish someone were. It is so lonely here by ourselves."

"I'm afraid Piera Magga has found us and is watching everything we do," worried Aslak.

The next morning a good lasso, left by the skis on the snow field, had been taken. Aslak was sure then that his uncle was near, for no one else would steal.

"At least if Piera Magga is watching me, he has not found Grandfather's burial place yet." Aslak found

444

comfort in that. "But how can I leave the camp and begin my search without his seeing and following me?"

"Are you going to search soon?" asked Merja, anxious that it should be done so they could start their journey southward.

"Just as soon as the new calves are marked," promised Aslak, for important as his mission was, the herd still must come first.

So the next days he spent with Pirkka and Small Jouni up on the snow fields. With a swish of the lasso, Aslak caught a calf by the hind legs. Small Jouni tipped it gently to the ground, careful not to bruise its delicate new horns. Swiftly he cut the nicks of Great Jouni Magga's mark in one ear. Aslak saved a snippet from each, and when all the calves were marked, he threaded the snippets on a string and counted them.

"Four hundred!" For a moment his tiredness vanished, for reindeer were the true wealth of the Lapp. They were his food, his clothing, his transport, and his trade. Aslak had done well to bring so many new calves safely to a summer pasture over such a long and hazardous route. In his joy he said, "Merja, you shall have ten deer of your own to trade at the winter fair—for any pretties you want. Shawls and ribbons and brooches—"

Lonely as she felt, Merja praised Aslak then for his accomplishments.

"I shall sleep awhile," he told her, "but when I wake I will set off. I may return in a day or a week. But if I do not return in two weeks, then wait no longer. Pack up the camp and drive the herd south. It will be hard traveling, but you should reach the summer camp in time for the roundup. Then hire two herdsmen to help you journey to the winter village. Once you are there do as you think best. Sell the herd and go to school if you like. But I do swear to you that Piera Magga has no right to this herd."

Then Merja became frightened, for she saw how much it meant to Aslak to prove he owned the herd and could provide for his family. And she was frightened by what he meant—that he must go on a dangerous and lonely quest and might not return.

While they talked, a sudden storm swept over them, clouds closing around the constant sun and throwing shadows violently over the mountains. The whole sky thickened and darkened, while lightning burst about them. In the *kåta*, silver spears of rain thrust through

446

the smoke hole, while Petri clutched his puppy and Terhi clutched Petri. But Aslak went about his plans, gathering food for his trip—dried reindeer milk so rich it was always diluted with water; dried meat and smoked fish; cheese kept in leather pouches. He stored it all inside his tunic, where his belt kept it from falling out. In the points of his cap were coffee beans, rock sugar, and the nugget he had found on the river bank and split in two. He sharpened his *puuko* and threw a lasso over his shoulders.

"Pirkka, I leave you the gun. You will need it on the homeward journey against lynx and wolverine."

"God save you!" said Merja.

"Stay in peace," replied Aslak, and stepped out of the *kåta*. At that moment a flash of lightning traced the tops of the mountains to the east and south. Among the peaks was one of the three he wanted to explore because its shape could be that of an eagle's head. Again the lightning emphasized its form, and he suddenly was convinced that was the place. Perhaps, like his ancestors, he should trust a sign brought by a storm as much as if it were a message brought by a drum.

He called Merja and Pirkka and pointed the mountain peak out to them. "It is nearer than I thought. If I find the cave there, I should return in a week. Merja, you must do all the things I have told you."

But as he looked at her in farewell, he saw how he could perhaps fool his uncle. "Quick! Lend me one of your dresses. Take my other tunic and wear it for two days. You can hide your long hair in my other cap.

I will put on your dress and start away as if I were you, going up to milk the deer. If Uncle Piera is hanging about, he will see two boys at work and not realize I have gone away."

Merja enjoyed a part to play and delighted in Aslak's short tunic and breeches. Aslak felt foolish with Merja's skirts over his clothing and her red cap with its ear flaps nodding in the way. But he wore them until he had walked a day's journey and then bundled them also into his tunic.

He stopped at last to rest, and after a few hours' sleep the scream of an eagle woke him. He saw a small brown lemming trying to escape the searching bird.

Aslak made his second day's journey at a steady pace until he reached the snow field below the peak of the mountain which was his goal.

Under a huge rock he left his sister's dress and hat, and much of his food, for he knew a hard climb stretched up above him. He wished for his skis as he sank deeply into the snow without them. He wished, too, for his eyeshades of deerhorn scraped thin to soften the glare of the sunlight on snow. There were crevasses, which he had to leap across or climb around, but at last he reached the rocky mountain top. Where was the Cave of the Great Hunters? And what would he find there?

Above him was rock so steep no snow could cling to it. A wind-whipped ledge lay under his feet, leading up in a spiral path to a shadowy crevice that stared blackly out of the cliff like the eye of an eagle. Aslak climbed wearily to the cleft and walked into an arching cave.

Turning from the dazzle of snow and sun outside, he was suddenly as blind as old Kuisma. But when at last he could see in the dimness, he knew it must be the Cave of the Great Hunters, for painted with a red-brown stain on the stone walls were primitive drawings of reindeer and men. And against the back of the cave, preserved in the eternal cold which even now needled Aslak's bones, lay the body of his grandfather, and beyond another, and another. Aslak bowed his head in the presence of his ancestors and felt sorrow in his heart that his own father, who knew of this place, was not resting there. For here was the unconquerable pride and wildness and mystery of his race, the Samer, and of his family, the Magga— and Aslak felt that whoever stood humbly there received new courage and strength and faith.

Had his uncle reached the cave before him? Aslak hesitated to disturb his ancestors. But on his grandfather's chest lay a small box. Aslak carried it to the light at the cave mouth and opened it. Inside were good-luck stones and wooden charms strung on deer sinews, and—a half-nugget of gold. He saw also the wide ring of gold which his grandfather had always worn with pride.

Aslak took the ring and half-nugget from the box, wrapped them carefully in moss and a cloth he had brought, and put them in a peak of his hat. Then from his hat he took the larger piece of the nugget he had found and smashed, and placed it in the box. Promising himself that next summer he would return the box to his dead grandfather's clasp, he tucked it now inside his tunic.

Too cold to rest in the cave, he began the downward journey, elated that he had found the sacred resting place and the half-nugget with which to prove himself head of the family.

Forgetting caution, for in all the day's journey the only voice he had heard was the scream of an eagle, he began a *joik* of thankfulness and joy. Even as he plodded through the snow field he hummed a song, and he stopped singing only as he came at last to the rock where he had hidden his sister's dress and hat. Now he was tired and planned to sleep. But when he bent over to look, he found the dress and the hat were gone.

Fear leaped through his body and left his limbs shaken and weak. Then, as he slowly straightened up, he heard the *whoo-whisk* of a lasso.

He jumped aside barely in time to escape being caught around the neck.

"Ho!" shouted his uncle, who stood above on the rock triumphantly twirling the rope.

Aslak remembered that this man was known for two things—his poor skill at gambling and his superb skill at lassoing.

Whoo-wheesh! Before he could move again, the leather circle fell around Aslak's shoulders, and he felt the shock as his uncle jerked it, trying to pull it tight about his neck. He intended to strangle him!

451

But luckily Aslak could reach the knife on his belt, and with a swift slash he cut the lasso before Piera could tighten it enough to finish squeezing off his breath.

Then Piera leaped from the rock and seized Aslak. He knocked the knife from his hand, and it fell out of sight in a patch of moss. They pummeled each other as Aslak fought to keep his uncle from jerking the cut end of the lasso and breaking his neck.

But his uncle was strong and fresh, and Aslak was exhausted from climbing. His hat fell off and he kicked it under the rock. Then his uncle knocked him down and Aslak fell so heavily on his back that his breath left him and he could not move. Seeing a box outlined under Aslak's tunic, Piera ripped open the boy's blouse and seized it.

Gloating, he held it up, while Aslak lay on the ground, weak and dizzy and breathless. Piera put a heavy foot on the boy's chest to keep him down.

"You are not so smart, Aslak. Did you think I would let you escape me? I'll admit you fooled me when you walked off in Merja's dress and left her behind in your clothes. But like all women, when her sister Terhi washed her hair, Merja had to wash hers, too. It looks very foolish when a figure in a belted tunic suddenly takes off a cap and washes long, long hair. And luckily through my glass I saw you struggling up the snow field this morning. A half-day's walk and I found where you had hidden your costume and heard you singing gaily up above me. And now—you did all the hard work for me and I have the box!" He proceeded to open

453

it. "And there is the other half of the luck of the Karasjoki. Now all Great Jouni's wealth is mine."

Aslak took comfort in having changed the nuggets — knowing that his uncle gloated over a nugget which could prove nothing, for the true nugget was half in his own hat and half in the mayor's safekeeping. But since his uncle had already provided the mayor with his own half nugget, he must also be planning a substitute for the nugget now in the box. That being so, his uncle was apparently counting on the box itself, painted with Jouni Magga's name and designs representing the kill of the biggest bear in all Lapland — to convince the mayor that Piera had found it and was handing him the right nugget.

Aslak saw then that his only chance lay in reaching the mayor before Piera could make his claim. Perhaps his grandfather's ring would be his proof that he was the one who reached the burial place. But Aslak began to feel that it was the truth and right of his tale which must finally convince the mayor.

Yet how could he manage to reach the mayor before his uncle? Piera took his foot from Aslak's chest, and the boy tried to move and could not. A horrifying weakness crept through his body. He wondered if he had broken his back and would be unable to move ever again.

Exhaustion seemed to be overcoming him. He must not let it, but he would use it if he could.

"You have won," he whispered to his uncle. "You have the box with its nugget. You can show it to the mayor at the summer roundup. But since the deer are your wealth, you must take them with you. As you cannot herd them alone, you must take Small Jouni and my brothers and sisters to help on the trail. Besides, you made great promises to the mayor about caring for them. It would look strange if you came to the camp with several thousand deer and none of us. And what do you intend to do about me? Leave me here to die? I am too weak to move, for when you knocked me down you must have broken my back."

But Piera Magga was not troubled by the boy's plight. "So you cannot move? Then I can only say that on my way back from the burial place of my ancestors I saw you lying on the trail, broken from a fall. And I shall say that I heard your last words. For who else will hear them? Because by the time I reach your camp, you will be dead. No one lives long lying in this cold."

Fear showed in Aslak's eyes that he indeed might freeze to death. Or Piera might kill him then and there. But Piera only kicked him, and even though he wore reindeer-skin boots, the blow sent splinters of pain ranging through Aslak's body. But he did not flicker an eyelash or flinch or show that he felt it in any way.

"You see I am paralyzed and beyond help," Aslak told him. "So why waste your time with me? Show Merja the box and tell her it makes you head of the family and she must obey you on the trip to the summer camp."

His uncle did not answer, but scrambled about, hastily thrusting his telescope and some of Aslak's supply of food into his tunic, until he looked like an odd-shaped being indeed—as odd and cruel as the dim-wit monster Stalo of the Samer legends. The thought of Stalo and his magic, evil though it was, made Aslak realize it would take some magic for him to carry out the rest of his plan—for he knew he must be hurt, although how badly he could not yet tell. As he stared up at Piera, one of the shapes pushed against his tunic looked familiar.

"Now you have the box, give me the magic drum you are carrying, so I can ask the spirits to help me if I must pass from this world," he begged. "After all, I am your flesh and blood and I lie in the shadow of my ancestors' resting place. You owe me at least that comfort."

If only to be gone the sooner, Piera pulled out the magic drum, dropped it onto Aslak's body, and departed.

slak did not stir until his uncle had been out of sight a long time. Then as his strength returned, he found he could move. Painfully he crawled to the mossy patch, found his knife and cut the lasso from his neck. Standing, he discovered none of his bones broken, but he was bruised from the fight and aching from his climb. He knew that sleep was the only healer close at hand, so he wrapped himself in Merja's dress, which his uncle had left behind, put his own valuable hat on his head, rolled under the shelter of the rock, and slept.

He awoke to the same bright light of the unsetting sun. Eating dried reindeer tongue and cheese and some rock sugar restored his strength. He packed his few bundles and Merja's clothes inside his tunic. Before he added the magic drum he studied it carefully. It did look like blind Kuisma's, and it would be like Piera to have stolen such a thing from a defenseless man. Aslak tapped his fingers on it softly, and then fearing what he did not know about it, stored it away in his blouse. He set out for the south by a different pass than that his uncle would use for the herd.

He climbed and descended stony ridges and crossed moss-covered plateaus; he found tiny freshets of purest water to drink and occasional berries to eat; he slept when he could no longer march on, and marched on when he could no longer sleep. Part of him found great joy in the freedom of traveling without the chores and worries of the herd and his brothers and sisters. The grandeur of the sky and the mountains gave him peace. But the other part of him worried about his family

457

and the treatment they would receive on the trail from his uncle. He wondered if they would think he really was dead, and how much they would miss him!

After a few days of walking he came to the region where mountains alternated with valleys slanting to the southeast, and the freshets became brooks that sparkled into streams that swept into rivers or swelled into lakes. Soon there should be a river that would lead him to the plateau of the summer roundup. But even if he stood on tiptoe on a peak of the highest mountain, he could not peer beyond the horizon to see which was the right river. The sun rolling about the horizon gave him no clue. There was no one to consult. Aslak had never felt so alone in his life.

But on the next day he saw over the horizon on the southeast a flock of eagles and, deciding to take them as a sign, followed the first brook leading in their direction.

For three days he descended from the mountains, while the voice of the brook changed from its first small babble over pebbles to a deeper conversation with its stones and fish. Now dwarf willows and birches occasionally edged its banks, and with each hour Aslak longed to catch sight of a column of smoke in the sky; or to look up at the white of the snow fields on the lower mountains to see reindeer moving; or to hear a dog bark — for some Lapps measure distance by sound and say that something is as far away as a *baenagulam*, or as far as a dog's bark is heard.

And with each hour he worried more that he had taken a river valley that would not open into the big plateau but cross above it and lead him only to more mountains. He saw no signs that a herd of reindeer had traveled before him, nor heard any sign that they might be close behind. He began cursing himself for entrusting the children and the herd to his uncle's greed. He woke from an ugly dream, thinking that he heard voices, and saw a mother bear fishing in the stream with her cubs. As he was defenseless except for a knife and his lasso, he lay still and did not move until they splashed out of sight.

Then with another day's travel he saw—looking as tiny as the gadflies they sought to escape—reindeer on a snow field far ahead to his left. He shouted for joy and then began a *joik* about his journey, singing as he ran. And in that burst of happiness, jogging on the bank of the stream, he suddenly slipped on a sharp stone. He heard the crack of a bone as his ankle twisted and he fell heavily. When he tried to stand, he nearly fainted from the pain.

Despair overcame him, for how could he go on? He had no reindeer to ride, no ski-sticks for a splint. He was helpless, while the pain of his leg pushed along his back and weakened his arms. Slowly he dragged himself to a large rock and leaned against it, half-hidden from the passing stream. He fell into dazed sleep.

When he woke he found a mist sweeping down the valley so dense that he could scarcely see across the river. The cold numbed his pain, but he knew it could also kill him. Somehow he had to find help.

Then out of the mist sounds swelled against his

ears and drummed against his mind. The sounds were the clicking of thousands of reindeer hoofs, and the grunting of a large herd. Bells rang through his aching head and dogs barked.

Any second he expected to be engulfed in the rush of reindeer as they dashed past his rock. Surely he could make himself heard to any man who followed them—even if it could only be his uncle. He cried out, "I am here—here! Come and help me!"

Then to his despair he realized the herd was on the farther bank of the river, and the noise was such that no one paid him heed. Nor did anyone see him through the mist.

Aslak knew it could be only one herd—that now led by his uncle. If only he could hear his sisters' voices, high and light as the bluethroat's song, and know they were safely back to the world of people!

But he still must get safely back too. For unless he could be there to tell the truth about all that had happened, his uncle would deceitfully produce the box in which he would have already substituted half a nugget that would match the one marked with his name and now in the mayor's safekeeping. Aslak must find a way to be there!

He wondered if some *kåtor* of the summer camp ground were as near as the sound of a dog's bark. He threw back his head and howled—but there was no reply. The sounds of the herd had long since faded away.

For some time the mist trapped him in desolation, and then silently it disappeared. Shapes of rocks and tiny trees and ptarmigan berry bushes returned. He shifted against the rock, and inside his tunic the magic drum slipped. His elbow struck it and made it vibrate.

Quickly Aslak pulled it out. Closing his eyes and thinking only of being heard, Aslak beat upon the skin over and over, on and on, until his hand and his arm ached.

When he thought he could go on no longer, there was a rustle of sound, and a white owl floated up from a bend in the river. Then the pad of paws suddenly seemed loud on the stones, as a white dog came to him and threw back his head and howled. And walking over the stones as easily as if they were a solid crust of snow came Kuisma.

"You have found my drum!" Kuisma stopped by the dog and stretched out his hands. Aslak reached up and put the drum into them. "I could feel its beat in my heart and its pulse in my head even as I sat by your mayor's hearth."

"And did you pass my herd and my family, led by my evil uncle, on your way?"

"They are still on the far side of the river from the camp. If you hurry, you can reach the mayor's *kåta* before they swim across."

"My ankle is broken, or I would not have sat here trying to make myself heard with your drum. How am I to hurry when I cannot walk at all?"

"But I have brought a *härke* to carry you, for I felt your need."

Looking up, Aslak saw a large reindeer waiting in a

patch of moss. With Kuisma's help he managed to sit in the saddle, and, holding the pommel tight, he endured the ride to the mayor's *kåta*. Kind hands lifted him down and put him on a bench of twigs and skins outside the door, and fetched him water to drink. But Aslak refused to lie down or take his hat from his head.

"Tell us what has befallen you," said the mayor.

But before Aslak could begin his tale, there was a great commotion at the far river bank. The famous herd of silver deer swam out into the stream, their magnificent antlers like a forest moving over the water. Crossing in a boat were Aslak's two uncles and his brothers and sisters. Straight to the mayor came Piera Magga, the others following him.

When Merja and Terhi suddenly looked up and saw Aslak, they screamed in fright! But Pirkka came running to touch his brother's hand and feel its warmth. He turned to Piera Magga in fury. "How could you tell us such a lie—that you heard our brother's last words—and make us think he was dead!"

Piera Magga stared down at the boys. "So Aslak played a trick on me. He lay there and claimed he was dying. And all the time he intended to let me do the work of bringing down the herd while he ran here by himself. But for what purpose? No matter what lies and tales he has told you since he came, I bring what we agreed upon—the other half of Great Jouni's Karasjoki nugget. It is safely here in his box of secret belongings."

"Aslak has told us nothing," said the mayor. From

462

his tunic he took out a leather pouch and unwrapped two half nuggets—one nicked with the initials of Piera; the other with the initials of Aslak. Kuisma held out his magic drum, and the mayor placed the two halves upon it.

Everyone gathered close as Piera Magga handed the mayor Great Jouni Magga's box. The mayor opened it and took out the half nugget which lay within. "This," he announced, "I take from Great Jouni Magga's box of secret belongings. It is known as the Luck of the Karasjoki and it should fit with the half nugget given me last spring by Piera Magga and marked then as his own."

He picked up the piece marked Piera and after studying it a moment, deftly fitted the halves together.

Terhi and Merja and Pirkka sucked in their breath and waited in suspense to see what their brother would do.

"Of course the two halves would fit!" Aslak spoke quickly. "Because on his travels here with the box he substituted half a nugget that he knew matched the half he had already given the mayor, pretending it was a talisman from his father. A false talisman, for ask blind Kuisma here if his tale of receiving it with a message from his father was not a lie!"

The mayor turned to the peddler. "Is there truth in his tale that you brought him a talisman and a message from his father?"

"None," said the old man.

Aslak cried out, "Seize Piera and search him. For somewhere on his body or in his baggage you will find a half nugget that I can match. For you see I met his deceit with trickery of my own. And it was I who first reached the Cave of the Great Hunters and took the box of secret belongings from my grandfather's clasp. And before I left that cave, I took the true half nugget from the box and placed in it a false one to deceive my uncle."

"You dare not search me!" cried Piera. "You have no right because of a young boy's lie."

"You lied when you told us Aslak was dead!" Pirkka shouted. "You are the one who cannot be trusted."

Two men seized Piera's arms, and Merja said, "Look in the pocket of his *atsaslieppa*, for I saw him take out a nugget and look at it and put it back there only last night when he thought we were all asleep."

They looked and they found it, and turned to Aslak, who took off his hat. From it he took a small bundle and unwrapped half a nugget. "This will fit the

464

unmatched half now lying on the drum—the half my uncle took from the box when he stole it from me. But it is lucky for me that he was too greedy to throw that half away—for it proves that he stole the box and changed the nuggets."

Piera Magga tried to pull away from his captors. "Do not believe him. He admits to trickery himself. He is only bragging that he reached the burial place of his grandfather."

Silently Aslak took out another little packet from a peak of his hat. Silently he unwrapped the cloth and from the moss inside plucked the ring from his grandfather's hand and the half nugget he had first seen in the cold light of the cave. He handed it to the mayor.

The mayor took up the nugget with Aslak's mark, which he had kept. The halves did fit, just as Aslak said they would. Merja and Terhi and Pirkka stared at their brother with awe.

"You have won the right to be head of your household and true owner of the silver reindeer," said the mayor. "I believe that you have the right half of the right nugget. But most of all, you proved you have the right in the way you took your deer and your household from our winter village to your summer pasture safely and with an increase in your herd. From now on you will need to make no secret journeys, and the name Aslak Magga will be remembered among men."

THINKING IT OVER

1. Aslak's problems concerned both things and people. Which ones were caused by things? Which problems related to people?

2. How did Aslak solve five of these problems? Do you think he made wise decisions? Why or why not?

3. What actions show that Aslak was both clever and quick-witted, that he had skill, courage, and endurance? What did you learn about human nature from this story?

THOUGHTS AT WORK

1. What do you think Pirkka will be when he grows up? Be ready to support your answer with evidence from the story.

2. Retell the story of Uncle Piera's treachery as Merja, Pirkka, or Kuisma might have told it.

3. How would your life be different if you lived in Lapland?

4. Mention several places in the story where the author keeps you in great suspense. How was this suspense built up?

5. Look back at the following scenes in the story and find the details that create a special effect. Why do you think the author concentrated on these details?
   a. The scene at Kuisma's *kåta*
   b. The coming of spring

6. What events led to the climax of the story? What followed this high point?

7. Were there any unanswered questions in your mind at the end of the story? What answer could you suggest for each of these questions?

Pronunciation Key

The symbols and key words listed below will help you tell which sounds to use in reading the words in the glossary.

a	hat	e	let	o	hot	u	cup
ā	age	ē	be	ō	go	u̇	put
ã	care	ėr	term	ô	order	ü	rule
ä	far	i	it	oi	oil	ū	use
		ī	ice	ou	out		

ch in child   th in thin   ə *represents:*   a in about   i in April
ng in long   ŦH in then   e in taken   o in lemon
sh in she   zh in measure   u in circus

Abbreviations

n. noun   *v.* verb   *adj.* adjective   *adv.* adverb   *interj.* interjection

The pronunciation system and key are from *Thorndike-Barnhart Junior Dictionary*
© 1968 by Scott, Foresman and Company

GLOSSARY

A

ad duc tor (ə duk′tər), a muscle that adducts, or pulls, a part of the body inward. *n.*

ak ja (äk′yah), a sledge pulled by reindeer. *n. pl.* **akjor.**

al ba tross (al′bə trôs), a very large sea bird with webbed feet. *n.*

an guish (ang′gwish), great pain or sorrow; suffering of body or mind. *n.*

an i mat ed (an′ə māt′id), 1. full of life; lively; gay. 2. alive; living. *adj.*

anoint (ə noint′), 1. to put oil on a person in a religious ceremony. 2. to rub or smear with a healing oil or with an ointment. *v.*

an tic i pa tion (an tis′ə pā′shən), the act of anticipating, or of looking forward to; expectation. *n.*

an vil (an′vəl), an iron block on which metal is hammered into shape. *n.*

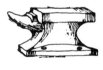

ap pa ra tus (ap′ə rā′təs or ap′ə rat′əs), the things that are necessary for a certain purpose, such as a set of tools or a piece of machinery. *n.*

ap pre hen sion (ap′ri hen′shən), 1. a seizing; an arrest, as of a burglar. 2. understanding; a grasping with the mind. 3. fear of what may be going to happen; dread of the future. *n.*

467

ar ba lete (är′bə let), a type of spear-gun used by divers for catching fish. *n.*

as tro nom i cal (as′trə nom′ə kl), of or having to do with astronomy, the science that studies and explains facts about the heavenly bodies. *adj.*

at oll (at′ol or ə tol′), a ring-shaped coral island that surrounds or partly surrounds a lagoon, a pond or small lake of sea water. *n.*

B

bac te ria (bak tir′ē ə), tiny plants so small that one usually needs a microscope to see them. Some bacteria cause disease; others are helpful, such as being active in yeast. *n.*

bal last (bal′əst), 1. to put something heavy in a ship to keep it steady. *v.* 2. anything heavy used in a ship to keep it steady. *n.*

bane ful (bān′fəl), very harmful; liable to cause injury or death. *adj.*

bar ri er reef (bar′ē ər rēf), a long ridge of rocks or a coral reef roughly parallel to, and fairly near, the shore. *n.*

bath y sphere (bath′ ə sfir), a water-tight chamber, with glass windows, in which men can go to the great ocean depths for the purpose of observing and studying the plant and animal life. *n.*

berth (bėrth), 1. a position; a job. 2. a bed on a train or ship. 3. a place for a ship to dock. *n.*

bos'n (bō′sn), a boatswain; a ship's officer who oversees and directs some of the work of the crew. *n.*

bow sprit (bou′sprit), a strong spar or pole that projects forward from the bow of a ship. *n.*

bran dish (bran′dish), 1. to wave or shake in a threatening way; to flourish. *v.* 2. a threatening shake; a waving in the air; a flourish: *the brandish of a sword. n.*

brig (brig), a sailing vessel with two masts that are square-rigged, or that have sails set across the mast. *n.*

brig an tine (brig′ən tēn), two-masted ship, the foremast of which is square-rigged, or with sails set across the mast. The mainmast is  fore-and-aft rigged, or with sails set lengthwise of the ship. *n.*

bril liance (bril′yəns), great brightness; sparkling light. *n.*

brine (brīn), an ocean, a sea, or a salt lake; also, the water of an ocean, a sea, or a salt lake. *n.*

bung (bung), *Slang.* 1. to throw; to hurl; to toss. 2. to bruise. *v.*

buoy (boi or bü′ē), 1. to hold up; to keep afloat; to keep from sinking. *v.* 2. a float- ing object anchored in a certain place in a body of water to mark a channel or to warn of rocks or shallows. *n.*

buoy ant (boi′ənt), 1. able to float in the air or on top of water. 2. light-hearted; cheerful; hopeful. *adj.*

C

ca lyp so (kə lip′sō), a type of song that originated in the British West Indies. A calypso is composed or sung without preparation, usually about some matter of current interest. *n.*

ca pac i ty (kə pas′ə tē), 1. the amount of space or room inside a thing: *This pitcher has a capacity of one quart.* 2. power to receive or contain something: *The hall has a seating capacity of five hundred. n.*

cap size (kap sīz′ or kap′sīz), to turn bottom side up; to upset; to overturn: *They feared the rough water would capsize the boat. v.*

cap stan (kap′stən), a machine for pulling or lifting that revolves, or turns, on an upright shaft. A capstan is used to pull up the anchor. *n.*

car bon di ox ide (kär′bən dī ok′sīd), a heavy, odorless, colorless gas that is present in the air. Plants absorb this gas and use it to make plant tissue. *n.*

cen sus (sen′səs), an official count of the persons living in a city, town, or country. *n.*

cen ti pede (sen′tə pēd), a small worm-like animal that has many pairs of legs. Some centipedes have poisonous fangs. *n.*

chem is try (kem′is trē), the science that studies facts about substances, their make-up, and what changes they undergo. *n.*

cir cuit break er (sėr′kit brāk′ər), a device, such as a switch, that automatically opens or interrupts an electric circuit when the current becomes too strong. *n.*

cleat (klēt), 1. a wedge - shaped block, which is fastened to something, and used to secure ropes or lines, especially on boats and ships. 2. the strip of wood or metal fastened across something to give support, to prevent slipping. *n.*

cleav er (klēv′ər), a type of cutting tool with heavy blade and short handle. *n.*

con cep tion (kən sep′shən), 1. the power of the mind to form ideas or to think up plans and designs. 2. something, such as a work of art, that results from such a power of mind. 3. an impression; an idea; a thought: *to have little conception of time. n.*

con found ed (kon′foun′did), detestable; hateful. *adj.*

con stel la tion (kon′stə lā′shən), a group of stars, such as the Big Dipper: Leo is a northern constellation in the shape of a lion. *n.*

con ster na tion (kon′stər nā′shən), dismay; fright; terror. *n.*

con ven tion al i ty (kən ven′shən al′ətē), conventional, or customary, behavior; the careful following of a way of behaving established by long use and custom as correct. *n.*

hat, āge, cãre, fär; let, bē, tėrm; it, īce; hot, gō, ôrder; oil, out; cup, pùt, rüle; ūse; ch, child; ng, long; sh, she; th, thin; ŦH, then; zh, measure; ə represents *a* in about, *e* in taken, *i* in April, *o* in lemon, *u* in circus.

cor mo rant (kôr′mə rənt), a large, dark-colored sea bird with a pouch under the beak to hold fish. *n.*

cove (kōv), a small, sheltered bay or an inlet on the shore. *n.*

crev ice (krev′is), a narrow opening caused by a split or crack. *n.*

cu li nary (kū′lə ner′ē or kul′ə ner′ē), of or having to do with cooking or the kitchen. *Cooking is a culinary art. adj.*

cut lass (kut′ləs), a short, but heavy sword that is slightly curved. *n.* Also **cutlas.**

D

daft (daft), 1. foolish; silly. 2. insane; crazy. *adj.*

dam sel (dam′zl), a girl; a maiden; an unmarried woman. *n.*

de cap i tate (di kap′ə tāt), to behead; to cut off the head of. *v.*

de fi ance (di fī′əns), a defying; an open or bold resistance to power or against authority. *n.*

de fy (di fī′), to set oneself boldly against power or authority; to resist or oppose in an open and bold way. *v.*

de mure (di myur′), 1. prim; pretending to be very modest; proper or shy. 2. sober in manner; thoughtful: *a demure young woman. adj.*

der e lict (der′ə likt), 1. a ship deserted at sea. 2. a person or thing deserted and considered of no worth. *n.* 3. deserted; abandoned. *adj.*

de ri sion (di rizh′ən), scornful or mocking laughter; contempt; ridicule. *n.*

de ri sive (di rī′siv), expressing derision; mocking: *derisive laughter. adj.*

de test a ble (di tes′tə bl), deserving to be detested; causing great dislike; hateful. *adj.*

di a bol i cal (dī′ə bol′ə kl), devilish; like a devil; evil; wicked; cruel; also, having or showing cunning. *adj.*

di min ish (də min′ish), to make or become smaller, as in size, amount, or number; to lessen; to decrease or reduce. *v.*

di min u tive (də min′yə tiv), 1. a very small person or thing. *n.* 2. very small; little; tiny. *adj.*

dire ful (dīr′fəl), dire; causing great fear or dread; terrible. *adj.*

dirge (dèrj), a song or tune to accompany a funeral or memorial service. *n.*

dis ci pline (dis′ə plin), training; a condition of obedience or order. *n.*

dis tinc tion (dis tingk′shən), 1. the act of distinguishing, or noting, a difference: *the distinction between good and evil.* 2. a special recognition: *the distinction of being the winner of a race.* 3. honor: *to serve one's country with distinction. n.*

doc ile (dos′l), 1. easy to teach; willing to learn: *a docile child.* 2. easy to lead, control, or manage; obedient: *a docile horse. adj.*

do ry (dô′rē), a large rowboat with a flat bottom and high sides that

curve upward and outward. Dories are often used by fishermen. *n.*

drave (drāv), an old-fashioned word for **drove**, the past tense of **drive**. *v.*

du bi ous (dü′bē əs or dū′bē əs), uncertain; open to question; doubtful: *to feel dubious about something. adj.*

E

ebb (eb), 1. of the tide, to flow away from the shore. 2. to decline; to weaken: *His courage did not ebb. v.* 3. a flowing of the tide away from the shore. 4. a passing from a high point to a low one; a decline. *n.*

ecol o gy (ē kol′ə jē), the branch of science that deals with the relation of living things to one another and to their surroundings. *n.*

elec tron ics (i lek′tron′iks), the science that deals with such things as vacuum tubes, radar, radio, and television. *n.*

em ber (em′bər), a piece of wood or coal that still glows in the ashes of a fire. *n.*

en vi ron ment (en vī′rən mənt), the surroundings of living things; the conditions and influences that affect the development of a person, animal, or plant. *n.*

es sen tial (ə sen′shəl), 1. that which is needed to make a certain thing what it is; a necessary element. *n.* 2. of great importance; absolutely necessary: *Air is essential to life. adj.*

ex ec u tive (eg zek′yə tiv), 1. the branch of government that has the work of putting laws into effect; also, the persons who make up this branch. 2. a person who manages or directs, such as the president of a bank. *n.* 3. of or having to do with managing business or public affairs. *adj.*

ex hil a rate (eg zil′ə rāt), to make gay or lively; to stimulate. *v.*

ex ter mi nate (eks tėr′mə nāt), to get rid of; to destroy completely: *We must exterminate the mosquitoes. v.*

F

fam ine (fam′ən), 1. a great lack of food in a place; a time when many persons may starve. 2. a great lack of anything; a shortage, as of coal or other fuel. *n.*

fath om (faŦH′əm), 1. to measure the depth of water. 2. to understand fully: *to fathom a mystery. v.* 3. a unit of measure equal to six feet, used mainly to measure the depth of water and lengths of a ship's ropes and cables. *n.*

fi na le (fə nä′lē), the close; the last part; especially the last part of a piece of music or a play. *n.*

fjells (fyel), the rolling open country. *n.*

fjord (fyôrd), a long narrow inlet of the sea between steep banks or cliffs. *n.*

flail (flāl), 1. to strike; to beat; to thrash. *v.* 2. an instrument or tool for thrashing grain by hand. *n.*

flot sam (flot′səm), the wreckage of a ship or its cargo found floating on an ocean or a sea. *n.*

flout (flout), 1. to treat with contempt or scorn; to mock; to insult. *v.* 2. a mocking speech or act; an insult. *n.*

flu o res cent (flü′ə res′nt), having or showing fluorescence, the giving off of light from a substance during the time it is exposed to certain rays, such as X-rays or ultraviolet rays. *adj.*

hat, āge, cãre, fär; let, bē; tėrm; it, īce; hot, gō, ôrder; oil, out; cup, pu̇t, rüle, ūse; ch, child; ng, long; sh, she; th, thin; ŦH, then; zh, measure; ə represents *a* in about, *e* in taken, *i* in April, *o* in lemon, *u* in circus.

fo cus (fō′kəs), 1. to adjust something, such as one's eyes or a camera lens, so as to get a clear image or picture. 2. to concentrate; to center; to focus one's attention on some activity or on a problem. *v.*

fore bitt (fôr′bit′), one of the bitts of the foremast of a ship. A bitt is a strong post or metal casting around which ropes or cables may be made fast. *n.*

fore deck (fôr′dek′), the fore, or front, part of a ship's deck, especially of the main deck. *n.*

fore stay sail (fôr′stā′sāl′ or fôr′stā′sl), a triangular, or three-cornered, sail in front of the foremast of a ship. This sail is set on hanks, or rings,

on the forestay, a strong rope or a cable reaching from the top of the foremast to the bowsprit. *n.*

fra cas (†ra′kəs), a noisy quarrel or fight; an uproar; a brawl. *n.*

fre quen cy (frē′kwən sē), 1. the number of complete cycles of current per second of an alternating-current generator. 2. a frequent occurrence, or happening: *the frequency of snowstorms in winter. n.*

fri ar (frī′ər), a member of one of certain religious orders of the Roman Catholic Church. *n.*

fund (fund), 1. a sum of money that is to be used for a special purpose, as for building a church or hospital: *The money was invested in a mutual fund.* 2. a supply; a stock: *a fund of good jokes. n.*

fun gus (fung′gəs), a plant which does not have flowers, leaves, or green coloring, such as the mushrooms, toadstools, mold, or mildew. *n.*

furl (fėrl), to wrap tightly; to roll up or fold up: *Please help furl this flag. v.*

G

gait (gāt), a way of walking or running: *a slow gait. n.*

gal ley (gal′ē), 1. the kitchen of a ship. 2. a long, narrow ship of earlier times, moved by oars and sails. *n.*

gen er a tion (jen′ər ā′shən), 1. all the persons born about the same time: *the younger generation.* 2. a step or degree in the line of descent of a family: *The family had lived in the same house for five generations.* 3. the average period of time between one generation and the next one, about thirty years. *n.*

grav i ty (grav′ə tē), 1. the natural force that tends to draw all objects toward the center of the earth. Gravity gives weight to objects. 2. the attraction or pull that tends to draw bodies toward each other; gravitation. *n.*

griev ance (grēv′əns), something to complain about; a real or imagined wrong; a reason for being annoyed or angry: *He made his grievance known. n.*

grue some (grü′səm), causing fear or dread; horrible; also, disgusting; revolting. *adj.*

gun wale (gun′l), the upper edge of the sides of a boat or ship. *n.*

gut tur al (gut′ər əl), 1. of or having to do with the throat. 2. made or sounded in the throat; harsh. *adj.*

H

hack le (hak′l), one of the long, narrow feathers on the neck of some birds. *n.*

hal yard (hal′yərd), a rope or tackle on a ship, used to raise or lower sails. *n.*

har ried (har′ēd), worried; troubled. *adj.*

her e tic (her′ə tik), anyone who holds a belief that is different from accepted or generally approved doctrines. *n.*

her o ine (her′ō in), a woman or girl who is admired for her courage, brave deeds, or noble character. *n.*

hi ber nate (hī′bər nāt), to spend the winter in a condition that resembles sleep, as do certain wild animals, such as bears and woodchucks. *v.*

hoary (hôr′ē), 1. white; whitish, or gray: *The old man had hoary hair.* 2. white or gray with age. 3. very old; ancient. *adj.*

hos tel ry (hos′tl rē), a lodging place, such as an inn or hotel. *n.*

hy dro gen (hī′drə jən), a very light gas, without odor or color. Hydrogen combines with oxygen to form water. *n.*

I

im mo bi lize (i mō′bl īz), to make firmly fixed, or not capable of moving. *v.*

im mu ni ty (i mū′nə tē), 1. a condition of freedom, as from any charge, tax, duty, or the like. 2. the power of resisting the development of a disease, as by vaccination. *n.*

im pe tus (im′pə təs), the force with which a moving object tends to keep moving; momentum. *n.*

in con ven ience (in′kən vēn′yəns), 1. to cause trouble, bother, or difficulty: *You did not inconvenience me. v.* 2. the condition of being unsuited to one's comfort or ease; a trouble; a bother. *n.*

in ev i ta ble (in ev′ə tə bl), that which cannot be avoided or prevented; sure to happen. *adj.*

in hab it ant (in hab′ə tənt), a person or an animal living in a place. *n.*

in tri cate (in′trə kit), complicated; difficult to follow or understand. *adj.*

J

jib (jib), a triangular, or three-cornered sail in front of the foremast of a ship. *n.*

jibe (jīb), to shift suddenly from one side to another, as the sail of a ship may do under certain conditions. *v.*

joik (yoi′k), improvised verses for a primitive sort of song. *n.*

jokk (yōk), a mountain brook, also a river. *n.*

ju bi lant ly (jü′bl ənt lē), in a jubilant way; in a manner showing happiness or joy; joyfully. *adv.*

K

kåta (kä′tə), the tent or hut of a Lapp. *n. pl.* **kåtor.**

hat, āge, cāre, fär; let, bē, tėrm; it, īce; hot, gō, ôrder; oil, out; cup, pùt, rüle, ūse; ch, child; ng, long; sh, she; th, thin; ᵼH, then; zh, measure; ə represents *a* in about, *e* in taken, *i* in April, *o* in lemon, *u* in circus.

khaki (kak′ē or kä′kē), 1. a dull, yellowish-brown color. 2. a strong cotton cloth of this color, much used for uniforms. *n.* 3. made of khaki. *adj.*

L

lath (lath), 1. one of the thin, narrow strips of wood used as a base for plaster, or for making a trellis or lattice. 2. any thin, narrow strip of wood. *n.*

lav ish (lav′ish), to spend, use, or give very freely or too freely: *to lavish money on clothes. v.*

ledg er (lej′ər), in bookkeeping, the book in which business or money transactions are recorded. *n.*

leech (lēch), the edge of a sail that is not attached to a rope or spar. *n.*

leer (lir), sly, sneering, or evil glance. *n.*

lee ward (lē′wərd or lü′ərd), 1. the lee side, which is the side away from the wind. *n.* 2. in the direction toward which the wind is blowing. *adv.*

lem ming (lem′ing), a small, mouse-like animal of the arctic. *n.*

lim pet (lim′pit), a small shellfish that clings to rocks. *n.*

loath some (lō̄TH′səm), causing loathing or strong dislike; disgusting; sickening. *adj.*

loft (lôft), a room under the roof of a building; an attic. *n.*

loin cloth (loin′klôth′), a piece of cloth worn around the hips by some natives of warm countries. *n.*

luff (luf), 1. to turn the bow of a ship or a boat toward the wind. *v.* 2. the forward edge of a fore-and-aft sail, a sail running lengthwise of a ship. *n.*

lu nar (lü′nər), of or having to do with the moon. *adj.*

lynx (lingks), a wild cat. *n. pl.* **lynxes** or **lynx.**

M

mac ad am (mə kad′əm), 1. small, broken stones. 2. a pavement of such stones closely packed and rolled until smooth and solid. *n.*

ma hog a ny (mə hog′ə nē), 1. a large evergreen tree that grows in the warm parts of America. 2. the hard, reddish-brown wood of this tree, which is much used for furniture. *n.*

ma lig nant (mə lig′nənt), 1. very hateful or unfriendly; evil; malicious. 2. very dangerous; liable to cause death: *Some diseases, such as cancer, are malignant. adj.*

mam mal (mam′əl), an animal that has a backbone and that feeds its young with milk. *n.*

ma neu ver (mə nü′vər), 1. to plan or scheme in a skillful way; to manage in a clever manner. *v.* 2. a clever plan or action. *n.*

med i tate (med′ə tāt), to think carefully about; to consider in a careful way; to plan. *v.*

mel an choly (mel′ən kol′ē), 1. low spirits; sadness. *n.* 2. in low spirits; sad; gloomy. *adj.*

men ace (men′is), 1. to threaten; to be a sign of possible harm or danger. *v.* 2. a threat; a danger: *The flooding of a river is sometimes a menace. n.*

mer chant man (mėr′chənt mən), a ship used for carrying cargo: *The merchantman carried tea from Ceylon. n.*

me te or (mē'tē ər), a mass of stone or metal that travels through space with great speed; a shooting star. *n.*

mo not o ny (mə not'n ē), 1. lack of variety; tiresome sameness. 2. sameness, as of tone or pitch. *n.*

mor tal i ty (môr tal'ə tē), 1. condition of being mortal, or destined to die. 2. the loss of life of large numbers, as by war or disease. *n.*

murk i ness (mėr'kē nis), darkness; dimness; gloom. *n.*

N

na val en gage ment (nā'vl en gāj'mənt), a naval battle; a fight between navy vessels, or warships. *n.*

ni tro gen (nī'trə jən), a gas, without color, odor, or taste, that forms about four fifths of the air's volume. *Nitrogen is necessary for the growth of all plants. n.*

no mad (nō'mad), a member of a people that moves from place to place in search of food and pasture for its herds. *n.*

nor'east er (nôr'ēs'tər), a shortened form of **northeaster**, a strong wind or storm coming from the northeast. *n.*

nos trum (nos'trəm), 1. a medicine recommended or sold by the person who makes it. 2. a favorite remedy, such as a scheme for doing some wonderful thing; a cure-all. *n.*

nov ice (nov'is), 1. a person who has entered a religious order but who has not yet taken any vows. 2. a person who is new at what he is doing; a beginner. *n.*

nu cle ar (nü'klē ər or nū'klē ər), of or having to do with a nucleus, or central part of a thing, especially of an atom: *nuclear energy. adj.*

nymph (nimf), in Greek and Roman mythology, one of the lesser goddesses of nature, represented as beautiful maidens who lived in forests, hills, rivers, and other outdoor places. *n.*

O

om i nous (om'ə nəs), like a bad omen; threatening or seeming to threaten some evil or danger. *adj.*

or a cle (ôr'ə kl), 1. in ancient times, an answer to a question given by a god through a priest or priestess. 2. a person who gives wise advice. *n.*

or nery (ôr'nər ē), *in common speech,* of a mean disposition; hard to manage. *adj.*

os cil lo scope (ä sil'ə skōp), an instrument for showing changes in a varying electric current, especially by means of the  wavy line made on a fluorescent screen by the bending or turning of a beam of cathode rays. *n.*

out rig ger (out'rig'ər), 1. a certain kind of framework extending outward from the side of a canoe to prevent the canoe from upsetting. 2. a boat equipped with such supports. *n.*

ox y gen (ok'sə jən), a colorless, odorless gas that forms about one fifth of the air. *Oxygen is necessary to life. n.*

hat, āge, cãre, fär; let, bē, term; it, īce; hot, gō, ôrder; oil, out; cup, put, rüle, ūse; ch, child; ng, long; sh, she; th, thin; ҭH, then; zh, measure; ə represents *a* in about, *e* in taken, *i* in April, *o* in lemon, *u* in circus.

P

pan da nus (pan dā′ nəs), a tropical plant, with swordlike leaves and usually large roots, found growing in certain warm climates, the leaves of which furnish useful fibers. *n.*

pen e trate (pen′ə trāt), 1. to get into; to enter and pass through; to pierce. 2. to fill: *A strong odor penetrated the room.* 3. to understand: *We tried to penetrate the mystery. v.*

per ceive (pər sēv′), 1. to be aware of through one or more of the senses; to see, hear, smell, taste, or feel. 2. to grasp the meaning of; to understand; to observe: *to perceive that a friend is determined to learn to swim. v.*

pes ti len tial (pes′tə len′shəl), 1. of, having to do with, or like, a very serious disease that spreads rapidly. 2. of a very troublesome kind. *adj.*

phe nom e non (fə nom′ə non), 1. any fact or event that can be observed; an outward sign of the working of a law of nature: *A hailstorm is a phenomenon.* 2. a remarkable or very unusual person, thing, or happening. *n. pl.* **phenomena.**

phoe be (fē′bē), any-one of several small fly-catching birds of America, grayish-brown on the back and yellowish-white below, with a low crest on its head: *The phoebes built a nest in the old carriage house. n.*

plague (plāg), 1. to strike or afflict with disease or misfortune. 2. to annoy; to pester; to bother. *v.* 3. a very contagious disease. 4. anything that causes suffering or trouble. *n.*

476

plaint (plānt), 1. in poetic use, a mournful poem or song. 2. a complaint; a protest. *n.*

poi (poi), a food made from the starchy root of the taro, a plant of the Pacific Islands and other tropical regions. *n.*

pol li nate (pol′ə nāt), to carry pollen from the stamens of a flower to the pistils. This fertilizes the seed-bearing part of the flower. *v.*

pre car i ous (pri kãr′ē əs), not safe or secure; dangerous. *adj.*

pre cise (pri sīs′), 1. exact; definite; distinct: *precise rules.* 2. careful, as in following rules or customs: *precise behavior. adj.*

prej u dice (prej′ə dis), 1. to cause a certain opinion about something without good reason; to influence in an unfair way. *v.* 2. an opinion formed without good reasons. *n.*

pre oc cu py (prē ok′yə pī), 1. to take up the attention of. 2. to occupy beforehand; to take possession of before another or others. *v.*

prim i tive (prim′ə tiv), 1. of long ago; of ancient times: *primitive people; primitive custom.* 2. very simple; like that which people had in early times: *primitive tools. adj.*

pri va teer (prī′və tir′), 1. an armed ship that is privately owned but is permitted by its government to attack and capture enemy ships. 2. the commander or one of the crew of such a ship. *n.*

pro tein (prō′tēn), an important substance which is found in the living cells of animals and plants, a necessary element in diet, supplied by such foods as meat, fish, milk, eggs, and beans. *n.*

prow (prou), the pointed front end of a boat or ship. *n.*

puuko (pü′kō), a knife with a bone or horn handle. *n.*

Q

quake (kwāk), 1. to shake or tremble; to quiver. *v.* 2. an earthquake. *n.*

quest (kwest), 1. to search for; to seek. *v.* 2. a search; an attempt to find or obtain something: *to be in quest of riches. n.*

quoit (kwoit), a heavy, flattened ring of iron or rope to be thrown over a peg stuck in the ground. *n.*

R

rajd (rähd), a group or string of sledges tied together. *n.*

ramp (ramp), to rush or jump about in a wild or excited way; to behave in a violent manner. *v.*

ram page (ram pāj′ or ram′pāj), 1. to rush about wildly or excitedly. *v.* 2. (ram′pāj), act of rushing about wildly or excitedly; reckless behavior; a wild outbreak. *n.*

ran kle (rang′kl), to give pain; to be sore or cause soreness; to fester: *to have an unkind remark rankle in one's mind. v.*

rav ish (rav′ish), 1. to seize and carry off by force. 2. overcome with delight or joy; also, to overcome with grief or sorrow. *v.*

re flex (rē′fleks), a movement not under control of the will but caused by a nerve impulse, such as a sneeze. *n.*

ref or ma tion (ref′ər mā′shən), the condition of being changed for the better; improvement. *n.*

ref uge (ref′ūj), protection or shelter from danger or trouble; safety; also, a place of protection or shelter. *n.*

re per cus sion (rē′pər kush′ən), 1. a return effect of an action; an action in response to something one has done: *Telling lies may have unpleasant repercussions.* 2. the throwing back of sound waves; an echo. *n.*

re proach ful ly (ri prōch′fəl ē), in a way expressing disapproval, criticism, or displeasure. *adv.*

rep u ta tion (rep′yə tā′shən), 1. a person's character as judged by people in general; also, the quality of a thing as judged by people in general. 2. a person's good name: *to keep one's reputation. n.*

res o lute ly (rez′ə lüt lē), in a resolute, or determined, way; boldly. *adv.*

re source ful ness (ri sôrs′fəl nis), the condition of being resourceful, or good at handling situations, or getting out of difficulties. *n.*

res pite (res′pit), a time of rest, as from work; also, a time of relief, as from suffering. *n.*

rig ging (rig′ing), 1. the ropes and chains used to hold and move masts, sails, and spars on a ship. 2. tackle; gear; equipment. *n.*

rile (rīl), *in common speech,* to roil; to rouse the temper of; to annoy; to irritate. *v.*

hat, āge, cãre, fär; let, bē, tèrm; it, īce; hot, gō, ôrder; oil, out; cup, pùt, rüle, ūse; ch, child; ng, long; sh, she; th, thin; ͲH, then; zh, measure; ə represents *a* in about, *e* in taken, *i* in April, *o* in lemon, *u* in circus.

rip tide (rip tīd), 1. a stretch of water made rough by the meeting of opposing tides or by cross currents. 2. a rapid current made by the tide. *n.*

rud dy (rud'ē), 1. red or reddish: *a ruddy glow from the fire.* 2. having a healthy reddish color. *adj.*

S

sac ri fice (sak'rə fīs), the giving up of one thing for another; especially, an unselfish giving up: *to make sacrifices for one's family. n.*

scance (skans), 1. to glance; also, to comment; to blame. *v.* 2. a glance; a comment; blame. *n.*

schoon er (skün'ər), a ship with two or more masts and also fore-and-aft sails. *n.*

scor pi on (skôr'pē ən), a small animal, somewhat like a spider, with a long tail that has a poisonous sting at the tip. *n.*

scourge (skėrj), 1. to punish, as by whipping. 2. to trouble very much; to cause suffering. *v.* 3. a person or thing that causes trouble or suffering. *n.*

scull (skul), 1. to move a boat forward with an oar worked over the stern, or end, of the boat. 2. of a fish, to move forward in water by a slow sideways motion of the tail. *v.*

sea sponge (sē spunj), a kind of sea animal with a tough springy skeleton. *n.*

serge (sėrj), a kind of woolen cloth with slanting lines or ridges on the surface, used especially for clothing, such as suits and coats. *n.*

shroud (shroud), 1. to wrap for burial, as a dead body. 2. to cover or conceal. *v.* 3. a cloth in which a dead body is wrapped for burial. 4. something that covers or conceals: *The darkness of night was a shroud over the land. n.*

sin ew (sin'ū), 1. a strong, tough cord or band that joins a muscle to some other part, as to a bone; a tendon. 2. strength; muscular power or energy. *n.*

skep ti cism (skep'tə siz əm), a doubting state of mind; unbelief. *n.*

slat (slat), to swing or sway about loosely; to move with a beating motion; to flap. *v.*

sloop (slüp), a sailboat that has one mast, a mainsail with a jib, and sometimes other sails. *n.*

snub bing post (snub'ing pōst), a post around which a line is thrown in order to snub, or check, something. *n.*

son net (son'it), a poem that has fourteen lines and a certain arrangement of rhymes. *n.*

southard (south'ard), southward. *adv.*

spar (spär), 1. to fight with the fists in a cautious way; to box. *v.* 2. a boxing match. *n.*

spar (spär), a long, strong pole used to support or extend a ship's sail; the mast, yard, or boom of a ship. *n.*

spe cies (spē'shēz), 1. a group of animals or plants whose members are very much alike, being different only in unimportant ways. 2. a sort; a particular kind: *a species of adventure stories. n.*

spiel (spēl), *Slang.* 1. to talk, especially in a common, noisy way. *v.* 2. a talk, of a common, noisy nature. *n.*

squall (skwôl), a sudden, strong gust of wind, often with rain or snow. *n.*

staunch (stônch), 1. firm; strong: *The house has a staunch foundation.* 2. loyal, steadfast; true: *staunch friends.* 3. watertight; sound: *a staunch ship.* *adj.* Also **stanch**.

stra mash (strə mash′ or stram′ash), 1. to smash; to break to pieces; to destroy. *v.* 2. a disturbance; a crash. *n.*

surge (sèrj), 1. to rise and fall in waves, or like waves. *v.* 2. a rolling swell of water. 3. an onward rush like a sweep of waves: *a surge of joy. n.*

sur mise, 1. (sər mīz′), to form an opinion without certain knowledge; to guess. *v.* 2. (sər mīz′ or sèr′mīz), an opinion formed without certain knowledge; a guessing. *n.*

sur vey or (sər vā′ər), a person who surveys, or carefully examines, something; especially a person who measures a piece of land. *n.*

T

tac tics (tak′tiks), 1. any clever plan, trick, or scheme to gain an advantage or success. 2. the art or science of moving troops or ships in action in such a way as to gain an advantage. *n.*

tal is man (tal′is mən), 1. a stone or ring engraved with figures or symbols that are supposed to have magical powers. 2. anything that acts as a charm to ward off misfortune. *n. pl.* **talismans.**

tap es try (tap′is trē), a heavy kind of cloth with pictures or designs woven in it, used for furniture coverings, wall hangings, and carpets. *n.*

taunt (tônt), 1. to mock; to jeer at; to treat with scorn. *v.* 2. an insulting, mocking, or spiteful remark. *Her taunts made me furious. n.*

ten ant (ten′ənt), a person, animal, or thing that occupies a certain place: *A squirrel was a tenant in the oak tree. n.*

tex ture (teks′chər), 1. the way in which anything is put together; structure; make-up. 2. the way in which a fabric is woven: *a cloth with a smooth, fine texture. n.*

the o ry (thē′ə rē), an explanation based on observation and reasoning; an opinion offered as possibly but not definitely true: *the theory of evolution; a theory of how a building caught fire. n.*

throt tle (throt′l), 1. a valve for controlling the flow of steam or fuel to an engine. 2. a lever or pedal that works such a valve. *n.*

tier cel (tèr′sl), the male of certain birds, such as hawks, falcons, and eagles. *n.*

trans mit ter (trans mit′ər), 1. an apparatus or device for sending out radio or television waves. 2. the part of a telephone or telegraph by which messages are sent over the wires. *n.*

tran som (tran′səm), 1. a window above a door or another window, usually with hinges for opening it. 2. a crosswise piece that separates a door from the window above it. *n.*

hat, āge, cāre, fär; let, bē, tèrm; it, īce; hot, gō, ôrder; oil, out; cup, pùt, rüle, ūse; ch, child; ng, long; sh, she; th, thin; ᵺH, then; zh, measure; ə represents *a* in about, *e* in taken, *i* in April, *o* in lemon, *u* in circus.

trough (trôf), 1. a long, narrow, box-like container for holding food or water for cattle, horses, or other livestock. 2. a channel for water; a gutter. 3. any long channel or hollow between two ridges, as between two ocean waves. *n.*

U

un com pre hend ing (un kom′pri hend′ ing), not comprehending; not understanding the meaning of. *adj.*

un quench a ble (un kwench′ə bl), that cannot be quenched or extinguished; that cannot be stopped or done away with. *adj.*

ura ni um (yu̇ rā′nē əm), a metallic element that is radioactive, or capable of giving off radiant energy. *n.*

V

vac u um (vak′yu̇ əm), 1. an empty space that does not even have air in it. 2. a space inside a closed vessel from which almost all air has been removed. 3. a type of cleaner: a *vacuum to clean the rug.* *n.*

val iant (val′yənt), showing valor; brave; fearless; courageous. *adj.*

van i ty (van′ə tē), 1. too much pride, as in one's looks, ability, or accomplishments; conceit. 2. that which is vain or that lacks real value. 3. a small box or case for toilet articles. *n.*

van quish (vang′kwish), to get the better of; to conquer; to overcome. *v.*

vault (vôlt), 1. an arched ceiling or roof. 2. a room or place for storing valuable things for safekeeping: *a vault in a bank.* 3. a burial chamber. *n.*

480

venge ance (ven′jəns), punishment in return for a wrong; revenge. *n.*

vow (vou), a solemn promise binding a person to do or give something. *n.*

W

weld (weld), 1. to join two pieces of metal by heating them and then hammering them together while they are still hot. 2. to unite closely: *A common interest welded the three young men.* *v.* 3. a welded part, such as a joint in a pipe. *n.*

whip poor will (hwip′ ər wil′ or hwip′ər wil), a bird found in North America and named for its call. *n.*

wile (wīl), 1. a cunning way; a trick to deceive or tempt. 2. slyness; craftiness; trickery. *n.*

wol ver ine (wu̇l′vər ēn), an animal related to the weasel. *n.*

wrought (rôt), fashioned; formed: *a finely wrought bracelet. adj.*

Y

yaw (yô), 1. to turn suddenly from a straight course; to go in an unsteady way. *v.* 2. a movement from a straight course. *n.*

Z

zeph yr (zef′ər), 1. a soft, gentle breeze. 2. the west wind. *n.*